Traditions and Hearthside Stories of West Cornwall

William Bottrell

Alpha Editions

This edition published in 2024

ISBN : 9789357969161

Design and Setting By
Alpha Editions
www.alphaedis.com
Email - info@alphaedis.com

DUFFY AND THE DEVIL.

AN OLD CHRISTMAS PLAY.

Part First.

Open your doors, and let me in,
I hope your favours I shall win;
Whether I rise, or whether I fall,
I'll do my best to please you all.

Christmas Play of St. George and the Dragon.

ASSOCIATED with Trove and the ancient family who lived, for many generations, in that pleasant place, there is a tradition that one old Squire Lovell wedded a poor girl solely because he believed her to be the best spinster and knitster in Buryan; but that all the fine stockings and other knitted garments with which she provided her husband were made by a devil. This droll formed the subject of an old Guise-dance (Christmas Play) which is all but forgotten: yet, in our youth, we have heard a few scenes rehearsed, which may be interesting as an example of a primitive drama of West Penwith, that may have succeeded, or been contemporary with, the miracle plays which, about three centuries ago, were acted in the Plan-an-gwarre, St. Just, and at the Church-town cross in most other western parishes. This uncouth piece shows something of the rude and simple humour of old times, when people were quite as innocent, though less fastidious, than in our days.

Great part of the dialogue appears to have been improvised, as the actor's fancy dictated. Yet there were some portions in rude verse, which would seem to have been handed down with little variation. Mimical gesticulation expressed much of the story; and when there was unwonted delay in change of scene, or any hitch in acting, in came the hobby-horse and its licenced rider, to keep the mirth from flagging. This saucy jester being privileged to say whatever he pleased, kept the audience in good humour by filling up such intervals with burlesque speeches on any matters which had taken place during the past year, that furnished fit subjects for ridicule.

A hall, farmhouse-kitchen, barn, or other out-house, served for a theatre, and a winnowing-sheet, suspended from key-beams or rafters, made a drop-curtain. Father Christmas, as chorus, described the scene, and told the company what characters the actors represented, unless they introduced themselves, as was frequently the case, like St. George, saying, "Here comes I, a champion bold," &c. He also narrated such parts as could not be acted conveniently.

Our simple actors got up their dresses in as old-fashioned and smart a style as they were able to contrive them, by begging or borrowing cast-off finery from the gentry round. Male players were often seen rigged in long-waisted, gay-coloured coats, having their skirts spread out with straw, instead of buckram or bombast, and resplendent with brass or tin buttons, large as crown pieces, and long ruffles at their breasts and wrists; their breeches were of blue, red, or buff, slashed, puffed, and tricked out with ribbons, tassels, and knee-buckles. Their hose was of any bright hue, to make a strong contrast to the small clothes. High-heeled shoes were adorned with shining buckles or bows of ribbons. Yet their greatest pride was displayed in steeple-crowned or cocked hats, surmounted with plumes and decked with streamers of gay ribbons.

Our rural actresses also wore steeple-crowns fixed high above their heads on pads; stiffen-bodied, long-waisted gowns, with bag skirts or long trains; ruffles hanging from their elbows, wide stiff ruffs round their necks; and any other remnants of old finery that they could contrive to get.

It is somewhat curious that in this old guise-dance, or story about Madame Lovell and the devil, several ladies belonging to noted families who lived in Buryan, two or three centuries ago, are represented as bringing their corn to Trove Mill to be ground and as serging (bolting) their flour themselves. The names of Mesdames Cardew, Pender, Noy, Trezilian, &c., are taken by these ladies, whose gossip forms a kind of by-play.

We now purpose to reproduce a few well-remembered scenes, as we have heard them related many years ago, by old folks of Buryan, and to simply tell the story as expressed by others. Yet, with a feeling somewhat akin to regret, we have curtailed some portions, in order to exclude whatever might, now, be regarded as indelicate: there is sufficient, however, preserved to carry on the story as far as it is likely to interest or amuse any but antiquarian students who might prefer, with all its blemishes, an unmutilated picture of such "merrie disports" as were usual at Christmas-tide with our simple-honest forefathers.

Characters :—

SQUIRE LOVELL, *of Trove.*
DUFFY, *a poor girl, who became Madame Lovell.*
HUEY LENINE, *Duffy's lover.*
JENNY CHYGWIN, *Duffy's stepmother.*
A BUCKA-BOO, OR DEVIL.
BETTY, *the witch of Trove Mill.*
JONE, *Squire Lovell's housekeeper.*
Several ladies and gentlemen, and witches.

SCENE I.—Father Christmas, with long hoary hair and beard enters before the curtain, and says:—"Ladies and gentlemen,—Please to take it that we are in Buryan Church-town, in the cider-making time. Squire Lovell is come up to get help to gather in his apples. When the curtain rises you will see him at Jenny Chygwin's door."

Curtain raised. Squire Lovell is seen on his horse (a hobby horse); an old woman and a young woman scolding within.

SQUIRE:—"Hullo! in there! Jenny, what's all the caperrouse with you and the maid, I'd like to know?"

DUFFY rushes out, and round the stage, followed by old Jenny, her stepmother, who beats the girl with the skirt or kirtle of her gown, saying, "I will break every bone in her body; the lazy hussy is all the time out courseying, and corantan, with the boys. She will neither boil the porridge, knit nor spin."

DUFFY runs to the Squire, saying "Don't e believe her, your honour. I do all the work, whilst she is drunk from morning till night, and my spinning and knitting is the best in Church-town. Your stockings are nothing so fine as I can make."

SQUIRE:—"Stop beating the maid, Jenny, and choaking one with dust from the skirt of thy old swing-tail gown. And, Duffy, as thou canst spin and knit so well, come down to Trove and help my old Jone, who is blind on one eye and can't see much with the other, as any one may know by looking at the bad darns in my stocking and patches on my breeches. Come away, on to the heaping-stock. Jump up: you can ride down behind me without pillion or pad."

Squire rides off: Duffy follows.

JENNY:—"Aye, go thee ways with the old bucca, and good riddance of bad rummage."

(*Curtain drops.*)

SCENE II. AT SQUIRE LOVELL'S DOOR.—SQUIRE ON HORSEBACK: DUFFY STANDING BESIDE HIM.

SQUIRE calls:—"Jone, come here and take in Duffy Chygwin, who is come down to help thee knit and spin, give her some bread and cheese, and beer: dost thou hear?"

Squire rides off.

JONE comes out, and says:—"Oh, Duffy, my dear, I am glad to see thee here, for I want help sorely ever since that villain, Tom Chynance, put out the sight of my eye because I seed his thievish tricks in stealing from the standings one night in Penzance."

JONE tells us a long story which we omit, as it can be found in the first series of *Traditions and Hearth-side Stories of West Cornwall*.[1] She concludes by saying, "Now you needn't eat any bread and cheese, as dinner will be ready soon. You can go up to the loft whenever you please and card wool to spin in the afternoon."

SCENE III.—A room in which are seen fleeces of wool, a turn (spinning-wheel) and other appliances for spinning. Duffy seated, carding and making rolls of wool, which were placed in a cayer (winnowing sieve.) Over a while she rises and exclaims:—

"Cuss the carding and spinning! What the devil shall I do now the wool is carded, for I can neither spin nor knit, and the devil take such work for me."

From behind some wool comes a devil, in the shape of a black man, with half-cocked, squinting eyes, and the barbed or forked tip of his tail just seen below his coat skirts.

DEVIL:—"My dear, here I am, come at your call, ready to do all you wish for very little pay. Only agree to go with me at the end of three long years, and for all that time I'll do your spinning and knitting and everything else you wish for, and even then, if you can tell me my name at three times asking, you may go or stay, till another time."

DUFFY:—"Well, I don't mind much: anything for a change. What ded'e say you were called?"

DEVIL, winking:—"You have only to prick your arm and draw blood to sign our agreement you know."

DUFFY:—"My word is as good as my mark. Spin and knit for me if you will; and I'll have, that while, a courant in the orchard and a dance at the mill."

In leaving, DUFFY says:—"Bolt the door, that no one may see who is doing the work."

"Stop and let me take the measure of your foot," says the devil, in stringing the wheel as handy as if he had been used to spinning all his life.

FATHER CHRISTMAS comes before the curtain and says:—"Good people, you see that Duffy wans't at all scared at the Bucca-boo's appearance, because in old times people were so much used to dealings with the devil—women especially—that they didn't mind him. Duffy is now gone off by the outer door and stair, to merrily pass the day; and old Jone, hearing a rumble all through the house, thinks her to be busy at work."

Duffy passes a great part of her time at Trove Mill, near at hand; where a crowd of women high and low, meet to take their turn at grinding, serging, &c. Whilst some work others tell stories, sing, or dance on the green, near which grew many old oaks, sycamores, and elms, in a place still called the rookery, a little above.

There was a great friendship between Duffy and Old Betty, who worked the mill, because this old dame, having long had strange dealings, saw at once, by a stocking Duffy pretended to be knitting, that a stitch was always down and that the work was none of hers.

In the evening, Duffy hearing, when she came in, the devil still spinning, thought she would see him at work and try to learn something. Looking through the latch-hole she saw what she took to be a woman, seated, and spinning with a small treddle-turn such as is used for spinning thread, and the wool-turn (with a wheel as large as that of a coach) put aside. When she looked around she knew that it was only the devil dressed in clothes like what she wore. He had on a loose bed-gown, petticoat, and towser (large coarse apron or wrapper,) with a nackan (large 'kerchief) thrown loosely over his head and shoulders. As Duffy entered, he turned around and said, "How are'e, my dear? Here I am, you see, busy at work for'e. See what I've already spun," he continued, pointing to a heap of balls in the corner, and skeins of yarn hanging on the walls.

She stood wondering, with eyes and mouth wide open, to see how handy the devil spun, and yet seemed to do nothing with his hands but pull off the yarn whilst his foot worked the treddle, and a ball dancing on the floor wound up itself!

"Arreah! faix," said Duffy, "I should have taken 'e for a woman if I hadn't chanced to spy your cloven foot, and your tail hanging down, and I don't much admire 'e in petticoats."

"There's good reason for wearing them, however," replied he; "besides, they are handy for such work, and if you will come here on Saturday night you will find, under that black fleece, ever so many pairs of stockings, both for you and the squire. I know his measure, and see if I don't well fit both of ye. So now good night."

Before she could wish him the same he disappeared, and all the yarn of his spinning along with him, leaving nothing to show that he had ever been there but a strong smell of brimstone.

Duffy didn't wait till dark night on Saturday, but went up to the wool-chamber about sunset. The Bucca-boo had just left work, and, having thrown off his petticoats, stood before her dressed like a sporting gentleman. He bowed as she entered and, handing her half-a-dozen pairs of stockings, all as strong as broadcloth and as fine as silk, said, "Excuse me, my dear, from staying a moment longer, as I must be away before Buryan bells are rung; else, some mishap may befall me."

"I wish 'e well till I see 'e again, and thank 'e, Mr. What-shall-I-call-'e," said Duffy, taking the stockings from his hand.

"You may call me captain," he replied, and vanished in a flash of lightning with a roar of thunder that shook the house.

On Sunday morning, when Squire Lovell was getting ready to don his velvet suit, that he might ride to church in grand state, as was his wont, Duffy brought him a pair of stockings suitable for the occasion.

"You see, master," said she, "that I havn't been idle, to spin and knit ye a pair of such long stockings in three days and the work so fine too." He put on the stockings, admired the beautiful knitting and good fit; then to show his delight at having such nice hose, the like of which were never on his legs before, he kissed Duffy again and again.

It was late when he reached Church-town. After churching, he stopped, as usual, to exchange greetings with other gentry of Buryan. Everyone admired his fine stockings. The ladies enquired how and where he procured them, saying there was no one in the parish who could do such good work; one and all declared they were fit for a king.

The fame of Squire Lovell's stockings drew crowds of people to Buryan church on the following Sunday. Old and young wanted to feel his legs. They couldn't be satisfied with looking, and so they continued to come from farther and farther, Sunday after Sunday. Church-town, for some weeks, was full of people like on a fair or feasten tide.

[It will be understood that great part of the foregoing, as well as the narrative parts of what follows, is related by Father Christmas, in his character of Chorus. He enters into details about the devil's wonderful spinning with a turn (spinning-wheel) of his own invention, that took wool from the fleece, without carding, and passed it into the spinster's hands all ready for knitting or weaving. He also related many other surprising exploits of these sable gentry, such as their church-building in out-of-the-way places, like that of St. Levan, of their amiable intercourse with witches, &c. Thus, as fancy dictated, he entertained his audience until the curtain rose.]

We next behold Squire Lovell's kitchen, with Jone, rather the worse for liquor, on a chimney-stool or bench in a broad and deep fire-place, such as used to be found in every West-country mansion, when wood and turf were the only fuel. She makes awful groans and screeches, till Duffy enters. Then

Jone says "Oh Duffy, you can't think what cramps I have in my stomach and wind in my head, that's making it quite light. Help me over stairs to bed, and you wait up to give master his supper."

The old housekeeper is led off by Duffy, who soon returns and seats herself on the chimney-stool.

Then Huey Lenine enters and says:—"What cheer, Duffy, my dear? Now thee cus'nt (can'st not) say that the lanes are longer than the love, when I'm come to see thee with this rainy weather."

"Joy of my heart," said she, "come by the fire and dry thyself."

Huey sits on the outer end of the chimney-stool. After a long silence, the following dialogue takes place:—

DUFFY:—"Why dos'nt thee speak to me than, Huey?"

HUEY:—"What shall I say than?"

DUFFY:—"Say thee dos't love me, to be sure."

HUEY:—"So I do."

DUFFY:—"That's a dear.—Brave pretty waistcoat on to you, than, Huey."

HUEY:—"Cost pretty money too."

DUFFY:—"What ded a cost than?"

HUEY:—"Two and twenty pence, buttons and all."

DUFFY:—"Take care of an than."

HUEY:—"So I will."

DUFFY:—"That's a dear."

Another prolonged silence.

HUEY continues:—"I'm thinkan we will get married next turfey season if thee west (thou wilt.")

DUFFY:—"Why doesn't thee sit a little nearer than?"

HUEY:—"Near enough I bla (believe.")

DUFFY:—"Nearer the fire, I mean. Well, I'll be married to thee any day, though thee art no beauty, to be sure."

Huey gets a little nearer.

DUFFY, putting her hand on his face, "Thy face is as rough as Morvah Downs, that was ploughed and never harved (harrowed) they say; but I'll have thee for all that and fill up with putty all the pock-mark pits and seams; then paint them over and make thee as pretty as a new wheelbarrow."

The squire is heard outside calling his dogs. Duffy starts up in a fright, seizes a furze-prong, and says, "Master will be here in a minute, jump into the huccarner (wood-corner) and I'll cover thee up with the furze."

Huey hesitates.

DUFFY:—"Then crawl into the oven: a little more baking will make thee no worse."

Huey gets into an oven, opening on to the fire-place and behind the chimney-stool, just as the Squire enters and calls out,

"Jone, take up the pie, if its ready or raw. I'm as hungry as a hound."

DUFFY, rising to uncover a pie that was baking on the hearth, says, "Master, I have staid up to give ye your supper, because An Jone es gone to bed very bad with a cramp in her stomach and wind in her head, so she said."

"Why I heard thee talking when I came to the door, who was here then?" demanded the Squire.

"Only a great owl, master dear," she replied, "that fell down from the ivy-bush growing over the chimney and perched hisself there on the stool, with his great goggle eyes, and stood staring at me and blinkan like a fool. Then he cried Hoo! hoo! Tu-wit, tu-woo; and, when you opened the door, he flew up the chimney the same way he came down."

The Squire, satisfied with Duffy's explanation, advances, and puts his foot on the hearth-stone, looks at his legs, saying, "Duffy, my dear, these are the very best stockings I ever had in my life. I've been hunting all day, over moors and downs, through furze and thorns, among brambles and bogs, in the worst of weather, yet there isn't a scratch on my legs and they are as dry as if bound up in leather."

The Devil (supposed to be invisible) rises behind Duffy and grimaces at the Squire.

DUFFY:—"I may as well tell 'e master that I shan't knit much more for 'e, because Huey Lenine and I have been courtan for a long time. We are thinkan to get married before winter, and then I shall have a man of my own to work for."

SQUIRE:—"What! Huey Lenine! I'll break every bone in his carcase if he shows his face near the place. Why the devil is in it that a young skit like thee should have it in thy head to get married! Now I'll sit down a minute and talk reason with thee."

[The Squire sits close beside Duffy. The Devil tickles them with his tail. Huey is seen peeping from the oven.]

SQUIRE:—"Give up thy courting with Huey Lenine,
And I'll dress thee in silks and satins fine."

DUFFY:—"No I'll never have an old man, an old man like you,
Though you are Squire Lovell:
To my sweetheart I'll be constant and true,
Though he work all day with threshal and shovel."

The Devil tickles the Squire behind the ears. He sits nearer and places his arm round her waist.

SQUIRE:—"Thou shalt have a silk gown all broider'd in gold,
Jewels and rings, with such other fine things
In the old oak chest, as thee did'st never behold."

DUFFY:—"My sweetheart is young, lively, and strong,
With cheeks like a red rose;
But your time will not be long:—
You have very few teeth, and a blue-topped nose.
So keep your silks and keep your gold,
I'll never have a man so feeble and old."

Here the Devil tickles them both. The Squire hugs and kisses Duffy, who makes less and less resistance.

SQUIRE:—"You shan't find me feeble, though I'm near sixty;
I'm stronger still than many a man of twenty."

DUFFY:—"Your only son is now far away.
If he came home and found ye wed,
What think ye he would say?"

SQUIRE:—"I hope he is already dead,
Or'll be kill'd in the wars some day,
If alive he shan't enter my door,
I'll give thee my land, with all my store,
Thou shalt ride to church behind me upon a new pavillion,
Smarter than Dame Pendar or Madam Trezillian."

DUFFY:—"Dear master, hold your flattering tongue,
Nor think to deceive one so simple and young;

For I'm a poor maid, lowly born and bred;
With one so humble you could never wed.
Keep your distance, and none of your hugging;
You shall kiss me no more till you take me to church.
I'll never cry at Christmas for April fooling
Like a poor maid left in the lurch.
Look! the sand is all down and the pie burned black,
With the crust too hard for your colt's-teeth to crack:
So off to the hall and take your supper."

Duffy rises, takes up from the hearth a pie, which had been baking there, goes out with it, followed by the Squire and Devil dancing. Huey crawls from the oven, saying "Lack a day who can tell, now, what to make of a she-thing?" By the time he gets on his legs Duffy returns, and, assisted by the devil pushes him to doors, saying,

"Now betake thyself outside the door,
Nor show thy black face here any more;
  Don't think I would wed a poor piljack like thee,
When I may have a Squire of high degree."

Duffy and the Devil dance till the Squire returns and joins in a three-handed reel, without seeing the Old One, who capers back into a dark corner at the pass of the dance, and comes close behind him at the pitch. *Curtain drops.— Thunder and lightning.*

The scene changes to Trove Mill, where a long gossip takes place over the new "nine days' wonder" of Squire Lovell having wedded Duffy for the sake of her knitting. Some say she will behave like most beggars put on horseback, and all the women agreed that they would rather be a young man's slave, and work their fingers to stumps, than be doomed to pass a weary time beside such an old withered stock; they should wish him dead and no help for it.

In the next, Duffy (now Madame Lovell) is beheld walking up and down her garden, or hall, decked out in a gown with a long train, hanging ruffles at her elbows, ruff of monstrous size round her neck, towering head-dress, high-heeled shoes, with bright buckles, earrings, necklace, fan, and all other accessories of old-fashioned finery. The bucca-boo is seen grinning, half-hidden, in the corner; whilst Madam walks she sings:—

"Now I have servants to come at my call,
As I walk in grand state through my hall,
Decked in silks and satins so fine:
But I grieve through the day,
And fret the long night away,

Thinking of my true-love, young Huey Lenine.

I weep through many a weary long hour,
As I sit all alone in my bower,
Where I do nothing but pine;
Whilst I grieve all the day,
And fret the long nights away,
In dreaming of my true-love, young Huey Lenine.

Would the devil but come at my call,
And take the old Squire—silks, satins, and all,
With jewels and rings so fine;
Then, merry and gay, I'd work through the day,
And cheerily pass the nights away,
Kissing my true-love, young Huey Lenine."

DUFFY AND THE DEVIL.

Part Second.

"Refinement, too, that smoothens all
O'er which it in the world hath pass'd,
Has been extended in its call,
And reach'd the devil, too, at last.
That Northern Phantom found no more can be,
Horns, tail, and claws, we now no longer see.

    *   *   *   *   *   *

But with your like, when we the name can learn,
Your nature too we commonly discern."

GOETHE'S *Faust.*

Filimore's Translation.

IN a mill scene, after the Squire's marriage, there is a long dialogue, in rhyme, on "the cruel miseries to be endured" by both husband and wife, "when a young maid is wedded to an old man." This can not be given because much of it would now be regarded as indelicate.

In another scene, the Squire's man Jack, and Huey Lenine, discuss the same subject. This is also inadmissible for the same reason. We are reluctant to dismember this old piece, even by so much as may be deemed necessary by persons of fastidious taste, because students of ancient manners would doubtless prefer an unpruned version.

We shall give the remainder of the story as it may be gathered from the play, without dividing it into scenes. And indeed great part of it, for want of convenience in acting, was often recited by Father Christmas, in his character of Chorus. We also omit the mill scenes, as they afforded a kind of by-play, that had little or nothing to do with the main story. Whenever time was required for the principle personages to get ready, a bevy of women were brought on to gossip about old times and the past year's events, or they told stories, danced, or sung until their turn came to "serge their flour," (bolt their meal.)

Duffy complaind to the kind old witch that she was very dissatisfied with her aged spouse. The old crone advised her to have patience and well feather her nest, that she might secure a youthful successor to Squire Lovell, who was'nt likely to trouble her long. Notwithstanding Madam's griefs, she kept the Bucca-boo to his work, so that all her chests and presses were filled with stockings, blankets, yarn and home-spun cloth; and her husband was clad, from top to toe, in devil-made garments. Squire Lovell, as was his wont, being away hunting every week-day, from dawn till dark, and the housekeeper and other servants hearing a constant rumbling throughout the house like the noise of a spinning-wheel, only varied by the clicking of cards, thought their mistress busy at work, when she spent great part of her time at the mill.

The stocking that Duffy made out to be knitting, but never finished, had always a stitch down. By that old Betty suspected her of having strange dealings as well as herself.

Though the time seemed long and wearisome to Madam, the term for which the devil engaged to serve her drew near its end: yet she was ignorant as ever of his true name, and gave herself but little concern on that account, thinking it might be just as well to go with a devil, who was so very obliging, as to remain with old Squire Lovell; for all the time this Bucca-boo became, as it were, her slave, he was well-behaved and never gave her the least reason to complain of his conduct.

Yet when she walked through Trove orchards, and saw the apple-trees weighed down with ripe fruit, she had some misgivings, lest her next abode might be less pleasant than Trove, besides, she thought that the devil, like most men, might be very civil in courtship but behave himself quite otherwise when he had her in his power.

Madam being much perplexed made her troubles known to Betty, the witch, who, cunning woman as she was, had'nt found out the particulars of the bargain. She was'nt much surprised, however, when Duffy told her, because she knew that women and devils were capable of doing extraordinary things. Betty was somewhat troubled, but not much; for in old times, white-witches could perform almost incredible feats, by having devils and other spirits under their command. So, after twirling her thumbs a minute, and thinking what to do, she said, "Duffy, my dear, cheer up! I would'nt like for 'e to be taken away before me. Now do what I advise 'e, and it is much to me if we don't find 'e a way to fool this young devil yet, he is but a green one. So, to-morrow evening, soon after sunset, bring me down a black jack of your oldest and strongest beer. But before that, be sure you get the Squire to go hare-hunting. Fool him with the old story, or any thing else to make him go. Wait up till he comes back, and note well what he may say. Go 'e home now: ask me no questions; but mind and do what I have told 'e!"

Next morning, the Squire noticed that his wife ate no breakfast, and, at dinner, observing that she seemed very sour and sad, and appeared to loath everything on the board, he said,

"My dear wife, how is it that you have been so melancholy of late? What is the matter with 'e? Don't I do as much to comfort 'e as any man can? If there's anything to be had, for love or money, you shall have it. You don't appear to have much appetite, honey; what would 'e like to eat?"

"I could just pick the head of a hare, if I had it," she replied; "I am longing for hare-pie; but you have been so busy about the harvest that we havn't had one for weeks, and I'm feeling so queer that have one I must or the consequences will be awful to the babe unborn, and to you as well."

"You know dear," said the Squire, "that harvest is late. We have still much corn to get into the mowhay. Besides, it's full time that all should be ready for cider-making. I would do my best to catch a hare if that would please ye," he continued, over a bit; "but dont 'e think that the old story about the child, that according to your fancy has been coming to and again for the last three years, is ever going to fool me to the neglect of corn and apples."

"Hard-hearted, unbelieving wretch," replied she, "you don't deserve to be the father of my child. Know, to your shame, that innocent virgins, when first wedded are often deceived with false hopes. Now would 'e have our cheeld disfigured for the sake of such little good as you are among the harvest people? An old man's bantling," she continued, "is mostly a wisht and wizened-looking object! Would 'e like to see ours with a face like a hare besides an ugly nose, and a mouth from ear to ear? Go, do, like a dear, and stay my longing; but in the evening, after croust (afternoon refreshment), will be time enow for 'e to start, that we may have one for dinner to-morrow."

With coaxing, scolding, and hopes of paternal joys, she, at length prevailed.

Soon after the Squire and his dogs were out of sight, Duffy drew about a gallon of beer, that was many years old, into a strong leather jack, made small at the mouth like a jar, for convenience in carrying, and took it down to the mill. Betty, after trying the liquor, said it would do, and told Duffy to go home, make the devil work till dark, wait up for her husband, and keep her ears open to all he might say. When nearly dark and a few stars glimmered, Betty turned the water from the mill-wheel and closed the flushet. Then, having donned her steeple-crowned hat and red cloak, she fastened the jack of beer to one end of a "giss" (hempen girth), and her "crowd" to the other, slung them across her shoulder, under her cloak, took a black-thorn stick, closed her door, and away she went over the hill. She went up the "Bottom" (glen) between Trove and Boleigh, till she passed the Fuggo Hole, and there, amongst the thickets, she disappeared! All this Bottom was well-wooded, and the upper part thickly covered with hazel, thorn, and elder; and a tangled undergrowth of briars, brambles, and furze, surrounded a wood called the Grambler Grove. Few persons liked to pass near this place, because strange noises were heard, and fires often seen within it by night, when no one would venture near the place.

Duffy waited up many hours after the servants had gone to bed, in great impatience for her husband's return. Her fears and doubts increasing, she remained seated in the kitchen chimney-corner, attending to a pie on the hearth; that it might be kept hot for the Squire's supper. It came into her head at times, as a kind of forlorn hope, that the crafty old witch might somehow get the Devil to take her husband instead of herself. About midnight, however, her uneasy musings were interrupted by the dogs rushing in, followed by Squire Lovell, who seemed like one distracted, by the way he capered about and talked in broken sentences, of which his wife could make neither head nor tail. Sometimes he would caper round the kitchen, singing snatches of a strange dancing-tune; then stop, try to recollect the rest, and dance till tired out. At last the Squire sat down and told his wife to bring him a flagon of cider. After draining it, he became more tranquil, and, when Duffy asked if he had caught a hare, he answered,

"I've seen queer sights to-night, and the damn'd hare—as fine a one as ever was chased—most in the dogs' mouths all the while. We coursed her for miles, yet they couldn't catch her at all." Then he burst out singing,

"To-morrow, my fair lady,
You shall ride along with me,
Over land and over sea,
Through the air and far away!"

O! the funny devil! How he tossed up his heels and tail when he danced and sang,

"'To strange countries you shall go,
For never here can you know.'

"I've forgotten the rest," said he, after a pause; "but give me supper, and fill the tankard again. Then I will begin at the beginning, and tell 'e all about the strange things I've seen to-night. I wish you had been there; it would have made ye laugh, though I havn't seen 'e so much as smile for a long time. But give me supper, I tell thee again, and don't stay gaping at me like a fool frightened! Then, and not before, I'll tell thee all about our uncommon chase, and we will ride 'Over land, and over sea, with the jolly devil, far away, far away!'"

Duffy placed a pie on the board and helped the Squire.

After supper he came more to himself, and said,

"We hunted all the way down, both sides of the Bottom, from Trove to Lamorna without seeing a hare. It was then dark, but for the starlight: we turned to come home, and, up by Bosava, out popped a hare, from a brake of ferns close beside the water. She (the hare) took up the moors; we followed close after, through bogs, furze, and brambles, helter-skelter, amongst mire and water. For miles we chased her—the finest hare that ever was seen, most in the dogs' mouths all the way, yet they couldn't catch her at all. By the starlight we had her in sight all the way till far up the Bottom, between Trove and Boleigh; there we lost all sight and scent of her at last, but not till, tearing through brakes of brambles and thorns, we found ourselves in the Grambler Grove. And now," continued he, after a pull from the flagon, "I know for certain that what old folks say is true—how witches meet the Devil there of summer's nights. In winter they assemble in the Fuggo Hole, we all know; because one may then often hear the devil piping for their dance under our parlour floor—that's right over the inner end of the Fuggo. And now I believe what we took for a hare was a witch that we chased into this haunted wood. Looking through the thickets I spied, on a bare spot, surrounded by old withered oaks, a glimmering flame rising through clouds of smoke. The dogs skulked back and stood around me like things scared. Getting nearer, and looking through an opening, I saw scores of women—some old and ugly, others young and passable enow as far as looks go. Most of them were busy gathering withered ferns or dry sticks, to the fire. I noted, too, that other witches, if one might judge by their dress, were constantly arriving—flying in over the trees, some mounted on ragworts, brooms, ladles, furze-pikes, or anything they could get astride of. Others came on through the smoke as comfortable as you please, sitting on three-legged stools; and alighted by the fire, with their black cats on their laps. Many came in through the thickets like hares, made a spring through the flame, and came out of it as decent lasses as one might see in Buryan Church of a holiday. A good large bonfire soon blazed up; then, by its light, I saw, a little way back sitting under a tree, who should 'e think? Why no less than old witch Bet, of the Mill. And by her side a strapping dark-faced fellow, that wasn't bad looking and that one wouldn't take to be a devil at all but for the company he was with, and the sight of his forked tail that just peeped out from under his coat-skirts. Every now and then Old Bet held to his mouth a black leather jack, much like ours, and the Devil seemed to like the liquor by the way he smacked his lips. Now said I to myself I don't much dislike nor fear thee, devil or no, as thee art so honest as to drink hearty. So here's to thee, wife!"

Duffy was very impatient, but took care not to interrupt the Squire. After draining the flagon, he continued to say,

"Faix, I should think the Devil got drunk at last by the way he capered when the witches, locked hand-in-hand, danced round the fire with him in their midst. They went round and round so fast one couldn't follow their movements as Betty beat up on her crowd the old tune of

'Here's to the Devil, with his wooden spade and shovel,
  Digging tin by the bushel, with his tail cocked up.'"

"Over a while Old Bet stopped playing; the Devil went up to her, drained the jack, took from her the crowd, and sang a dancing-tune I never heard before. The words, if I remember right were,

'I have knit and spun for her
Three years to the day,
 To-morrow she shall ride with me,
Over land and over sea,
Far away! Far away!
 For she can never know
That my name is Tarraway!'"

"The witches then sung as a chorus,

'By night and by day
 We will dance and play,
With our noble captain—
Tarraway! Tarraway!'"

"I thought the words odd for a dancing-tune, but devils and witches do queer things."

"The witches, locked hand-in-hand, danced madder and faster, pulled each other right through the fire, and they wern't so much as singed, the bitches. They spun round and round so fast that at last, especially when the Devil joined in, my head got light. I wanted to dance with them and called out as I advanced, 'Hurra! my merry Devil, and witches all!' In an instant, quick as lightning, the music stopped, out went the fire, a blast of wind swept away umers (embers) and ashes, a cloud of dust and fire came in my eyes and nearly blinded me. When I again looked up they had all vanished. By good luck I found my way out of the wood and home. I'll have another hunt to-morrow and hope for better luck."

The Squire drank another flagon of ale; then, weighed down with fatigue and drink, he rolled from his seat on to the floor. Duffy covered him up. He often passed his nights thus, when too drunk to go over stairs. As she threw over him a rug, and kicked a pile of rushes from the floor, in under his head, he murmured, "To-morrow, we will ride over land and over sea, through the air and faraway!"

It was hours after sunrise when Squire Lovell awoke and found his wife sitting near him; but she didn't say a word about his going a-hunting; in fact she would rather not be left in the house alone, or with servants only. Late in the afternoon, however, he whistled to his dogs and away he went a hunting again. As he had a mind to see, by daylight, the ground he coursed over, and where the witches danced, he took his way towards the Grambler Wood. Now Duffy hadn't been upstairs for all that day, but, a little after sunset, she went up to the guest-chamber, as a large spare bed-room was called, to fetch something she much wanted. She took the garment from a hanging-press, and hastened to leave the chamber, but, when she passed round the bed she beheld the bucca-boo, standing before her, in the doorway. She never saw him looking so well, nor so sprucely dressed, before. From beneath a broad-brimmed hat and plume his coal-black hair fell in glossy curls on his shoulders. He wore a buff coat of fine leather, with skirts so long and full that they quite concealed his forked tail, or he might have coiled it round his waist for what we know, any how there wasn't so much as the tip of it to be seen.

Madam surveyed him, over and over again, from the golden spurs on his bright black riding-boots to the nodding plume on his high pointed hat, and thought she had never seen a more likely-looking fellow. Yet she was speechless from fear or surprise. The devil, advancing with stately step, doffed his hat, and bowing, said in courteous tones,

"Know, fair lady, the time is passed and some hours over that I engaged myself to work for ye, and I hope that you have no reluctance to fulfil your part of our agreement."

"Indeed no," said she, "I can't say I have much objection as you are a very well-behaved obliging devil, and, during the three years that I have had the pleasure of your acquaintance, you have given me no reason to complain of your conduct. Yet," continued she, after a moment's pause, "I'd like to know where you live when at home, and what sort of a country it is? I fear it may be rather hot, as you seem to be burnt very dark!"

"As to where my country is," replied he, "You wouldn't be much the wiser if I told 'e all about it, because you have hitherto seen so little of the world, and there would be great difficulty in making 'e understand. As a proof, however, that my country's climate isn't much to be complained of, you see me strong and healthy enow; besides, I'm not so dark-skinned under my clothes; and, if you were burned as black as myself, I would love ye all the same."

"I can't quite make up my mind," said she, "though no doubt you would please me as well, and make a better husband than Squire Lovell, who, if he isn't drunk, snores all night with his face to the wall. If I went how would 'e convey me to your far country?"

"I have brought to the Grambler Grove a noble steed," he replied, "that will go over land and sea, or fly through the air with lightning speed. Now do make haste, dear, and get ye ready for my horse is very impatient to be left alone; he may whistle for me and shake down the chimney-tops, or paw the ground and make all the country tremble; yet he is as gentle as a lamb when mounted. So come along as you are; there's no time for delay," said he, offering his hand.

"If you please," said madam, shrinking back, "I would like to stay in Trove a little longer."

"Now, no nonsense," said the devil, in an angry tone; "You know that I have been true to my word, as every gentleman ought, and trust you will abide by our bargain: and as for your knowing my name," added he, with a haughty air, "that's impossible, because it is long since that I, like other persons of quality, have only been known by my title, and even that is not familiar to vulgar ears." Assuming his ordinary courteous manner, he said, "Yet, my love, for mere form's sake I'll ask 'e three times if ye like! Besides, I'm curious to know what sort of a guess you will make at it. So now, for the first time asking, tell me if you can, what is my name?"

"My dear Mr. Devil," said she, "don't 'e take offence if I happen to misname ye in my ignorance. Now arn't 'e my lord Beelzebub!"

"No! be d——," replied he, choaking with anger, "how could ye even think me such a mean, upstart devil as Beelzebub, whose name isn't known in the place where I belong; and, even here, among those best acquainted with him, nobody ever heard of his grandfather! Now I hear my horse shaking his bridle and, for the second time, I ask ye my name?"

"Pray excuse my ignorance and don't 'e be vexed," said she, "for I don't doubt but you are a grand gentleman when at home and no other, I think, than Prince Lucifer!"

"What? Lucifer!" he exclaimed, more than ever enraged; "you make me mad but to think that I should ever be taken for one of such a mean tribe as Lucifer, who is no better than the other. As for me, I wouldn't be seen in their company. None of their family were ever known or heard of in this country till lately. Great indeed is your want of sense," continued he, with a scornful air, "to take me for one of these upstarts. Yet, forsooth, many fools—if one may judge by their fears—seem to reverence them; nay almost to worship them. But crafty folks, who profit by fools' fears, havn't a good word to say of these new buccas behind their backs, nor yet of their country; for that, they say, is full of burning brimstone, and one may well believe it, for when any of the tribe come here they stink of sulphur. But one like you— born and bred in Buryan Church-town—can't have any notion of the antiquity and dignity of my family! If you hadn't been the loveliest of Buryan ladies I would never have condescended to spin for 'e. And now, for the third and last time, I ask what is my name?" On the same breath he added, "come! Give me your hand love, and let's away, for you can never guess it."

Duffy didn't feel much reluctance to go with him, yet was proud to outwit the devil and answered,

"Don't 'e be in such a hurry, old gentleman, Buryan people mayn't be so ignorant as you think them; they live near enow to St. Levan witches to know something of devils and their dealings. YOU ARE TARRAWAY—you won't deny it!"

"No, by my tail," said he, almost speechless with surprise; "I am too proud of my ancient name to disown it. I'm fairly beaten; it's provoking though to be outwitted by a young thing like you, and I can't think however you found it out. But true as I'm a gentleman, if you don't go with me now, the time will come when you'll wish you had, and one day you shall spin for me yet."

Duffy shrunk back, and, in a moment, thick smoke gathered around Tarraway; the room became dark; and he disappeared amidst a blaze of lightning and a rattling peal of thunder, that shook the house from end to end.

Duffy, much frightened, ran down stairs, and, as she entered the hall, in tore old Jone, terrified out of her wits by the kitchen chimney-top rattling down on the hearth where pots, kettles, and pans were all smashed. Their dread was much increased by finding throughout the house a smother of burning wool. Other women servants ran shrieking into the hall. Old Jone said she felt a fit coming on; whilst she looked about for a place to fall down and have her fit comfortable; into their midst rushed the Squire, with nothing on but his hat, shirt, and shoes. At this sight all the women have fits; the Squire stands for some time, looking on, like one distraught, till the women come to; all rise and run out except his wife; she asked him how he came home in such a plight, and where he had left his clothes. The Squire told her that when he came to the Grambler he had a fancy to see by daylight the place where Old Nick and his witches had their dance the preceding night. He entered and searched all round—over bare places, between the trees, and elsewhere, but saw no signs of any fire having been made in the wood; there wasn't even a handful of ashes, or the grass so much as burnt on the spot where he was sure he saw a bonfire blazing the night before.

He turned to leave this haunted place, by taking his course down the Bottom, but, when he was just out of the wood, a blinding flash of lightning surrounded him like a sheet of flame, whilst he was stunned by louder thunder than he ever heard before. When he recovered his senses and opened his eyes he found that all his home-spun woollen garments were burned from his breech and his back, leaving him as he then stood. He believed it was all done by witchcraft, because he saw their devilish doings. He told his wife to fetch him a coat, stockings, and breeches.

Duffy, disliking to go upstairs alone, called Jone to accompany her, and great was her terror to find that every article of Tarraway's work had disappeared from chests and presses—nothing was left in them but Squire Lovell's old moth-eaten garments covered with dust and ashes. He was very dissatisfied with his old clothes, but there was no help for it.

As clever a conjuror, or pellar, as any in the west country was fetched. He declared that it was all exactly as Squire Lovell thought—the devil and witches had served him out because he wanted to pry into their doings, and had chased one of them in the form of a hare. The wise man nailed old horse-shoes over the doors, and promised, for little pay in proportion to his services, that he would take Trove and the Squire's household under his protection, so that they need fear no more mischief from witchcraft, nor bad luck.

Madam, by the witch's aid, had a happy riddance of Tarraway, yet greater troubles were in store for her. Squire Lovell, disliking to be seen again wearing his old stockings, would neither go to church nor to market, and instead of hunting, as was his wont, from dawn till dark, he stayed indoors all day, in a very surly mood, to keep his wife at her spinning; and she knew no more how to spin than when she summoned the bucca-boo to work for her.

The Squire having forbade Betty the witch to come near his house, Duffy had little chance to see her; but one Thursday evening when he was off guard—up to the blacksmith's shop in Boleigh, to hear the news from returning market-people, as was his custom—Duffy hastened off to Mill and made known her troubles, and the next market-day Betty went to Penzance and bought the best stockings she could get. On Sunday morning Duffy brought them to her husband and passed them off as her own work; but he wasn't at all satisfied, because they wern't so fine and soft as what he had been accustomed to for three years. He wouldn't go to church in them; he went a-hunting, however, and returned very cross, for his new stockings didn't protect his legs from brambles, furze and wet, like Tarraway's. He again staid indoors to keep his wife to spin, and Madam was obliged to twirl her wheel all day though she only spoiled the wool, for unless he heard the sound of turn or cards, he would be up to the wool-chamber door calling out, "art thee asleep Duffy, lazy slut that thee art, I havn't heard cards nor turn for an hour or more, and unless thou very soon makest me better stockings than the rags on my legs, and a good breeches too, I'll know the reason why, that I will, you lazy faggot you, what the devil else did I marry thee for I'd like to know." She would threaten to card his face if he entered, so they led a cat and dog life for months, that seemed years to Duffy, shut up as she was in a dusty wool-loft and not a soul to comfort her or to share her griefs. Her spirits sunk and her beauty faded fast, she thought it had been better by far to have gone with the devil, than lead such an irksome life with old Squire Lovell. Often she prayed Tarraway to come for her, but he turned a deaf ear to her cry, and was never more seen in Trove.

By good luck, when winter and muddy roads came, the Squire took it into his head one Sunday morning to don his jack-boots and jog off to church, that he might learn what was going on in the rest of the world.

It was the Sunday before Christmas. He wished his wife to mount behind him, but she, pretending illness, begged to be excused and said she would be glad to accompany him next time.

Madam watched her good man spurring his Dobbin till he was clear of Trove town-place, then down she ran to Mill and told old Betty that unless she got a speedy release from her irksome task she would drown herself in the mill-pool.

Bet sat a moment on the mill-bed, twirling her thumbs so quick that one could hardly see them spinning round each other, and said, "No, my dear cheeld, dont 'e think of such a thing yet, young and handsome as you are it would be a pity, let's try a scheme that I've thought of, a woman never should despair of finding a trick to fool an old man, and if need be the old witch will stir her stumps and trot again to help 'e, if one plan don't serve we'll try another, for as the old saying is 'nobody ever got out of a ditch by grunting,' what's just popped into my head may answer!" "Do tell me what it is," said Madam. "No, there's no time now," Betty replied. "You have wasted so much already in bemoaning your griefs instead of thinking how to get rid of them, like a sensible body ought, that old master will soon be back from church, and he musn't know that you have been here, so only mind now what I am going to tell 'e."

"Next Saturday, being Christmas-Day, the Squire will no doubt go to church and desire you to go with him; by all means go, and when, as usual after churching, you stop at the cross to exchange greetings with other gentry, I'll come near enow for 'e to hail me with 'A Merry Christmas to 'e An Betty, and a Happy New Year when a do come.' I shall wish 'e the same, and you invite me, before the Squire, to come up in the evening to taste your Christmas beer. And in the afternoon when, according to custom, there will be a hurling match from Church-town to Boleigh, the Squire and you, with scores of gentlefolks, on horseback and afoot, will be near the goal to see the ball brought fairly in, and to hinder fighting; then look 'e out for me, give your kindest greetings again, and don't 'e be surprised at anything you may hear and see, or if you be don't 'e show it, and invite me again to partake of your Christmas cheer. That's all I have to tell 'e now," said she, opening her door for Duffy to depart, but going a few steps on the Green she continued, "It don't cost 'e any pain, no not a bit, to speak kindly to a poor body now any more than before you became Madam Lovell, and as good a lady as the best in Buryan, for you are no ways vain; but if you had ever shown any scornful pride be assured I would never have gone a trotting for 'e, nor do what I intend, to get 'e relieved of your troubles: besides it isn't your fault that you can neither knit nor spin, you never had a kind mammy to teach 'e. And no one can blame ye for deceiving old Squire Lovell—lying and deceit come to us poor women by nature—so hasten home, leave the rest to me, and hope for better times."

Madam got home just in time to see that dinner was ready, when her husband returned in a good temper after his morning's ride.

"Duffy, my dear," said he, as she assisted him to pull off his boots, "I wish you had gone to church, everybody was enquiring for 'e, and asking what was become of us this long time that they hadn't seen sight nor sign of us. And some of the women—cuss their itching curiosity they can never be satisfied—wanted to roll down my boot-tops and undo my knee-buckles that they might have a peep at my stockings. But on Christmas-Day come ye along with me, they won't be so foarthing if you be there."

Duffy replied, "my darling man, I'll go with all my heart and see if they carry their impudence so far again, and now dear, make a hearty dinner, and tell me all the news you have heard."

Christmas-Day in the morning, Duffy, as richly attired as any lady in Buryan, mounted on a pillion behind her husband, and away they went to church. After service, a great number assembled at the Cross and sung old charols. Squire and Madam Lovell exchanged many kindly compliments with the Cardews, Harveys, Noys, Penders, Vivians, Gwennaps, and other ancient gentry of Buryan, who were waiting for their steeds.

Whilst wishing her neighbours a Merry Christmas Madam Lovell had kept a sharp look out for old Betty; but had nearly given up all hopes of seeing her, and was about to mount behind the Squire, when glancing around for the last time she spied her steeple-crown and red mantle among the crowd of singers, through whom she had great trouble to lead her fat and lazy Dobbin to the heaving-stock. Madam went to meet her, shook hands heartily and said, "good morrow to 'e Dame Chymellan, how are 'e an; I am glad to see ye looking so well and wish 'e a Merry Christmas and a Happy New Year, and many of them. I hope you liked the sermon and the singing, and so on;"—we can't tell all the fine compliments that passed so long ago.

"Thank your honour, and I wish 'e the same," the old dame replied, making a low curtsey to Duffy. Then turning round to other gentlefolks, she continued to wish all their honours—as she styled them—the compliments of the tide, calling each by name as she curtsied to every one.

Now there was nothing remarkable in An Betty's civil words; but as she stood close beside the Squire, who was on horseback, and bestowed her old-fashioned greetings at every curtsey, an unseemly noise was heard. Squire Lovell got vex't, the ladies looked confused, glanced at him and rode off.

Betty, however, without appearing to hear or to heed anything, mounted the heaving-stock, settled herself comfortably on her high-peaked bow-pad, and jogged away with Dame Pendar; Squire Lovell and others going the same road. At parting Duffy said to her, "now be sure An Betty you come up early to try our Christmas-cake and ale." "Thank your honours I will," replied she, in turning off to the Mill.

It was customary for the Squire's tenants, and all who choose, to assemble at his house every night from Christmas-Eve till twelfth-night, to freely partake of his abundant cheer and help in the merry disports of the tide; yet he wasn't at all pleased because his wife invited the old dame. "I should'nt have minded her coming at any other time," said he, "but to-day a good many from the hurling will come home with us and pass the evening; I hope however, she will be on her best behaviour before the quality: to be sure one don't like to offend the spiteful old witch for fear of her tricks."

In the afternoon Squire Lovell and his wife, with many others—mostly on horseback—were got together near Daunce-Mayn when old Betty stalked in to their midst, and just such another scene was acted there as took place in Church-town.

Many who came from a distance went down to Trove to pass a merry Christmas night.

A score or more of ladies and gentlemen, seated in the hall, pledged each other in hot-spiced-ale, brandy, punch, and wine, when Betty, Jone and others entered, holding aloft their horns of foaming liquor. The Squire fearing another display of Betty's unbecoming behaviour, rose in haste to prevent her drinking their healths with all the honours. "Stay a moment An Betty," said he, "come into the kitchen, I must tell 'e that twice already to-day you have made me ashamed of 'e, how could 'e do so and show so little respect for the company both in Church-town and Boleigh?"

"O dear master, you musn't mind such a trifle as that," replied she, without budging an inch, "for it will soon be all the same with madam there, your honour's wife, if you keep her to spin so much, she won't be able to help it for her life. You may look scared and misbelieving, but indeed she won't; no! no more than I can whenever I move quick, or curtsey to your honours as I am, in duty, bound to do; and if your honours would like to hear how it happened to me I'll tell 'e."

Many of the company having intimated that they would like to hear how she became in such a condition, Squire Lovell placed her in a settle near the hearth, she emptied her horn and gave the following relation:—

"Know then, your honours, that in my first husband's time,—more than thirty years ago,—we lived at Trevider. I did out-door work and helped old mistress besides, when there was extra house work, such as great brewings, cheese-making, the baking and roasting at feasten-tides, spinning for the weavers, besides the regular spinning of winter's nights, and such like. Though I say it, there wasn't a brisker lass in Buryan than I was then; just like mistress there, your honour's wife. There was no woman and but few men that could beat me in shaking liners (threshed wheaten sheaves), leading trusses, branding turves, raking tabs (roots, grass, &c.), reaping, rulling, aye, or binding either on a push; and I could make an arish mow as well as any man. Old master used to say that at the windan-sheet (winnowing-sheet), there wasn't my equal in the parish for handling the sieve and kayer (coarse sieve), and that I made a better sample of corn, and not half so much after-winding and waste, as any other windster he ever met with; but I needn't blow my trumpet any more on that score. My old mistress, Madam Pendar, was a noted spinster, as you may have heard, and of winter's-nights she, with her servant maidens and I, took our places at the turns (spinning wheels); master and the servant men carded and sung three-men's songs or told old drolls the while. My spinning-work was soon equal to Madam Pendar's though she would never allow it; but my yarn was strong, even, and fine, just like your honour's wife's," said Bet, addressing Squire Lovell to fasten his attention. "And often I was kept spinning all day for days running, just like mistress there. But one Christmas night every body belonging to Trevider, young and old, went off in a Guise-dance, except old mistress and I. 'Now they are all gone, Betty,' said she, 'and left us all alone, see if we don't enjoy ourselves.' Mistress drew a good joram (jug) of strong old ale, boiled, sweetened, and spiced it whilst I roasted the apples; we brewed a drink fit for a king; for hours we pledged each other's good health and drank to our heart's content. Over a while mistress began to brag of her spinning, she was proud of her work and so was I of mine, just like your honour's wife. I shall ever remember that Christmas-night and how cherry the old hall looked with the Christmas-log burning bright, and faggots of oak and ash blazing up the chimney, showed every window, dresser and wall decked in holly, box, and ivey; with branches of bays and rosemary around the pewter flaggons, plates, and platters, that shone like silver among the Christmas greenery.

Old mistress boasted much of her spinning, and wager'd a bottle of brandy—which she placed on the board—that she would spin a pound of wool in a shorter time, and make a finer yarn than I could. I took her to her word, rolled up the rushes from the floor, to make a clear run all the length of the hall, and placed our turns, while mistress weighed and carded the wool, divided the rulls, and gave me my choice of them. When all was ready, to cheer our hearts and put life in our heels, we each drank a noggin of brandy. Then I tripped backward and forward as light as a feather, and for more than three hours we twirled our wheels by the bright fire-light, keeping good time together. My yarn was suant (even) and fine as a flaxen thread; just like that spun by my lady there, your honour's wife, and I was then about her age. I had nearly spun my pound of wool, and never felt in better heart for dancing to the turn, when, as bad luck would have it, my twadling-string—weakened with so much stepping backwards—burst. I fell to the ground, and ever since I've been in the sad predicament that so surprised your honours. Though it's comforting to have companions in affliction," said she, after a pull at the flaggon, "yet from the regard I have for your honour and mistress there, I have spoke of my ailment to warn 'e that as sure as I sit here with a broken twadling-string it will soon be the same with my lady there, if it's true, what I do hear, that you keep her to spin from morn till night most every day of the year. When that do happen you will be frighten'd into fits; old mistress was so scared that she nearly lost her senses, she thought the house falling about her ears, to save herself she snatched the bottle and tore up stairs; next day she was found asleep under a bed with the empty bottle close by her head."

Old Betty's story rather surprised the company, and Squire Lovell, much concerned, said "I'm glad you told me An Betty, now drink another horn full like a dear; I wouldn't for the world that my darling Duffy should be in such a plight, nevermore shall she spin from this very night. I would go bare leg'd all my life, rather than such a mishap should befall my wife."

The entertainment concludes with a dance, to music made by Father Christmas on a crowd.

CELTIC MONUMENTS OF BOLEIGH AND ROSEMODRASS.

Dear land of old romance,
Legend and mystic dance;
Lost towns and temples, and that buried shore
Where thy great hero fought his last sad fight,
Cromlechs and quoits and cairns and hills of war,
Circles of mystery and mounds of might.

W. K. D.

ABOUT a furlong south-west of Trove, but on a tenement of Boleigh, is the Fuggo. It consists of a cave about six feet high, five feet wide, and near forty long, faced on each side with rough stones, across which long stone posts are laid. On its north-west side a narrow passage leads into another cave of similar construction and unknown extent; as it has long been blocked up by a portion of the roof having fallen in. One may be pretty sure, however, that much of the stories about its great length are fabulous. They say that it extends from its entrance, at the foot of Boleigh hill, to the old mansion at Trove; in proof of this the old one has often been heard piping under a parlour of the house. It is supposed he meets the witches down there, who have entered by the Fuggo to dance to his music. Hares are often seen to enter the Fuggo which are never known to come out the same way; they are said to be witches going to meet their master, who provides them with some other shape to return in.

There are also traditions of this cavern having served as a place of refuge to some of the Levelis in troublesome times; and of its having frequently been used by our fair-traders, as it afforded them a secure hold for storing their goods, and to have a carouse therein.

Old traditions about the far-reaching and unknown extent of the Fuggo, may not, however, be altogether void of foundation. At the annual excursion of the Royal Institution of Cornwall, in 1871, Mr. H. M. Whitley, of Truro, remarked that the bank, just opposite the branch cavern, sounded hollow, from which he is persuaded that there is a chamber underneath to be yet explored.

There are the remains of a triple entrenchment near, and this subterranean passage might have been connected with it.

Old folks of the neighbourhood say that there was another Fuggo in Trove Hill, on the opposite side of the Glen, but the entrance has long since been closed, and no one knows exactly where it opened.

The track of moor and croft between Trove and Boleigh has indeed never been thoroughly examined by our antiquaries; yet as the vestiges of ancient British habitations are generally found in the vicinity of prehistoric monuments, the Daunce-mayn, Menheres, and holed-stones on the hill, would seem to indicate that this sheltered glen might be a likely place in which to find the remains of old crellas or circular huts, similar to those of Bodennar, Busullow, and Chysauster. And farther up, near the brook, amidst brambles and furze may yet be discovered traces of ancient Celtic dwellings, with ashes still on the hearth and quern and muller beside it.

A short time ago an old inhabitant of Boleigh informed us that many persons in that neighbourhood are afraid to enter the Fuggo, even by day, as they believe that bad spirits still frequent this place. Women of villages near often threaten their crying babies that they will carry them down to the Fuggo, and leave them there for the Bucca-boo if they don't stop their squalling. There are traditions that almost all these caves were haunted by beings of a fearful nature, whose path it was dangerous to cross.

The fuggo at Bodinnar, called the Giant's Holt, was a few years ago much dreaded, as it was thought to be the abode of ugly spriggans that kept watch and guard over treasures which still remain buried in that ancient hiding-place.

There is a somewhat graceful creation of fancy associated with the Vow, or fuggo, at Pendeen, which is said to extend from the mansion to Pendeen Cove, and some say it has branches in other directions, which spread far away from the principal cavern.

At dawn on Christmas Day the "Spirit of the Vow" has frequently been seen just within the entrance, near the Cove, in the form of a beautiful lady, dressed in white, with a red rose in her mouth. There were persons living, a few years since, who had seen this fair but not the less fearful vision; for disaster was sure to visit those who intruded on the spirit's morning airings.

Many of the "sawns" in the western cleaves have also similar legends connected with them, only the dwellers in sea-side caverns, are either of the mermaid race, or what we call Hoopers. The latter are beneficent spirits who warn fishermen from going to sea when there is an approaching tempest.

The Hoopers shroud themselves in a thick fog which stretches across coves frequented by them. There are well remembered stories of Sennen Cove

Hooper that used to rest in a cloud of mist, on Cowloe, and thence emit its doleful notes as a danger signal.

BOLEIGH OR BOLEIT.

Although we never heard of any Household Stories connected with this interesting spot, yet we cannot pass it without some notice of its prehistoric remains.

Our antiquaries follow the fashion of spelling the name of the hamlet on the hill as above, yet everyone here who ought best to know the name of the place in which they live, call it Bolé. Most likely it has been thus pronounced from long before it was ever written. All sorts of contradictory meanings have been given for the name of this noted place; as the dairy-house, place of slaughter, &c. It was once the residence of an old Norman family, whose name, spelt Bolleit, may be seen on a long coffin-shaped slab, which lay on the floor within the tower of Buryan Church a short time ago. The inscription in old Norman-French which borders the edge of this curious tomb says that

† CLARICE: LA: FEMME: CHEFFRIE: DE: BOLLEIT: GIT: ICI: DEV: DE: LALME: EIT: MERCE: KE: PVR: LEALME: PVNT (PRIUNT:) DI: IOR: DE: PARDVN: AVERVND.

This means, in plain English, to say † "Clarice, the wife of Geoffry de Bolleit, lies here: God on her soul have mercy: Who prays for her soul shall have ten days' pardon."[2] Now the "Bo" we know to be another form of Beau, in ancient French names. Leit may be a variation of lieu. The provincial pronunciation of Beaulieu is, in many parts of Northern France, simply Bolè. And this is the nearest approach to the proper sound of the name that a Cornish man would be likely to turn his tongue to form. This old Norman family, as in many other instances, might have done their best to give to their new inheritance a name which was a common one in their former home. This conjecture respecting the derivation is at least as probable as the others. We know of no Cornish name which terminated in leit, yet, if the name be Cornish, it is safer to take the traditional pronunciation of those who live in Buryan than to go by any mode of spelling.

MENHERES.

The most striking objects seen after passing through the hamlet are two large long stones or pillars of granite, sometimes called the pipers, but formerly known as the hurlers, which stand in the fields on the north side of the road. Antiquaries are far from being unanimous in their conjectures as to the purpose intended to be served in the erection of these remarkable stones.

Whether they were astronomical, sacerdotal, or sepulchral monuments—whether erected for all or neither of these objects—the learned think it premature to decide. There is no mark on these mysterious stones to throw any light on the subject. Yet it is pretty certain that all the large menhere stood in pairs; that their bearing is generally east and west; that they are mostly found on an open plain near other Celtic monuments, and the vestiges of ancient British habitations; and we may be sure they were formerly more numerous and regarded as objects of great importance, from the number of dwelling-places, enclosures, and names of old Cornish families terminating in Menhere, as Tremenhere, or Tremener, (Longstone place) Polmener, (Longstone pool) Goonmenhere, (Longstone downs) and many others. Probably many of the companion stones of the erect single pillars may be still found lying along in some hedge, at no great distance, (about the twelfth of the circle north of east or south of west), from those which remain where placed thousands of years ago.

If the menhere (as has been conjectured from being found in pairs, bearing nearly east and west) were intended to mark the times of the equinox or solstice, these seasons being sacred festivals of Baal or the Sun, the desire of the early Christians to obliterate all remembrances of Pagan rites may account for the prostration or destruction of such objects as must have been regarded with religious veneration, from their importance to show the times to sow the grain, and do various kinds of work pertaining to pastoral life; and, above all, to denote the sacred festivals of our forefathers, which we still commemorate in our Midsummer bonfires. These long stones at Boleigh are the more interesting because there are not many of the original pairs to be found standing in the west. There is another pair near Newbridge, and one may be seen lying prostrate in Escols lane, Sennen, at a short distance from the stile on the pathway to Escols village.

There is a tradition that this menhere was taken down from where it stood, in the middle of the field, by a giant, who lived in Escols, by him rolled into the hedge, and his son, ten years of age, placed the trigg (propping stone) as we may still see it. An old lady of Escols informed me that the other stone of the pair was in a hedge at no great distance, prostrate also. The erection of these huge monoliths proves that the animal powers and mechanical skill of our ancestors were of no mean order.

HOLED STONES, &c.

Continuing on the road towards Boskenna, a minute's walk from the Menheres brings us to a holed stone standing in the hedge on the right hand side. This stone has been removed a considerable distance from its original site to form the side of a gateway. The upper portion of the stone is very much broken, and is irregular in shape, yet its head appears to have been triangular and worked to an angle similar to the Men-an-tol at Lanyon.

In the lane near the holed stone is an ancient cross, seemingly placed in the midst of the Druidic monuments to sanctify what the old Celts would not permit the Christian teachers to remove.

There is another holed stone near by, in Rosemodrass lane, placed head downwards, and it serves for the hanging-post of a gate. The form of the head of this stone cannot be easily ascertained, as it is buried so deeply in the ground that only a small portion of the hole is to be seen.

The aperture in both these stones (about six inches in diameter) is too small to pop the smallest, or all but the smallest, baby through; yet the people call them crick stones, and maintain that they were so-called before they were born. Crick stones were used for dragging people through, to cure them of various diseases. As these holed stones at Boleigh have been removed from their original site no satisfactory conclusion can be arrived at as to their primitive use. Some have thought that these stones, in common with the men-an-tol at Lanyon, the tolmen in Constantine, and many others, might have served the same important purpose as the menheres—to fix the proper time for the celebration of the autumnal equinox, by the stones being so placed that the sacred index of the seasons on rising above the horizon would be seen through the perforation, at a right angle to the face of the stone, and that the triangular head of the stone formed such an angle that when the sun was on the meridian, (at certain periods of the year, which were required to be known,) its altitude would denote the time, by its place in the heavens being in a line with the slope of the primitive time-piece, which would then cast no shadow on the ground at mid-day. If these monuments were intended for stone calendars, and any can be found in their original position, it might be possible, at least approximately, to fix the time of their erection, by their present variation from true east and west. If the deviation is in the direction demanded by the precession of the equinoxial points, the difference might be calculated at the allowed rate of fifty seconds a year. There is but little doubt but the men-an-tol still remains where it was first erected.

As urns, or crocks of ashes and charred bones, have frequently been found near these, and other mystic stones, which were generally regarded as Celtic relics, it has been conjectured that long stones, holed-stones, and quoits (cromlechs) were all raised to mark the last resting-places of some noted personages. Is it not as probable that they were erected for the use of the living, and, by being associated with the religious observances of the time and people, came to be regarded as garrac-zans or holy stones; and that the priest, or chief, would desire to be buried near them, prompted by a feeling identical with that of the present time and common to all ages, which makes many desire that their poor dust and ashes may rest near the shrine at which they worshipped, within the bounds of what they regard as holy ground? Sacerdotal communities have always been ready to grant this distinction to the rich, and encouraged this enshrining of the relics of mortality, because the presence of the King of Terrors in the temple augments that mysterious awe with which all ancient theocratical hierarches endeavoured to invest themselves, and all their ghostly appurtenances; as by this means they acquire more power over those who live in dread of the spirit world, easily conjured up by morbid fancies, when surrounded by whatever engenders melancholy.

Besides the tolmen noticed above there are several others in the western part of Cornwall. Some thirty years ago, two holed stones, about the size of those at Boleigh, might be seen in Treen Cliff, at no great distance from the end of Pedny vounder lane, on the sea side of the wheel-road to Castle Treen and the Logan Rock. These stones were amidst other rocks. One was standing upright and the other lying flat on the ground a few feet from it. The old people of Treen did not know what these stones were placed there for.

In a field on the southern side of the lane is the circle of upright stones called by the people of Buryan, Daunce-Mayn. The name is most probably a corruption of Zans Mëyn (sacred stones,) and has nothing whatever to do with dancing maids. The legend that the (originally) nineteen posts were damsels, thus fixed for dancing on Sunday, was evidently suggested by the name to some manufacturer of such wares, who as readily converted the two long stones, in the field across the road, which we have already noticed, into the Pipers, who took to their heels and left the damsels to their fate as soon as their metamorphosis began; but their ungallant action did not avail, as the petrifying power of the cursing saint, who stopped their sweet pipings, overtook them when they ran thus far, and laid them up in stone as we now see them.

No such legend, however, is native to the place, as the old folk only know it from having it repeated to them by visitors, who have seen it in books. They never regard the name as having any connection with dancing maids any more than dairy maids, and the Menhere, changed into Pipers, were known to them by the name of the Hurlers, from their having been a goal for the hurling-run, when the starting-post (where the ball was thrown up) was the cross in the Church-town.

This story affords another example of the way in which the meaning is lost of many an ancient Cornish name, (which tells a history,) from the foolish desire to assimilate the expressive old Cornish name to some unmeaning English nickname. Thus, goon-here-an (the long downs) near Tregonebras, is become goldherring. And the town-arms of Penzance is just as bad a punning kind of Blazon. It is easy to understand how Zans-Mëyn became Daunce-Meyn. A common form of mën is mêdn, as pen changes into pedn, in Tol-Pedn-Penwith. And this is near enough to maiden, for the legend to spring up to account for the name.

Another common name for the Celtic circles is the Nine Maidens. Now, as the usual number of stones in the circle is nineteen, that number may have something to do with the first part of this name, and the latter would come from the Cornish, as before, mêdn.

The Daunce-Mêyn is the best known of all the Druidic circles in the west, as it is within sight from the road frequently taken by those visitors to the Logan Rock who care for seeing the many interesting objects, and fine sea views, visible from the lower road, as we call this route near the sea shore. Yet the circle at Boscawen-un, in the higher side of the parish, is invested with a peculiar interest, from the fact of the opinion held by Dr. Borlase that these circles were places of council of judgment, has been confirmed by an old Welsh triad, which makes this place still more remarkable by naming it as one of the three Gorsedds, or places of judgment for poetry and bardic minstrelsy. This valuable relict of Welsh poetry, as translated by the eminent Welsh scholar, the late Rev. Thomas Price, is in English:—"The three Gorsedds of Peetry of the Island of Britain; the Gorsedd of Boscawen Damnonium; (Damnonium included Cornwall and great part of Devon;) the Gorsedd of Salisbury, in England; and the Gorsedd of Bryn Gwyddon in Wales."

We hope that when the laureate revisits Cornwall he may be induced to go there, and, sitting on a granite throne, by the side of the tall central stone, sing the "Idyls of the King," if only in honour of the Welsh bard who has preserved the remembrance of this remarkable temple where ancient minstrels sung of how Merlin, the enchanter, deceived the beautiful Igerna, so that she received King Uter Pendragon as her husband—how King Uter died, and Arthur, his son, by Igerna, kept his court at "Wild Dundagel, by the Cornish sea"—and how our own Prince Arthur, and his knights of the table rounde, slew all the enemies of Britain. Here they sang of the beauty and guile of the fair and frail Guenever—of the honour and truth of Arthur's knights, and the treachery of Mordred. Here the Bard sounded a lament for the lost lands of Lethowsow, and the submerged City of Langona:—

"Between Land's End and Scilly rocks
Sunk lies a town that ocean mocks.
    *   *   *   *   *
Where breathes the man that would not weep
O'er such fine climes beneath the deep?"

We owe a debt of gratitude to Dr. Borlase for preserving to us a graphic description of these, and many other, Druidic circles which have disappeared since his time.

Fortunately, the work of destruction has been arrested at Boscawen-un circle, as the lady to whom the property belongs has caused it to be surrounded with a good hedge to prevent further spoilation. Some years ago a wholesome fear prevailed of bad luck following anyone who removed these landmarks of a long past age, but now our country folk think themselves more enlightened, and, unless those who have some respect for the monuments of ancient times, take measures to prevent the recipients of this questionable sort of enlightenment from exercising their vandalism, our Celtic remains will soon disappear. Pages might be filled with an account of the destruction which has taken place within the past half century.

That these circles were used for religious, judicical, or political purposes, (and in ancient times all three were combined), there can be no doubt, from the veneration with which they were formerly regarded. This solemn respect was expressed in the belief that the avenging deity, in the shape of Bad Luck (which was felt to be as real a personage as any other undefined invisible demon) would sooner or later overtake the sacrilegious destroyer of the ancient holy stones. In many of the oldest villages there were formerly altar-like stones, known by the name of garrac zans, (the holy stones) which were protected by the fear of the goddess of Bad Luck; and until within these last few years, no rude hand would dare to remove or spoil them. We remember one of these venerated rocks in the village of Rosekestal and another in Sowah town-place. The noted stone in Mayon was also called indifferently the garrac zans or table men. We have heard of many others which were formerly to be seen in the town-places of ancient hamlets, but their places know them no more.

Dr. Borlase describes many circles and other Celtic remains as being in his time almost as perfect as when left by our forefathers thousands of years ago. Of these public monuments, there is now scarcely a trace to be found. Recent investigation proves the trustworthiness of the information preserved by the antiquary, born and bred in Pendeen, in the very heart of a district which contains, even now, more Celtic remains of all kinds than any other portion, of equal space, in the British Isles.

By similar monuments to those we have noticed at Boleigh, the migrations of the ancient Celtic race may be traced from farthest Ind to the Scilly Isles.

THE LAST CARDEW, OF BOSKENNA, AND THE STORY OF NELLY WEARNE.

No ditch is so deep, no wall is so high,
If two love each other, they'll meet by and bye;
No storm is so wild, and no night is so black,
If two wish to meet they will soon find a track.

From KLAUS GROTH'S *Song "Keen Graff is so brut."*

Max Müller's Translation.

THERE are few places which afford such a variety of picturesque views as may be seen in and from the grounds of Boskenna ("dwelling-on-the-ridge.") The sylvan and rural are beheld, forming endless combinations with the grand, the wild, and the romantic. Glimpses of the boundless ocean are caught through overarching boughs in deep winding glens, where the brilliant plants of semi-tropical climes are seen growing in loving companionship with our more modest and sweet native shrubs, ferns, and flowers.

From the height called the Rockery, (surely there must be an old Cornish name,) the view embraces towering carns, distant hills, and headlands, including Castle Teryn and the Lizard Point; scenes of many wild legends and poetic traditions, of Danish invaders, of witches, saints and hermits.

"Far as the eye can peer,
The waters roll, divinely blue and clear;
With white sails flashing in the sunlight's ray,
Of countless vessels, near and far away;

Here the wild sea-gull plumes her snowy breast,
Then skims the wave or perches on the crest
Of some majestic cairn, or cromlech where
Long ages past the Druids knelt in prayer,
Till, with stretched wing, she cleaves the fields of blue,
Dips 'neath th' Atlantic, and is lost to view."

One of the most delightful spots on the grounds of Boskenna is a little wooded glen, through which flows a clear stream, embowered by luxuriant foliage and fringed with ferns, flags, and sedges, amongst which many rare wild flowers show their elegant bells of pale blue, and star-like blossoms of every tint. The brooklet and shady walk wind down this little vale to St. Loy Cove, where, within a few years, there stood on the verge of the cliff, the walls and altar of a chapel dedicated to St. Eloi; but, a few years ago, this interesting relict of the piety of ages past, with its wrought-stone altar, was thrown over cliff by the, then, occupier of an adjacent cottage, without the knowledge or permission of the owner of the property. The vestiges of this sacred building were thus toppled into the sea, merely that a few feet of land might be gained for growing early potatoes; and now nothing remains but the name of St. Loy to connect this romantic spot with the saint by whom Chaucer's "Wife of Bath" was accustomed to swear. We fear that the mention of this realistic, marriage-loving dame may put to flight all poetic notions; yet hear what our Cornish poetess, Mrs. S. E. Tonkin, (from whom we have quoted above) says of this hallowed shrine.

"A pleasant ramble through a bosky vale;
A pause to hear a babbling brooklet's tale;
A moment's lingering by its mossy well,
And I, once more, am in St. Loy's green dell.

Ages ago, as old traditions say,
The monks devout stole here to fast and pray;
Within these wilds they communed by the sea,
And reared for worship a fair chapelry,
Where pious souls, and needy, found them rest,
And by their prayers and sanctity were blest.

Naught now remains to whisper of the past;
Still, o'er the spot a holy light is cast,
In gothic arches yon fair trees entwine,
Low-drooping o'er the consecrated shrine,
And waves come singing, as they inland flow,
Thrilling the heart with strains of long ago."

The place thus favoured by nature and Mrs. Tonkin's verse, was an ancient seat of the Cardew family, who, between two and three centuries ago, also owned Boskenhal and several other farms in the neighbourhood. The last of this decayed family, who lived in the old home of his ancestors, mortgaged this place, and other lands, to the predecessors of the present possessor. The Paynters resided here for some generations, and the late Mr. John Paynter will long be remembered in the West Country as a liberal landlord and kind neighbour; and for being more learned in the law than country justices usually are. It was a common saying in the West, that "the Squire of Boskenna knew more law than all the lawyers of Penzance put together!" This place is now the residence of Charles Dacres Bevan, Esq., Judge of the district County Court. Mr. Bevan has much improved and beautified both the mansion and grounds. Many years ago, the late Mr. Cardew, of St. Ives, (who was descended from a collaterial branch of the Boskenna family) informed us that there were several old family portraits of the Cardews in the mansion of Boskenna during his remembrance. He also related the following traditional

STORY OF NELLY WEARNE.

This damsel was an illegitimate daughter of the last Cardew of Boskenna, and, (according to a very general custom which prevailed in the West) this love-child was bound a parish 'prentice to her father that he might be legally entitled to some degree of guardianship over his irregularly-begotten offspring. Children thus bound to their fathers were mostly regarded as a sort of poor cousins to the legitimate members of the family, and they were often taught a trade or handicraft, or portioned off with some small tenement. Nelly's spendthrift father, however, was a most unsuitable guardian for a young girl. He paid much more regard to his dogs and hunters than to his daughter, who, by all accounts, was very remarkable for her good looks and devil-may-care disposition. The Squire's mother did all an old dame could do to restrain her wild tendencies, and give her a little more gentle breeding than was thought requisite for an ordinary servant. Dancing was one of the accomplishments in which Nelly took most delight, and Madam was rejoiced to find that her damsel was soon the best dancer in Burian. However hard Nell might have worked during the day, she thought nothing of going three or four miles of an evening, in any kind of weather, to enjoy her favourite diversion at some village merry-making. She never missed Burian Fair, which was then regarded by our western lads and maidens as the most joyful holiday of the spring.

When Nelly had become a young woman it happened that one Burian Fair-day the weather was even more tempestuous than usual, though the storms of Burian Fair are proverbial. Madam Cardew had made up her mind that Nelly should remain at home that stormy night, but she protested that neither rain nor wind, thunder nor lightning, nor all the old women in Burian, should hinder her going to Church-town and dancing at the Fair, which only came once a year; and she swore that a reel she would have, before that night was passed, even if she danced with Old Nick. "She would never be married," she often said, "unless she could meet with a man who was able to dance her down; and she would find one that night or the Devil might take her." Off she went in a storm of wind, rain, and thunder, blaspheming and reviling the old lady, who tried to keep her home. Arrived in Church-town, Nelly found dancing going on in every room of the public-house; and violin, fife, or tambourine making music for the revellers in many other dwellings. Nell entered the principal room of the inn; and before she cast off her cloak and wrung the rain from her long black hair, many youngsters asked her to drink and dance with them, but she refused them all, saying they couldn't keep the floor half so long as herself—she would either get some better partner or not have a jig for that night.

Whilst she was declining the offers of her rustic suitors, two dark-complexioned, strapping sailors entered, and one of them, dressed in dashing style, with gold lace on his coat, broad leather belt round his waist, cutlass by his side, and glossy boots reaching to his knees, advanced to Nelly, doffed his hat, bowed, and said, "Pray dance with me, my fair pretty maid?" "With all my heart, sir," she replied, rising and giving him her hand. Nelly's partner called to his comrade, "Now pipe away, Bosun, and give us the good old tune." The seaman addressed as Bosun took a pipe from his pocket, marched round the couple prepared to dance, saying "A floor, a floor, for the lovely Nell and our gallant Capt. Black." The piper blew at first a rather slow measure, to which the captain's heel and toe, true as an echo, showed a new step at every change of pass and pitch. By slow degrees the tune became quicker till it was such as Nelly never moved her feet to before. The lively music soon drew such a crowd into the room to see the dancers, that the floor beams warped and showed signs of breaking. Then, as the storm lulled and a full moon shone bright, the dancers, followed by all the rest, left the house for an open space below the cross. Now every one wanted to treat the seamen, and they drank as much as they could, to show their good fellowship with every one, and Captain Black, giving a purse of gold to the landlady, desired her to send out her best cordials for the women kind, and to keep her beer-cocks running, that all might drink health to him and the lovely Nell.

When one and all had drunk as much as they liked, the Bosun's pipe again rung out so loud and clear that his music was heard for miles away. The Captain, Nelly, and scores of others again danced in joyous style. People from all parts flocked round them; every house in Church-town was soon empty. Old men and women hobbled and danced on their crutches; the piper's lively strains set every one in motion, till the road was covered with dancers, capering like mad folks, all the way from Park-an-cady to the cross and around the churchyard. Soon after midnight, however, whilst their mirth was at its height, there suddenly came on a more violent storm than ever of wind, hail, and thunder. The sky, black as pitch one moment, was all ablaze the next. Streams of lightning fell and ran hissing along the ground. All were terror-struck with the sudden rise of this awful weather. Yet, in the general consternation, some one had the happy thought to ring the bells, that their sound might allay the weather, and drive away the evil spirits who rode on the tempest. With the first stroke of the big bell the thunder-clouds rolled away to the eastward, and at the same instant Captain Black vanished with Nelly and the piper.

This terrific storm, joined with the sudden disappearance of Nelly and the dark looking strangers, so frightened many that they fell down in fits, and others, from the same cause, were never right in their heads again.

On a tract of uncultivated land north of Boskenna lane, there was then a barn, which usually contained a quantity of dry food for the cattle wintered on the downs. This barn, then full of straw and hay, was burned to the ground that Fair-night, and near its ruins were found a handkerchief, full of fairings, with some other things which belonged to Nell, but all search for the wilful damsel was in vain. Most people believed that Captain Black was the Old One, disguised as a seaman, and the Bosun some inferior devil in attendance—that Nell, by her blasphemous language, had brought them from below, whither they had now taken her to dance as best she might. Squire Cardew, being less superstitious than many of his neighbours, conjectured that the strange dancer and piper were nothing worse than two jovial sailors, who had carried her off to their ship—an occurrence far from unusual in these times; and in hopes of gaining some tidings of his stolen or strayed daughter, he rode into Penzance and over to Market-jew, to make enquiries; but he could learn nothing of her. Some said, however, that a strange craft had anchored in Guavas Lake, the Fair-day, and that part of her crew had landed in Newlyn, but nothing farther was known of them, as the ship made sail the next morning.

Nelly's gay songs were missed in Boskenna hall, where she often sung for hours, to cheer the old lady when they were together plying their spinning-wheels, or seated in the window, lighted with the evening sun, at their embroidery. Then, at night, she used to be foremost in the dance with her father and his roystering companions of the chase.

Grief for the strange fate of Nelly shortened the days of old Madam Cardew, who was soon at rest in Burian churchyard, and the Squire took to hunting, drinking, and rioting worse than ever.

Twenty years and more passed; Nelly and the Cardews were all but forgotten; new people possessed their ancient domain; none of their kin remained in the West, but an old well-to-do yeoman and his family, who resided at Sennen.

One dreary afternoon there was a very humble funeral at Burian Church, and the last Cardew of Boskenna was laid beside the dust of his forefathers. Soon after candlelighting on that day, whilst some few who came to see the last of the spendthrift, who had lavished his property upon them, were still drinking in the public house, there entered, dripping wet, and weary, an elderly foreign-looking woman, whose dress of rich stuff and of outlandish make, was travel-stained and much the worse for wear. The large hooped-shaped rings in her ears, joined with her dark complexion and long braids of black hair wound around her head, only covered with the hood of her scarlet mantle, made her appearance still more remarkable.

The stranger enquired if Betty Trenoweth, who many years ago lived in Boskenna, was still alive. She was answered that Betty was alive and well, and lived no farther off than a minute's walk would take her, in a comfortable dwelling of her own, over Trevorgans side of Church-town. Without giving any one the chance to question her as to who she was, or whence she came, the outlandish-looking dame proceeded to Betty Trenoweth's cottage. The elderly woman, who opened her door, asked the stranger in and placed her to sit by her fireside, wondering who she could be and what she could want of her, at that time of night. The stranger in a broken voice and speaking in an unfamiliar tongue, made many enquiries about the Cardews, and appeared to think they were all still living in Boskenna.

Betty informed her that none of the name were then in the place—that her old mistress had long been dead, and the young master was that day buried, having lost all his lands, she couldn't tell how, and the new people had, for years, only kept him there in a condition little better than that of a servant to hunt the same dogs which were his own a short time ago. "But who can you be," she continued, "not to know anything about them now; yet, from what you say, you must have known them all long ago? Oh! if I could but believe that dear Nelly were still alive, from the sound of your voice, so like the tones of the one laid in his grave to-day, I would say that you were she; and if you are, I have kept everything that belonged to ye, and what was found on the morning after the Downs barn was burnt is now in my chest."

"My dear old friend," the stranger replied, "I'm your Nelly. The night I lost that handkerchief I found my husband, but we must have some rest before I can tell ye our history."

Dame Trenoweth showed her delight at again beholding Nelly, by preparing her a good supper and a comfortable bed. In the morning Nelly rose refreshed, and knowing the old woman wished to hear how she had fared since they danced together at Burian Fair, commenced by asking, "Did it never come into your head to think who the dark seaman could be? You had often seen the one, whom many took for Old Nick, dance with me in Boskenna hall, when he, and scores of others, came to Feast. He had to leave the country, because a person he beat in fair fight died from the effects of his lusty blows, three years, or so, before that Burian Fair; and the Bosun, too, was a lad you very well knew."

"Oh," exclaimed Betty, "now I see it all: the one that took you off was young Billy Brea, and his comrade was his cousin Bosvargus, of Kelynack."

"You have rightly guessed," Nelly replied.

"Hundreds of times," Betty continued to say, "old mistress and I have wondered what was become of the wild youngster who was so fond of you, even when a young girl working your sampler; and he, foremost in the hunt or fight, always said he'd have no other wife than the lovely little Nell. And old Madam would often say that, though he might be as poor as poor might be, yet was he come of the gentle blood of the Breas of Brea, who at one time were as rich and high as any in the West Country; and their old mansion, with the chapel turned into a barn by those who now occupy their estate, and their chapel on the hill of Brea, still show how grand they once were! I remember, too, the many good offers you had from rich farmers' sons around, and wondered how you refused them all."

When the old dame had somewhat recovered from her surprise, Nelly told her, that, young and thoughtless as she was, until Brea, to avoid trouble to his family, escaped with great haste and secrecy, she had no notion how deep was her love for the unfortunate youngster, and that he, unknown to every one but herself, had been for many days and nights in Boskenna or Treviddern cliff, before Bosvargus found a merchant-ship, in which they both left on a long voyage. Nelly knew if all went right, when they might be expected to return; and Brea promised her that, whenever he came on shore, he'd take no rest till he met her again in the old chapel of St. Loy, where many a long and dreary night she had watched and prayed for his safe return, and often of an evening, or a winter's night, when the inmates of Boskenna thought her in bed, or miles away at some merry-making, she was wandering the cliffs, or waiting in the cairns near by, in hope of meeting with her absent lover. Yet she had only the chance to see him at long intervals, and then only for a short time.

Four or five years after Brea went to sea, he became captain of a ship. Then he proposed to take Nelly with him as his bride, and she, being nothing loath, they met at St. Loy, one night, a little before the Fair, and agreed that, at the Fair, a dance together they would have, and that should be their bridal night. He was so altered, as well as his comrade, the Bosun, that no person but Nelly knew them, and, if they did, no one would betray him, or turn informer.

When Nelly had come thus far in the history of her courtship, Betty said, "Now, my darling, one can understand how, in spite of wind and rain, you were so eager to go to Fair that night; and, faith, I'd go through fire and water for the man I loved when at the mad age you were then. One can see how drink, given without stint, by the open-hearted sailor, together with the music of the Bosun's pipe, set every one dancing in spite of themselves. Then, when the storm so suddenly came, and as suddenly broke, and you vanished in the midst of thunder and lightning, with Brea and his Bosun, everyone believed you were carried off by the Devil, and it's thought so still. But tell me what next became of ye?"

Nelly then related, how when the storm was at its height, Brea took her on towards Boskenna. They intended to see old Madam, say farewell, and take a horse from the stable to help them on their road; but, long before they came to Boskenna gate, with hard weather, drinking, and dancing, Nelly was unable to stand. Then Billy Brea took her up in his arms, and bore her along till they came to the Downs barn, where she fell on the straw half dead. Brea remembered every hole and corner about the place, and knew that a tinder-box, with candle and lanthorn, used to be kept in the barn that one might have light in winters' mornings to bundle up straw or hay for the cattle, and, being anxious to reach his ship early in the morning, wanting to know the time, and not being over steady in the head, when he struck a light and saw by his watch that there was still some hours to daybreak, he, neglecting to put out the candle, fell asleep and only woke to find the place on fire. He drew Nelly from the burning barn, and they hurried on to Mousehole, where they found the Bosun and boat's crew waiting for them.

"And have ye been lawfully married, my darling?" asked the old dame. "Indeed we have," answered Nelly, "not that I cared much about the ceremony; for to me his love was all in all, and from that moment I felt sure of his truth and affection I regarded him as my husband and freely gave him all that love requires. Yet as we were near a port when I was about to become a mother, my husband proposed we should go through the legal form which would entitle our children to bear their father's family name, if they chose; so one may say they are, at least, all truly born. But that was of little consequence, because he was no more known by the name of Brea."

Captain Black, as we shall henceforth call Nelly's husband, offered her a home either on land or on board. She decided to make her abode in his gallant ship; the Captain was pleased with her choice, and she not to be encumbered with an inconvenient dress for such a life, rigged herself in man's attire, and soon learned to do the duty of an able seaman. To act as cook and steward on board ship soon became as natural to her as the care of Boskenna mansion. Besides this, Nelly learned to keep the ship's reckoning and navigation so well, that often, when the Captain was laid low with wounds or fever, she took his place, and by that means saved the ship and ship's company.

During many years they traded from London to distant ports in various parts of the globe, without any serious mishap; but, on a return voyage from the Levant, a Barbary corsair gave chase and overtook them. At that time these sea-robbers seldom levied what they were pleased to call dues for coming into, or crossing, their waters, from any English ships, but often from a motive of revenge as much as for gain, confined their attention to Spanish and French vessels. This Levantine gang, however, attempted to board and take the *Buck*, and many of them were cut down by her crew, as they came up the side, before they gave over and made off. In this encounter Captain Black, Nelly, and several of the crew were badly wounded. This maddened the Captain, and he swore to serve out these cursed pirates if his crew would join him. Nell and all the ship's company, being as eager for revenge as their Captain, and hoping by this neck-or-nothing game to acquire riches quickly, as soon as their cargo was disposed of, the Captain having saved a large sum, procured a suitable craft for privateering which he called the *Lovely Nell*, and when she was well armed and victualled, they made sail for the Levantine seas, where, in a short time, they captured several rich prizes, and, among others, the galleon which was the cause of their becoming privateers. On this crew they took ample revenge.

Nelly, and all the ship's company, liking the excitement of this wild life, and not being over-scrupulous as to the means of getting rich, no sooner neared the Cornish coast that the Captain, Nelly, Bosvargus, and some few others, put ashore, in a boat, at Goonwalla Cove, and buried a quantity of gold in some secret nooks of the cliff. The *Lovely Nell* then took her course for the sea-rovers' rendezvous in the West Indies.

There, many years were passed in buccaneering expeditions to plunder the French and Spanish Settlements, until they had amassed a great quantity of treasure in money and jewels, taken in pillage and for the ransom of prisoners. Nelly said that, for many years, she much enjoyed this roving life. During that time several children were born. And all who lived were boys, who soon became expert sailors, and, after serving their apprenticeship with their dad, all but the oldest and youngest had then left for other vessels.

About a year before the time Nelly returned to Burian, she, with her husband and most of the crew, thinking they were rich enough, wished to give up this roving life, and decided to settle down in their native land. They disinterred the riches they had buried in various uninhabited islands and keys, which were only frequented by such as themselves. The chests of dollars, bars of silver, ingots of gold, ornaments, jewels, and rare gems, which belonged to the Captain's share alone, were worth more than would purchase half-a-dozen such estates as Boskenna, and the dearest wish of her heart was that they might return in time to free that place for her father.

They were many months collecting all their riches. They then set sail from the western main, and arrived with fair weather in sight of the Cornish coast. The wind being light and sea smooth they kept close in shore for the pleasure of gazing on the well-remembered carns and coves.

More than a week before they sighted land, Nelly was seized with a most intense desire to be put ashore at some cove near the Land's End, and, when they beheld the well-known landmark of Burian Tower, saw Castle Trereen, passed Penberth, St. Loy, and Lamorna Coves, her longing to land and see her father was such that she could neither eat nor sleep; and this was about the time he breathed his last.

She begged to be landed in Mount's Bay, but her husband, wishing her to remain on board till their vessel should be disposed of and their riches turned into English money, they passed the Lizard, when, to save her from going mad, she was put ashore at Falmouth. Thence she was brought on horseback to Market-jew, and walked from that place to Burian. Her husband agreed, should the weather permit, to return to Mount's Bay, and there cruise about until she might be ready to proceed along with him, when, as was arranged, she would be taken on board from Mousehole or the Mount. This is the substance of what Nelly related to her old friend, of her adventures up to that night; and when Dame Trenoweth told her how all the Cardews were dead and gone from Boskenna, she no longer desired to see the old mansion, but heartily wished herself again on the ocean with the one for whom she had left her native land and weathered the storms of more than twenty years; she endeavoured to cheer herself with the hope that, ere many days, she would again behold the *Lovely Nell*, sailing, in all her pride of flowing sails, and, walking the quarter-deck, her husband, near enough to be hailed from Reginnis Cliff.

The second day after Nelly's return to Burian, she became anxious to rejoin her husband, as she knew the wind had been favourable for him to beat back to Mount's Bay. It had been arranged that he should cruise about near the coast for a day or two, or until she might give him a signal, from Paul Cliff, to send a boat ashore for her at Mousehole. The following morning Nelly rose by break of day, dressed herself in a suit of seaman's clothes which she had brought with her, left her discarded woman's dress, and a good sum of money, with Dame Trenoweth, and wished her good-bye, saying that she hoped to see her again ere long, when she and her husband would settle down in the West, to end their days in peace.

Before sunrise, Nelly stood on the high headland west of Mousehole, straining her vision in a vain endeavour to pierce the clouds of mist which rolled over the water and hid both sea and shore. She could hear the fishermen's voices and the sound of oars rattling in the row-locks; but, only at the distance of a stone's cast, land, sea, and sky, were all shrouded in fog. A few hours later the mist cleared away. She saw boats returning from the fishing-ground, and a good many vessels passing across the Bay, but no craft that could be taken for her husband's ship.

Tired with watching, from the cliff, the ships as they sailed past, she descended to Mousehole to make enquiries there, if any vessel like the *Lovely Nell* had been seen on the coast. She met with no person until near Squire Keigwin's mansion, and there, near the balcony, were collected a number of people around a pile of such things as are usually found loose on a ship's deck. Nelly joined the crowd, who told her that the water-casks, hatches, buckets, spars, and other articles she saw before her had, that morning, been found floating near Lamorna Cove; and everybody thought that a ship, which was seen cruising near the shore, the night before, must have struck on some dangerous rocks west of Lamorna, sprung a leak, and foundered in deep water, with all hands on board. Nelly, hearing this, rushed through the crowd, examined the wreck, and there saw many well-remembered articles belonging to her husband's ship. Whether Nelly cried, fainted, or gave any other natural expression to her grief, we don't know. Without discovering herself, however, to the people of Mousehole, she remained there all day, hoping to hear something farther from others who had gone out in search of anything which might be floating near the place where it was supposed the vessel must have sunk; but nothing more was learnt of the disaster. Some fishermen, however, said that when the mist cleared away they saw a boat far out to sea, but that they concluded it to be a smuggling craft bound for France.

Late at night Nelly returned crushed with grief, to her old friend who did all she could to console her, and time, which alleviates all sorrows, at last brought relief to the bereaved woman. Then she assisted the old dame in her household work and in carding and spinning—more because constant exercise made her think less of her loss than from any necessity for exertion to gain a livelihood. She had brought with her a good sum of money, intended to pay off the incumbrances of her father's estate (in these times a small amount of gold would buy a large extent of land). She had many valuable jewels besides. An Betty was also well off. Having seen the last of Madam Cardew, the old servant had from her son many valuable dresses and old heirlooms of the family, saved, between them, from the clutches of those who got the besotted Squire into their power, and, long before he died, this old servant of the family was the only one in the wide world to care for him, or who showed him any kindness. Nelly, on her mother's side, being a near relation to Dame Trenoweth, she regarded the poor wanderer as her own daughter. When several months had passed a circumstance occurred which gave Nelly just that uncertain glimmer of Hope against Reason, which is more grievous to bear than the certainty of evil.

A sealed bottle was found in Mount's Bay, containing a paper on which Captain Black's name, and those of several others, were written. It was directed to "Nelly Wearne, Boskenna;" and the news came to her through the gossip of the village. The paper was lost or destroyed without reaching her, because everyone thought that she was an inhabitant of a warmer region.

An Betty one day said to Nelly, "'Tis as good as a play, my dear, to see how all the old women of Church-town try to discover who and what you are, and they can't find out, because, for the fun of the thing, I take good care to fool them." Seeing that Nelly roused herself and took some interest in her talk, she continued,

"They are mad to know how you are never to be seen anywhere out-of-doors, except down in the cliffs, early in a morning or late of moonlight nights."

"Well, and what did you answer to that?" Nelly asked.

"To puzzle them the more," said Betty, "I told the curious, prying fools, that you were a Wise Woman come from the East—that you ramble over cliffs and moors to gather herbs, whilst the morning dew is on them, or when the moon is near the full—that no one can beat you in making from them, ointments, salves, and still-waters—that you understand all sorts of complaints and can cure anything, from the gripes to the palsy. And now all the young wenches in the parish want to know if you can read fortunes; they think you can because you look like a gipsey, so they say. 'Why yes to be sure; nobody better,' I told them. Now listen to me," Betty went on to say, when she had recovered her breath, "I've made them believe that you can read the stars—that you know all that will happen to any body by the lines of their palms—that you can tell, by means of rushes, spring water, and ivy leaves, and scores of ways besides, who are to be married, as well as who are to die unblessed with a husband. And to everything they asked about your knowledge of white witchcraft, I assured them that you knew more about magic, conjuration, and so forth, than the Witch of Endor that we have all heard of."

"My dear old friend," says Nelly, "how could 'e go on so. I know no more about fortune-telling than you do—perhaps not so much, as you're a noted hand for charming."

"No matter for that," answered An Betty, "You know everything remarkable that ever happened in the families round up to the last twenty years or so, and what you don't know I can tell 'e. When they find that you're acquainted with what's past they are sure to believe that you can read them the future. Besides, this game will serve to divert your thoughts from ever dwelling on Billy Brea, or Captain Black, if you have a mind to call him so."

"I don't much mind trying, but how shall I manage to know who they are?"

"You keep in the hale," (best room) Betty replied, "and, before they see you, I'll come in and tell 'e who they are; then, when they enter to consult 'e, be sure, first of all, to give a hint at some scandal that made a noise about their families, no matter how long ago; everything bad is remembered for ages after the good is forgotten. Then promise the young lasses any number of sweethearts and a speedy marriage. You know what you used to wish for in your teens."

In spite of her grief, Nelly, to please the old dame, soon became widely known as the wise woman, or white witch, of Burian Church-town. She read the fortunes of young and old, much to their satisfaction and her own gain. Those who could'nt pay in cash paid in kind. The greatest trouble she had was with the sedate, plain, and sour elderly females, who were all but past hope. They would come, and come again, mad to know if they were ever to be blessed with a husband. By the old woman's advice, Nelly gave them dubious answers and advice for wheedling old hoary-heads and hobble-de-hoys, as they were easiest snared. 'Tis said some were supplied with love-powders, made from the bulbs of plants commonly called Adam and Eve, and that others were furnished with compounds for more questionable purposes. In a little while Nelly became famous for match-making. Her outlandish dress and the strange speech which she affected, made the simple folks, who had never been out of the smoke of their chimneys, think she must have been born and bred in Egypt, or in some other foreign land of which they had heard.

Sometimes, when at a loss to find a suitable response to the wishes or fears of her visitors, she would burst out with long, unintelligible words, as if forgetting herself, and end by saying, "Oh! my dears, know that, far away as I am from my native land, I often think that I am speaking to my cousins, the maidens of Jericho; all the tongues of eastern countries are easier for me than your Cornish speech." At other times she would entertain them with stories of what she had learned from an uncle in Babylon. Besides carrying on these profitable trades of soothsaying, charming, and deviltry, Nelly and Dame Trenoweth made and sold ointments that were in great demand for the cure of various skin diseases, which were more common in those times (when much salt meat was used all the year round) than the same class of distempers are at the present day. The way in which these ointments, salves, or unguents were prepared, was by seething in lard elder-flowers, betony, and other healing or drying herbs, cut fine, until their medical virtues were extracted; then the ointment was carefully strained from the herbs and ready for use. As a remedy for a troublesome distemper, now seldom heard of, they made an ointment from Skaw-dower, the English of the name is water-elder, (the *Scrophularia*.) sulphur was mixed with this unguent for the disease alluded to. Another noted preparation of this time was a golden-coloured salve, made from purified lard and celandine juice; this was much esteemed as a remedy for obscured sight. Our wise-women also distilled elder-flowers, eye-bright, and other cooling herbs for eye-waters.

Nelly and her aged friend had acquired much useful knowledge about the virtues of plants from Madam Cardew, who, like many other ladies of the West Country, at that time, prepared from simples, many useful medicines with which they supplied their poorer neighbours, and such was Nelly's fame as a skilful doctoress, that, before a year was gone, gentle and simple came from a great distance to consult her for her medicines. Her preparations might have possessed medical virtues which need not be despised even in these enlightened times. Though the faculty make a jest of old women's nostrums, yet in our great-grandmother's time, the uses and natures of various plants were much better understood by country ladies than they are at the present day; because those who are esteemed accomplished botanists pay more attention to the classification and nomenclature of plants than to their usefulness. In this kind of life, Nelly passed her time—seemingly tranquil. Knowing that any expression of gloomy feeling only makes it take the deeper root, she showed no outward signs of sorrow. Yet she was for ever grieving over the untimely fate of the lost ones; and, when alone with her old friend, she would often say that, in spite of all she could do to forget, her heart was ever with her husband and children at the bottom of the deep. However skilful the poor woman might have been in reading others' fortunes, she little knew what fate had in store for her.

One Autumn evening, about three years after Nelly returned, she was alone with her old friend relating some adventures of her seafaring life. As usual, her husband's reckless courage and bravery was the theme of her discourse. A knock was heard at the open door. Dame Trenoweth rose and saw, standing on the door-sill, a stout, dark man, who asked if any one lived there who could read his fortune? Nelly knew the voice, sprung to the door, and was clasped in her husband's arms.

"Whatever has happened," said Nelly, "thank the Powers, you are safe. But tell me where are my sons?" "Here's one of them," said a lusty young fellow, stepping into the doorway, from having stood on one side fearing the fortune-teller wouldn't turn out to be his mother, "and my eldest brother is on board our good ship anchored in Guavas Lake, which we left a few hours since."

The Captain then related how he had come to Boskenna, expecting still to find some of the Cardews there, and Nelly with them. He found none but strangers, who told him that the Cardews were all dead and their clothes washed—that Nelly Wearne had never been heard of since she was carried away by the Old One, as every body believed.

They came on to Church-town and enquired at the inn if a strange woman had come to the parish about three years since, and were told that a gipsey fortune-teller, who lived with Betty Trenoweth, came there about that time.

Before going to rest Captain Black related how, on the foggy morning, when he hoped to take Nelly on board, by a mistake in reckoning, he kept too near the shore, and their ship struck on a rock west of Lamorna. As the ship leaked but little at first, they hoped she had only sustained slight damage. They tacked off the coast, still shrouded in dense fog, and intended to bring her into Mousehole or Penzance; but, in an hour or so, the water poured in so fast that they had barely time to launch a boat and place in it a small part of their riches, when the *Lovely Nell* went to the bottom, with several of the crew in her hold. The Captain told all hands to let the jewels, gold, and silver go to Davy Jones's locker, but some of them, disregarding his orders, went below and were endeavouring to save a part of their riches when the ship sunk, and he being the only one then on deck swam off and reached the boat. They remained an hour or more, beating about where the ship went down, in hopes that some of the submerged crew might escape from the hold and rise to the surface. The fog still hid the shore, so that they knew not on which side of the coast they lay, and, before they had time to think much of their loss, or to form any plans for the future, a ship, with sails and rigging all out of order, loomed in the mist, within speaking distance.

There was not a soul to be seen on the dirty-looking craft. Black hailed her with the usual questions. No response. They were about to board her and hailed again, when a man rambled to the gangway and, in a drunken voice, answered "Here I am: this ship is the *Red Rover*." To the questions where bound, &c., he replied "We are from the Seas; we want to get to Madagascar; can't 'e tell us the way, mate, and where we are now? we ought to be near there by this time I should think, and seeming to me I have heard your voice before now, but can't call 'e by name, who are 'e an? and where do 'e hail from when you are home?"

On getting nearer, Captain Black perceived that the one who spoke to him was a St. Just man, who had sailed with him many years—a good fellow, and a first-rate seaman when sober, but he was so seldom capable of performing his duty, that the Captain, to be rid of him, and others of the crew equally fond of rum, had, a year or so ago, left them the good ship in which they sailed; but now from neglect, those who built the strong and swift-sailing craft wouldn't know her.

"Oh; I know 'e now," said the St. Just man, after he had stared at Captain Black awhile. "You are our old commander, and I am brave (very) and glad to find 'e; and where have 'e left your ship, the *Lovely Nell*?"

Black inquired for their captain and quarter-master.

"I'm cappen to-day," he of the *Red Rover* replied, "we are all commanders in turn when we arn't too drunk, like all the rest of us are now. As for quarter-master, we haven't wanted any yet to share the prizes; but we want a captain who can keep the reckoning, and you shall take charge of the ship with all my heart, if you will."

With the St. Just man's full consent, Black and the remnant of his ship's company, among whom were his two sons, took possession of the *Red Rover* which, for strength and swiftness, was almost equal to his former craft. Before the drunken crew came to their senses all the arms and ammunition were secured in the cabin. Then, over a bowl of punch, Black was elected Captain; a quarter-master was chosen, as was usual with these hardy seamen; and they had a carpenter among them who always performed the surgical operation: in case of need he would take the wounded limb under his arm, and, with his big saw, separate it from the body of his patient, with as much ease and as quickly as he could have cut a spar in two, and with his red-hot axe cauterize the wound.

Rules were drawn up, agreeably to the sea-rover's code, and sworn to on an axe—the *Rover's* old crew consenting to all Captain Black required on the condition that there should be no stint of rum.

Now a few days after this, whilst the old and new hands were working in company, clearing the deck of all lumber, that they might have a fair stage for fighting and otherwise getting things into ship-shape, it leaked out and was known to the Captain that, only a few months since, the *Rover's* former crew had chosen a commander and officers who knew something of navigation, but when the crew was augmented by half a score desperadoes from the lawless multitude swarming about the islands, these officers, for trying to check the riotous proceedings of their ship's company, got themselves marooned; that is, they were put ashore on an uninhabited island, that they might take their chance to die or live. As these deserted men were the only ones on board who had any notion of keeping a ship's reckoning, the drunken crew, who took possession, when found in Mount's Bay, had a very vague idea as to what part of the world they were sailing in, and they had, by fits and starts, a week or so past, given chase to the *Lovely Nell*, thinking her to be some richly laden merchant-man. She and her crew had been altered in her rig, and otherwise, so as to pass for a ship pursuing an honest vocation. Some of the marooned men were well known to Captain Black and esteemed by him to be worthy fellows, as pirates go, and as brave men and true—for gentlemen of their profession. Without enlightening his crew as to their destination, he made sail for the desolate island, and by the time they had their guns, pistols, and cutlasses clean and fit for service they arrived at the place of exile only just in time to save the deserted men from starving in the midst of plenty; all for want of a tinder-box, or any other means of kindling a fire. The rescued men told Captain Black and the sober portion of his ship's company, that they would repay them for their deliverance with something more substantial than words. The fact was that in wandering over and round the island in search of water, yams, roots and fruits, or whatever would contribute to sustain life, they had discovered an immense quantity of buried treasures, probably the concealed spoil of former pirates, which were taken on board to be shared among all but those who marooned them. The drunken mutineers, when their former officers were brought on board, were sent on shore with a tipsey fiddler to take their places.

Among the rescued Captain Black found one of his own sons. This did not surprise him, as he had left his father's ship many years ago, that he might enjoy more liberty elsewhere; but it accounted for the silence of the crew. It was only in their drunken bouts that an intimation of the occurrence escaped, on which the Captain acted.

Some provisions, a tinder-box, and materials for striking fire, were left with the sailors on the island. The rescued officers soon recovered their strength, and, falling in with a strong and swift-sailing Spanish ship, the *Rover* gave chase, and captured the prize, which, as one captain was enough in a ship, was handed over to those delivered from the island, who retained part of the crew and made the rest walk the plank.

Captain Black, with his share of the treasures found on the island, was as well off as ever he was for returning; but, as the greatest part of his ship's company preferred to enjoy their free-and-easy life a few years longer, they bore away to the Spanish Main, where they sometimes acted in concert with other buccaneers.

Nothing worthy of note is related of their adventures. One of their practical jokes was whenever the buccaneers took a priest in any of the Spanish settlements, they conveyed the sable gentleman on board, placed him on all-fours, and rode him round the deck, or made him dance by sweating him with pricks of knives or forks, &c., as long as the fiddler or piper could play.

In about three years they had treasures to their hearts' content, and those who chose to give up their adventurous career returned with Captain Black. Best part of the night was passed by the returned Captain in relating his adventures to his wife and the old dame.

Early next morning three horses were procured, and Nelly, with her husband and son, were on Newlyn beach by break of day.

Captain Black hailed the *Red Rover*. A boat, well manned, left the ship and soon grounded on Newlyn beach. Then such a man as the Captain was when he danced at Burian Fair, on his stormy bridal night, sprang from the boat and beat through the sea to meet his mother. With little delay great store of money, jewels, rich stuffs, and other valuables were landed and conveyed to Betty Trenoweth's dwelling. The *Red Rover* with Nelly's eldest son appointed commander, proceeded on her voyage to London, that her valuable merchandise might there be disposed of. Now the Captain and younger

Black, by Nelly's earnest desire, consented at least to try the landsman's peaceful life. They had more riches than would suffice to purchase a good farm and enable them to live at their ease. The son, too, seems to have had no great love for a sea-rover's profession. Black leased, or purchased, a large old house at Trevorgans, with about thirty acres of tillable land, and a great run of downs and moors which, though they could not boast of much in the shape of game, were well stocked with rabbits, and the moors, in winter, were resorted to by wild-fowl—a substitute for beasts of chase not to be despised when but little fresh meat could be had. Then hunting was pursued as much for necessity as for pastime. The younger Black took to farming kindly, for one who had only been used to plough the deep, and soon acquired a sufficient knowledge of the simple husbandry practised at that time.

When the only crops grown in fields were corn and pulse, green crops for winter's consumption were unknown, and potatoes, just introduced, were regarded as something more curious than useful, and to be cultivated in the gardens of rich folks only; just as Jerusalem artichokes, asparagus, sea-kale, salsify, beans, and many other useful plants, which ought to be grown in every farmer's field or garden, are still neglected here. The bold Buccaneer, Black, was well received and made much of by the neighbouring gentry, who, for the most part, were very poor; yet they contrived to keep up a show of gentility on very inadequate means. Then in Burian parish alone, one might count seven or eight gentlemen's seats, or, more correctly, what by courtesy were called such, which were inhabited by different branches of the Pendars, Tresillians, Davieses, Jenkins, Harveys, Hutchenses, and others. The Levealises had become extinct, and the Noys, Boscawens, Vivians, &c., had shortly before then removed from their ancient homes to other parts of the country. Portions of their old mansions still remain in the condition of dilapidated farm-houses in Trove, Trevider, Treveddern, Pendrea, Baranhuel, Alsia, Tresidder, Rissic, &c. A country church was then, (perhaps even more than it is now,) the principle stage on which the rural gentry displayed their state and grandeur to admiring rustics. Captain Black, not to be eclipsed, would appear in Burian Church on Sundays and holidays dressed in crimson damask waistcoat and breeches, silk hose, diamond knee and shoe-buckles, a red feather in his cocked hat, a gold chain round his neck with a diamond cross hung to it, jewel-hilted sword, hanging by a silk sash at his side; his naval-blue coat resplendent with gold buttons, lace, and other trappings proper to the Buccaneer's costume. Nelly, decked out in rich velvets, lace, silks, satins, and jewels which once belonged to dark-eyed senoras of Mexico or Peru, eclipsed all the ladies of the West Country.

Such a man as Captain Black, notwithstanding his former profession was not a person to be treated with contempt at any time, and much less "In the days when we went a pirating, a long time ago." These gentlemen were looked upon as heroic adventurers, who served the dons, by way of reprisal, no worse than they deserved. Because then, if an English, French, or Dutch ship put into a Spanish-American port she was likely to be confiscated, and her crew kept prisoners, or treated no better than slaves, if they escaped with their lives, till dearly ransomed. We have little to do, however, with the morality of sea-highwaymen. Yet, if old stories may be credited, our brave Buccaneer Black soon became a greater favourite with certain ladies of the parish than he was with their lovers and husbands.

One tale is often told of his adventures with a gay lady of the Tresillian family, who then lived at Tresidder, and how a noted smuggler called Ackey Carn, one both landless and lawless, who cared for no man, being a rival for the gay dame's favour, by way of a jest spoke of certain amatory passages which he had witnessed between the Captain and lady, whose powerful and proud relatives constrained Carn, under pain of their displeasure, to do penance in Burian Church for thus thoughtlessly exposing the scandal. But the culprit, who, according to custom, came into church barefooted and clad in a sheet, instead of kneeling before the priest or parson, to beg pardon, and otherwise express contrition, and receive the priestly reprimand with becoming humility, stood up in front of the rud-locks (rood-loft,) turned his back to the priest and, facing the congregation (crowded to behold the show) made the well-remembered speech which begins:—

"Here am I, compelled by the law
 For to deny what my own eyes saw, &c."

Here follows a minute relation, told in language more quaint than choice, which was calculated to spread the scandal far and near. Then, throwing off his sheet, he showed himself well armed and bade defiance to all priests, pirates, and Tresillians, this side of a disagreeably warm place, as he would have said, if paraphrases of gentle words and equivocations had been the fashion then; however, he said he didn't care a rap for any one before him, and he would fight them all one after the other.

Black took up the challenge as soon as given, and offered to fight him there and then, any way he chose, either with arms or naked fists. Their partisans decided that they should fight unarmed. Black threw down his sword and would have fought in the church had there been a clear field for their encounter. They passed through the hundreds who were assembled at a clear space or bowling-alley, below the cross. Ackey Carn, finding that Black was too dexterous for him in the use of his fists, and that he was getting the worst of it in boxing, turned the Captain over his hip and brought him down a fair back fall; and, as often as Black rose, the smuggler laid him down at full length, yet always with the greatest care not to harm the man who had often treated him like a prince. Carn only wanted to convince the Captain that he was his match one way or another in the art of self-defence. The two men having fought and wrestled till they were bruised black and blue, acquired the greatest respect and admiration for each other's courage, fair play, and prowess; and they were taken at last into the public-house and, over a bowl of punch, the Buccaneer and smuggler Carn became sworn friends, which they ever remained until their day of doom, when they left this world together.

Notwithstanding the favours of country ladies and gentlemen, Black soon became tired of what he was pleased to call a landlubber's lazy life. Caring little for hunting, and less for farming and other sports or occupations which make rural life glide pleasantly away, he passed much of his time in the public-house, surrounded by a gang of loafers who drank at his expense and applauded his stories of savage warfare, told in such infernal language as is seldom heard except from the lips of sea-robbers. His greatest delight was to beat everyone in hard drinking—no easy matter in those times. An old song of that jovial age thus describes what was deemed fair enebriation:—

"Not drunk is he who from the floor,
Can rise alone, and still drink more!
But drunk is he who prostrate lies,
Without the power to drink or rise!"

After days and nights of drunken revelry, Black, in gloomy fits, would often wander down to the cleves and pass many days alone, in the carns and sawns of the sea-shore, or was only seen in company with the smuggler Carn, who, from the Sunday when they fought for the honour, or disgrace, of the fair lady, became the Captain's favourite companion. Yet time hung heavy on the Captain's hands, and by way of a change, he had built from his own designs, a strong, swift-sailing, half-decked craft, which might serve for fishing and fetching liquors and other goods from France. There was a high duty on salt then.

When she was all rigged and ready for sea Captain Black took Carn for his mate, and they, with a crew of such dare-devils as suited them, set sail one Friday morn in the Fall and shaped their course for Gunwallo, where they landed, dug up and shipped the treasures taken from the Moorish galley some five-and-twenty years before. Thence our free-traders bore away for their usual trading port in Brittany. They soon procured the goods they required, then passed several days drunk and rioting, and often fighting, with anyone they encountered, for mere pastime. As smugglers spent abundance of money in the place, they were allowed to do much as they pleased. At last they made sail for home with a fair breeze, which, however, soon died away; and, for several days, there was scarcely a breath of wind. The sky continued overcast and the air sultry. During this heavy weather Black lay among the goods like one worn out, and scarcely spoke or moved. After a tiresome spell of beating about and making but little progress, the wind freshened, and one evening, about night-fall, they sighted the Lizard. Then, suddenly, black clouds gathered over-head, and a thunder-storm came on. With the first flash of lightning Black sprung up and said, "Hoist all sail, boys, for by all the devils we'll get home this night." The crew wished to shorten sail or lay to till day-dawn, but the Captain's spirits rose with the storm. He took the helm, and shaped his course in almost total darkness, for Penberth Cove. The boat going before the wind, bounded over the waves like a thing of life; the crew expected every moment to become a wreck; they could only see the cliffs by the flashing lightning; when Black, as if sporting with their fears, cried out, "Bravo, devils of the whirlwind, fire away, we will give ye a salute with our thunder;" then, giving the helm to Carn, he loaded and fired their swivel-gun, in answer to a cannonade from the clouds. The crew were confounded by the blasphemous talk of their commander, who, amidst the crash and roar of wind, waves, and thunder, seemed rejoicing in his native element. Their terror was at the utmost when, amidst the awful tumult, he stood up and, tearing out a handful of hair, threw it away in the blast, bellowing out, "There, fellow devils, take that; stand by me now, and I'll be with ye soon."

That instant the lightning burst out in such bright flashes over the cliffs, that rocks and carns were seen as plainly as at noon-day, and a sheet of flame hung over across the cove, from Pednsawnack to Cribba Head, till they ran safely in and the storm died away.

With the help of farmers' men and others, who had been several days and nights watching for the smugglers' return, the goods were soon landed, taken up to a level spot above the capstan, and covered with a tarpauling. Then two or three kegs were broached, a fire made, and the smugglers, with those who assisted them, sat round to enjoy the good liquor and other things.

At the height of their carousal the Captain drew the keg he sat on close beside the pile of blazing wood. He had not long settled himself there to drink and smoke, when his breath appeared to be all ablaze and his body in flames. His mate, Carn, threw himself on him, and swore he would save his Captain or perish with him. And perish with him he did; for, before the rest of the company had power to hinder him, both the commander and his mate were blazing like a bonfire. They neither spoke nor struggled. The others, in great terror at beholding their fearful end, went off, in all haste, to Treen, there remained till morning; then they and many others went down to the Cove, and on the spot where the two men were burned, not a sign of them was to be seen: all their ashes, even, were blown away.

Now, when folks came to think of Captain Black's strange career and stranger departure, many believed that he was either an evil spirit in human form or else a man possessed with a devil, and it remained undecided by the people of the West, whether he was man or demon, or a compound of both. Yet, in all probability, this strange being was only mad at times, and his sudden exit, might have been a case of spontaneous combustion, (if indeed, there be such a thing.) Many of those who in former times were believed to be demoniacs, witches, or wizards, would, if they lived and played their pranks at the present day, be simply regarded as lunatics and most interesting cases for the medical student rather than for the rude treatment of inquisitor, exorcist, or other priestly operator. We hear but little more of Nelly. Her son purchased a farm in St. Just, she removed thither with him, and ended her days in peace. Some descendants of the rover, (whose name we have abridged) were living in the western parishes a few years since.

About a century ago an aged dame of the family kept school in Burian Church-town and used frequently to relate strange traditions of her buccaneering ancestor.

THE WITCH OF BURIAN CHURCH-TOWN.

These midnight hags,
By force of potent spells, of bloody characters,
And conjurations, horrible to hear,
Call fiends and spectres from the yawning deep,
And set the ministers of hell at work.
ROWE.—*"Jane Shore."*

Who rides my horse a' nights,
Who lamed the miller's boy,
Who raised the wind that blew my old barn roof down;
But I've a silver bullet ready for her that will lame her,
Hobble how she will.—*Old Song.*

ABOUT the time of Captain Black's exit old Betty Trenoweth from her superstitious usages and pretensions to mysterious science, became notorious as a witch, and her practice of the black art was discovered and put past doubt by some one in Church-town, against whom she had a grudge. A man, finding when all attempts to please old Betty failed, that his cattle still pined off their legs, and everything went wrong, and that there was nothing but bad luck about house and land. Then he or his wife determined to punish the witch and bring her to reason. He made her image in clay or dough, we have forgotten which, and, when the figure was fashioned to their mind, ran up a good long skewer through the lower part of its body. Now, that they might know the effect of their counter-spell, some persons in the plot, entered the witch's dwelling, at the moment the skewer pierced her effigy, and saw her fall suddenly on the ground, where she continued rolling, kicking, and groaning in great agony for some minutes, when she exclaimed, "Good Lord, what's in my body? I can hold out no longer; do run over to Dick Angwin's and tell am I'll make et up weth am ef he will!" Fearing the witch might die in her agony and leave her curse on them or the spell unbroken, they hastened to make friends with Betty and destroyed the image.

Yet this punishment didn't make the old dame desist from carrying on her naughty tricks; for, one Thursday about the end of harvest, Betty jogged away to Penzance, intending to buy a pig that she might fatten it for winter's use. She was in price, and had nearly come to terms for one which suited her fancy. There were only a few pence between her and the seller; yet, pretending she didn't care about it, and saying she wouldn't give a farthing more, she turned her back and went to look at some others. That while, one

Tom Trenoweth, a cousin of hers, offered a trifle more and purchased the sow.

Tom had paid the "earnest money," when the old dame came back and said she would have the sow. "You're too late, cousin," said Tom, "I've bought her." "And what made thee interfeer, I'd like to know, when I was in price for the sow?" said Betty; "ef I don't have her thee shust wish thy cake dough, and find the sow the dearest bargain thee hast ever had." Tom refused to give up his purchase. Betty went off mumbling threats and curses, and shaking her bony finger at Tom.

With much ado, the man got home the sow, put her in a crow (sty), filled the pig's-trough with wash, and firmly fastened the door. Tom rose early next morning, and found the crow-door open, the pig's-trough full of wash and his sow rooting in a neighbour's garden; and it took all the men and boys in Church-town many hours to get the troublesome beast of a sow back into her crow again; and in spite of all he could do, scarce a night passed but she would get out, be off to lanes miles away, and do some mischief that Tom would have to pay for.

Months passed, during which the sow had given to her corn, meal, milk, and everything else that could be thought of to satisfy her, but all without avail— the more she ate the leaner and more lanky she became. One day Old Betty met the owner of the pig and said, quite friendly-like, "well, cousin Tom, how es thy sow getting on? Will she be fat against Christmas? I hear she is very troublesome; perhaps you had better sell her to me. What do 'e look for her now?"

"No," Tom replied, "ef she esn't fat for seven years, in Sundays, you shall never be the better off for begrudging her to me; old black-witch that you are; I'll drive her to Penzance and sell her for less than I gave, rather than you shall have her."

More months passed, during which the old woman, in spite of Tom's rebuffs, made him various offers for the sow, but every time less than the preceeding, as she said the pig was getting poorer and would soon be reduced to skin and bone. Tom, finding that his sow had eaten and destroyed more than she was worth, and all the time getting leaner, fastened a rope to her leg and started early one Thursday morning for Penzance, determined to sell her for anything he might be offered rather than bring her back again. The sow went on, quiet as a lamb, till she came to a stream running across the road in Bojew-bottom; there was no bridge over Bojew water in Tom's time. The sow wouldn't take to the water, nor could the man make her; he tried to put her across, wheelbarrow fashion, holding her up by the hind legs; then he endeavoured to drag her through the water, but she turned right around, bolted in between his legs, upset him in the muddy stream, and the rope slipping from his hand, she took her way up the moors, over hedges and ditches. Tom followed her, through bogs, brambles, and furze for many miles, till they came out in Leah lanes on the Land's End road to Penzance and Sancreed; the sow seemingly never the worse. But Tom felt very tired, and his clothes were torn to rags with the thickets.

The sow, now on the road to Penzance, and near Tregonebris Downs, went along so quietly that Tom caught hold of the rope again, made a running noose in the end of it, and (that she mightn't jerk it away again,) passed it over his hand and reeved it round his wrist. That being done to his mind, "Now, ah es much to me," says Tom to himself, or to the sow, "late as et es, ef I don't get 'e to market yet." He hadn't spoken the words a minute when a hare leaped out of a bush beside the road, made a squeak that sounded like "chee-ah!" ran down over the moor, the sow followed after, dragging Tom along, and never stopped, going almost as fast as the hare, till she came to Tregonebris bridge, when in under the road she bolted, so far as the rope would let her. The opening under the road being little other than a drain, or "bolt," as we say, Tom couldn't even crawl in on all-fours, his arm was almost dragged out of joint, and the loop, reeved on his wrist, cutting through the skin; Tom by good luck having his knife in his pocket, managed to get at it, cut the rope, and let the sow go; but she only went as far as the middle of the bridge, where it was narrowest, and fell to lie in the water.

Tom could neither drive nor coax his pig from under the road. He threw all the stones he could find at her till he had nearly closed up the bridge on one side, but she hardly noticed him with a grunt.

About noon Tom got very hungry; yet he was afraid to leave his sow and go to the nearest house, that he might have something to eat, because whilst he was out of sight the devil-directed pig might bolt away, no one could tell whither. Tom sat down beside the bridge, wishing some one might go by or heave in sight within call. He had to wait there till near sunset, when who should come by, from Tregonebris way, but Old Betty, with her basket on her arm and knitting-stocking in her hand. She came on clicking her needles, knitting all the way, and looking as demure as if "butter wouldn't melt in her mouth and cheese choke her." When she saw Tom sitting beside the road she seemed all surprised like, and said "Arrea! cousin, es that you? Have 'e sold the sow and got drunk on the profit, that you have missed your way back, an soas?"

"Well, Old Betty, es that thee? I must say that thee hast beaten me hollow," Tom replied. "The sow is under the 'brudge,' and thee dust know it well enow; for who but thee crossed the road and went over the moor in the shape of a hare? Thy friend, the devil, lent thee his hounds, I suppose, to drive her in where she can neither turn, go forth, nor come back, et seems to me."

"Well, thank the powers," said she, according to her custom, when anyone came to grief, "I am'at the only one in trouble this day; but as you are a cousin of my own, I'll give 'e the value of the sow still, and that es about half of what she cost 'e, because she's now gone to skin and bone, et will take months to get her up again."

"If you will give me something from your basket to eat, and what you last offered, you may take her, get her out ef you can, and be d——d to 'e."

But no, the old witch stood out, and wouldn't give a farthing more than half of what Tom paid for the sow; and he was glad at last, to get that and a two-penny loaf which she took from her basket. Then the dame went down to the mouth of the bridge, or bolt, only just said "Chee-ah! Chee-ah!" and the sow came out and followed her home like a dog.

Tom took the road to Sancras Church-town, and stayed at "The Bird in hand" as long as his money lasted. "It was no good to lay by; he might as well spend it first as last," he said, "because every shilling of the devil's coin will go and take nine more with it." All who heard Tom's story agreed that what seemed a hare, to cross his path, was no other than Old Betty in that shape, and wished they could send a silver bullet through her. It is said here as elsewhere that lead has no effect on a witch-hare. The old woman kept her pig many years for a store-sow and she became the parent of a numerous progeny.

THE STORY OF MADAM NOY.

After Betty had gained her ends with Tom Trenoweth, nobody ventured to deny her anything she coveted except Madam Noy, of Pendre. From the little known of this lady, she seems to have been a strong-minded close-fisted termagant. She was fond of going to law, and had always suits on hand concerning the bounds and common rights of her lands. She is said also to have kept the best hunter and hounds in the West Country, and that she coursed with them daily as she rode over her farms, across hedges and ditches, to inspect her work-people and stock. We suppose she was a widow then, or if she had a husband he made too little noise in his time to be remembered. She took great pride in her poultry; above all, in her rare breed of hens with large tufts or cops on their heads. Now Betty knew that Madam had often refused to give or sell any eggs from her coppies to her best friends, yet one morning early she put on her steeple-crown hat and mantle, took her basket and stick, hobbled down to Pendre, and seated herself on a style entering the town-place. In a few minutes she saw Madam Noy come from the barn with a bowl of corn in her hands to feed her poultry of all sorts and sizes. "Good morrow to your honour," said Betty, as she went up curtseying and nodding to Madam, "Dear me, how well you are lookan, you're gettan to look younger and younger I do declare, and what beautiful hens, ducks, and geese, you've got! The finest in the parish I do believe. Do 'e know, Madam dear, that I've got an old cluckan hen that I should like to put to set, ef you would spare me a dozen eggs, the sort of your coppies I'd like best." "Arrea! Betty, I suppose you would," said Madam, "but I've no eggs to spare from my hens with cops nor the ones without, while I've so many of my own clucking hens about. And dust thee think, than, that when I've refused to sell any of my new sort to my own sister Dame Pendar, or to my cousin Madam Trezillian, that I would spare them to the likes of you?" "I don't care a cuss whether you do or no," Betty replied, "but if you won't sell me some eggs you shall wish your cake dough." "Now go thee way'st home thou deceitful old bitch," said the lady in a rage, "and what business hast thee here pryan about the place and covetan all thee cust spy with thy evil eye, I'd like to know. Begone, or I'll set the dogs at thee, and throw fire over thee, dosn't think that I'm afraid of thy witchcraft."

"I am on the church-road through the town-place," said Betty, "and here I will stop as long as I like in spite of you and your lawyers too." Madam Noy and Betty continued their threats and abuse until the lady became so enraged, at the old woman's persistence to stay in her town-place, that she snatched up a stone, threw it at Betty, and hit her right on her noddle, with a blow that made her jaws rattle. Betty limped to the stile mumbling to herself, "now may the devil help me and by all that's evil here I will rest till I've curst thee to my heart's content." Standing on the stile she pointed her finger at Madam Noy and made the lady 'shake in her shoes;' whilst she nodded her head, waved her out-stretched hand, and ill-wished her by saying,—

"Mary Noy, thou ugly, old, and spiteful plague,
I give thee the collick, the palsy, and ague.
All the eggs thy fowls lay, from this shall be addle,
All thy hens have the pip and die with the straddle.
And before nine moons have come and gone,
Of all thy coppies there shan't live one:
Thy arm and thy hand, that cast the stone,
Shall wither and waste to skin and bone."

Madam Noy was never well from that day, her fowls' eggs were always bad, and all Betty's spells took effect. Before six months were past she lost her coppies every one; for, in place of gay tufts of feathers, the chickens' brains came out on all those hatched from her coppies' eggs.

A noted old droll-teller and clock-cleaner of Sancreed, called Billy Foss, used to recite this, and many other stories, in a sort of doggrel, in which he mostly half said and half sung his drolls. We remember but little more of Billy's verse, in this story, than the few lines given above; these are enough, however, for a sample of the kind of composition that was much in vogue with our old droll-tellers.

'Tis said that Betty owed her proficiency in the black art to her frequent conferences with Old Nick, (or her familiar, whatever his name might have been,) who almost nightly took the form of An' Mally Perase's black bull, and, under that shape, met the witch on the northern side of Burian churchyard. Much more is related of Betty's transactions, but nothing new in the annals of witchcraft; and enough has been stated to serve as an example of the faith and practices in such matters long ago; indeed, we may say that such beliefs and doings are anything but extinct; something turns up, every now and then, to show that, notwithstanding all the teaching and preaching, faith in witchcraft, and other dreary superstitions, are nearly as rife as ever.

We give the following instance as just related.

A Modern Sancreed Witch.

Only t'other day a farmer of Sancreed had three or four dairy-cows to let, and a woman who lived near by offered to take them, but as he didn't altogether like this woman he wouldn't close the bargain with her, and another neighbour soon agreed for the dairy. When the woman heard who had been preferred, she told everybody she met with that Jemmy—the man who took the cows—should rue the day that he ventured to cross her path. "For if I didn't know the right hour and minute," said she, "I would ill wish him every minute of the day till the spell was cast." A week or so after the first cow was in milking, Jemmy and his wife came to the farmer's house one night and said, "we believe that our cow must be ill-wished, for her milk is all bucked and gone to cruds (curds), with only a mere skin of cream on the pans; if you don't believe it come and see for yourself." The farmer and some of his family went home with the dairy-man, and found the milk like it often is in summer when the buck (spittle-fly) is on the grass, that, so it is believed, makes milk curdle then without becoming sour. The farmer and his wife couldn't tell what to think of milk being in that state early in spring; he took home the cow, however, and let the dairy-man have another, and when she was milked by Jemmy her milk 'runned' too, like that of the former one, which was then all right in the master's dairy. And so it continued with all the other cows Jemmy had; it was only for a day now and then, that any cream rose; other things went wrong with him and his family, and the farmer was at last obliged to take back his cows because there was no chance of his dairy-man making the rent. Meanwhile the woman who coveted them bragged how she had served Jemmy out for interfering.

"The very night I heard that he had took the cows," said she, "I went on my knees under a white-thorn tree by the crossroads, and there, for best part of that night, I called on the powers till they helped me to cast the spells that gave old Jemmy and his family plenty of junket and sour milk for a time." In fact she was proud to make her neighbours believe her to be a witch.

We suppose the reason why this would-be witch chose the cross-road thorn as a suitable place for her hellish work, was because many such trees are said to have sprung from stakes driven into suicides' graves; also on account of those sites being often visited by Old Nick and his headless dogs when they take their nightly rounds to see if any spirits have wandered from their assigned resting-places.

We may remark that, although the Black-huntsman's hounds are said to have neither heads nor tails, yet according to our popular mythology, they are believed to have the former appendages, with the same lineaments they bore when they dwelt on earth in human forms, but they make their heads invisible, to ordinary mortals, that they may not be known.

The same applies to apparently headless coach-drivers, horses, &c., that were frequently seen in old times.

A Queen's Visit to Baranhual.

At all feasts where ale was strongest,
Sat this gracious Queen the longest,
First to come and last to go.

LONGFELLOW, *slightly altered.*

THERE is a tradition,—that has taken the form of a droll, as it is related by old people of Buryan,—which sayeth that when the Pendars lived in grand style, in Baranhual, a Queen and her retinue landed from a Man-of-war, at Moushal, for the sake of seeing the Logan Rock and Land's End. News of the intended trip soon spread, and reached Buryan ere sufficient horses could be procured to furnish out the cavalcade. On the morning of the royal progress, work was at a stand still, and nearly all who could "lift a leg" started off from house and field towards Burian Church-town, as it was rumoured that Her Majesty intended to inspect Buryan Church on her way. So, in the morning early, Buryan bells were set a ringing; and Church-town folks arrayed themselves in their best to receive the Queen with due honours.

Every soul left Baranhual except old Dame Pendar, who was rather infirm. "My lady, the Queen," said she, "is but a woman, and make the most of her, even if she do wear a crown on her head every day of her life, with velvet robes all broider'd in gold, silk stockings, and diamond-buckles on her satin shoes, with rings on her fingers and bells on her toes, yet she's much like myself under all her fine clothes; and it esn't worth while to leave the house alone, and all that's in it, and go so far to see her at my time of life; besides there's the milk to scald and many jobs to be done at all hours. No, verily," said she to her son and his wife, "you may be off to Church-town with the scabble-angow (rag, tag, and bob-tail), but, indeed, I'll stay home and guard the house, and all that's in it. That shall never be left alone whilst I draw breath."

At that time the Pendars kept a capstan in repair, and gave other aids to the fishery at Penberth,—which is partly in Baranhual ground,—and received for it a certain portion of fish from the owners of each boat kept in the cove.

An hour or so after all the household, but old mistress, had started off to behold a queen, An' Joan Taskes came up from Penberth with a cowal full of fish, as the Squire's dues from all the boats which landed that morning. Madam told An' Joan to take the fish to the river, and that she would be down in a minute to help clean them. Before Joan had taken all out of her cowal, and laid them on the stepping-stones, that stood in the water where

Baranhual bridge now crosses it, old mistress arrived, knife in hand, ready to help clean and split her fish. They had nearly finished their job,—the old lady standing on a stepping-stone, with her skirts tucked up to her knees, taking the fish from An' Joan, who waded in the stream to give them a last rinsing,—when the old fishwife, on hearing a clatter of horses' hoofs coming down hill, looked up, turned round, and bawled out, "Can I believe my eyes; look 'e mistress, dear; ef I live, there's hundreds of kings and queens ridan down the hill. I can see more than a score, and there's more a coman round the turnan; pull down your petticoats, do! Oh, I wish to gracious I had a clean towser on, and my best hat."

Before old Joan had ceased exclaiming, and fixing herself as tidy as she could—though Madam Pendar, intent on the fish, didn't notice her commotion—a score or so of ladies and gentlemen on horseback, were within a stone's-cast. They drew reins, and a horseman started forward, rode down into the water, accosted the old lady, enquired if Squire Pendar lived in the house on the hill, and informed the wondering women that Her Majesty, on her route to the Logan Rock, well remembering that the Pendars had always been staunch friends to the royal cause, had preferred coming that way to give him a visit, instead of seeing Buryan Church, which Her Majesty and her attendants might have a glance at on their return from the Land's End. Madam replied that she was very glad to see "my lady, the Queen;" and was sorry that her son and his wife, with all their servants, were gone to pay their respects to Her Majesty in Church-town, as everybody said that was the intended route, and nobody home but herself to receive them.

"My royal mistress approaches to speak for herself," said he.

Madam was still standing on a stone, knife in hand, her coats tucked up, and kirtle drawn through her apron-string, when the Queen, understanding that her gentleman was speaking to no less a person than Madam Pendar, rode into the water, shook hands with her, and said, "If all are gone to see the Queen and left 'e alone, the Queen is come to see you; and I, and my attendants, would be glad to rest a while to have something to eat, and to mend the rents in our clothes that are torn to 'skethans' with thorns and brambles that overhang the narrow lanes." "The Lord love 'e, my dear lady, the Queen," exclaimed she, making a low curtsey, and quite overcome with honour. "Do 'e put your hand, now—as mine, on that side, is fishy and wet—into my left pocket, take out the key of the fore-door, and my huzzey (housewife) you will find in it needles and thread of all colours, ride up to the house, let yourselves in, and I'll follow with the fish, and do the best we can to entertain 'e." "We should like nothing so much as some of that nice fish, draining on the stones," said the Queen, in trying to get a key, large enow for a church-door, out of Madam's pocket. "Bless your life, and you shall have them," replied the old lady. "I am so flambustered (confounded) with the honour you have done me, that I hardly know which end I stand upon. But you will want my scissors, pieces of stuff, and other things in my pockets, for mending," continued she, in untying the string from around her waist, that kept up her pockets; "take them all as they are; you will find most everything in them."

The precious pockets, like knapsacks, were handed to a gentleman who slung them across his saddle-bow, and the Queen rode on well pleased with Dame Pendar.

Joan stood gaping and staring, nodding and smiling, without speaking a word, though many spoke to her; but their backs were no sooner turned than she said, "Why, mistress, dear, can you make out their lingo? Can that lady, who spoke to 'e, be a Queen? Why, where's her crown? It wasn't upon her head, I'm sure." "Cease thy clack, be quick and gather up the fish," Madam replied; "she put her crown in her pocket, I suppose, that the thorns might'nt sweep it off her head and under the horses' feet; thee west see her wearing of it when she's seated in the great parlour, by and bye, eating bread and honey: I'm glad, though, thee hast brought up a lot of nice mullett, bass, whiting-pullocks, and other fish for pies and frying, besides good large cod and ling for boiling."

When Dame Pendar and Joan got up to the house, they found the Queen and her ladies in the parlour busy sewing up rents in their garments; and the gentlemen—having stabled their horses—had made a blazing fire on the hearth. A large brass brewing-pan was placed on a brandes (trivet); pounds of butter and lard cast into it, and the nicest frying-fish cooked therein.

Mullet-and-parsley pies were put to bake on the hearth; large fishes boiled, and conger stewed, with fennel, in as many crocks and kettles as it would contain, with other things. Ladies and gentlemen—Queen and all—helped: some got the best pewter platters, plates, and flagons—only used on grand occasions—out of a chest, those on dressers and shelves, for ordinary use, wern't half enough; others peeled garlic and hollick, chopped fennel, tarragon, and other herbs to flavour sauces. Several tried to grind mustard, but none could give the right motion to their knees to make the bullet spin round in the bowl, and old mistress was obliged to grind it all, or have it spoiled. They dished up fried and boiled fish, swimming in butter; bowls of cream were poured into the pies; lucky, too, Madam had a batch of barley bread just baked, hot and hot.

Two gentlemen placed a high-backed carved oak chair, with several pillows thereon, at the head of the hall table, and Her Majesty was seated in as much state as she desired. They ate, one and all, with such an appetite, as if they hadn't tasted "meat" for a week, so old Joan Taskes said. The Queen imbibed old ale from a silver goblet; her ladies from pewter tankards and flagons; her gentlemen drank beer and cider from black-jacks and brown-georges (leather drinking vessels), which were often replenished.

Wasn't Dame Pendar delighted to see it all, as she bustled about to help Her Majesty to all sorts of sauces, of her own compounding. Indeed it was, as she said, "the proudest day of her life." She was, above all, elated when her royal guest smacked her lips after a sip of brandy, and swore, "by cock and pie," that "true as she was a sinner, never before, in all her born days, had she so much enjoyed a repast."

When the Queen and her ladies returned to the parlour, Dame Pendar placed before them white bread, cream and honey, brandy, sweet-drink (metheglin), and other cordials, of which they all partook with great pleasure. Having mended their garments, the ladies thought it full time to proceed on their journey, if they were to see the Logan Rock and Land's End that day.

But Her Majesty, bless her honest heart, was so well pleased with her entertainment that she preferred to stay there with old Dame Pendar till her attendants returned; so they, with her permission, rode away to Castle-Treen.

When the Queen's suite had departed, Dame Pendar produced from her own private cupboard, a bottle of rare old mead, and a flask of extra strong brandy, for Her Majesty to taste; and she, liking them well, drank glass upon glass of mead, with several sips of brandy, to keep the fish from "flowing on her stomach," and to show their loving regard for each other, they exchanged all the contents of their pockets for keepsakes; yea, every item, except their crooked sixpences, which they kept for good luck.

At length the Queen, feeling drowsy, reclined in a long window-seat, thence rolled on the floor, where she lay puffing and snoring, unable to rise. Dame Pendar, by so often drinking "Here's health and long life to 'e, my dear lady, the Queen," was too fuddled to help her up, so she lay down with her for company; and old Joan, who had been sipping of all sorts, and drinking everybody's health, was stretched under the kitchen table.

The Queen's attendants, having passed hours in viewing the Logan Rock and other wonders of Castle-Treen, 'couranted' about amongst the rocks, where they found pleasant places for courting, till nearly sunset. They then, concluding it was too late for going to the Land's End, mounted and returned to Baranhual, that they might wait on their royal mistress, and reach Moushal in time to be on board before dark. They galloped away in hot haste, expecting to find Her Majesty impatiently awaiting their return; but, sad to say, they found her—all her state forgotten—lying helpless on the floor, beside Dame Pendar. The royal lady was hastily lifted on her palfrey; Joan Taskes—now the least drunk of the three—helped to fasten a giss (hempen girth) across her Majesty's lap, to keep her safe in the saddle, and they quickly departed.

Now it so happened that Squire Pendar, his wife, and their servants, tired waiting for the Queen, in Church-town, till near night, returned home across the fields, Selena way, arrived at the Green-court gate just in time to catch a glimpse of Her Majesty under the trees that darkened the avenue. He had the merest glance of her going down hill with her head drooping over her horse's mane, and a gentleman holding her steady; and that's the last seen of her in Buryan. Squire Pendar, his wife, and their servants were all rather muddled too, from having passed all day at Church-town with hundreds of gentle and simple, in drinking "Here's to the Queen and ourselves, comrades;" yet he and his wife expressed great surprise and ill-humour at finding their house all in disorder.

Joan told them how they all enjoyed their entertainment. "Bad luck to them all!" murmured he; "our cellar-floor is like mud with spilt liquor, and not a gallon of beer or cider left in the casks. What mother said was true enow; the Queen, for all her fine clothes, is much like another woman, especially when drunk." Next morning he could hardly be persuaded that Her Majesty had been there at all, till his mother showed him what fine things she had as keepsakes. "My thimble, as thou knowest, was brass," said she, "and my bodkin silver; but see, here's my gracious lady's silver thimble and golden bodkin:" then, with great pride, drawing from her pocket the Queen's huzzey, she continued "if anything more is wanted to assure thee how I've been honoured by my gracious lady, behold this!" She then displayed what one may conjecture to have been a remarkable contrivance for containing many requisites of a lady's work-box or bag, and several toilet articles besides. It was a yard long when unfolded; every little pocket and flap of a different sort of rich stuff, all worked in elegant designs, with gold and silver thread, coloured silks, intermixed with pearls and precious stones, or what passed for such. It folded into strong leather covers, fastened with silver clasps like a book; and the upper cover was lined with a mirror.

Hundreds of people came to see it suspended, at full length, the looking-glass at top, over the parlour fire-place, where it was kept in remembrance of the Queen's visit.

The shell-room was built after, and some say it was intended to commemorate that honour. This apartment was incrusted with shells,— mostly from Parcurnow. Among other devices, a cavalier was pourtrayed, as if pursued by robbers; and under this shell-picture, the legend,—"This is the heir, come let us slay him, that the inheritance may be ours."

We have frequently remarked to old persons, who related the above story, that nothing is said in any county or other history of a Queen having visited

Baranhual. "Perhaps your history-makers never heard of it," they reply: "no one belonging to Buryan saw her plainly, that's true, except the two old women." Squire Pendar and his servants only had a glimpse in the twilight of a company on horseback passing down the road, which was then overhung with large spreading sycamores,—three rows of them on each side,—which soon hid his royal guests. But the Pendars, even in our time, poor as they were,—many of them labourers and fishermen,—had always preserved something among them that the Queen was said to have left with old Madam hundreds of years ago; and all of the name, that we have met with, say that Pendre, Baranhual, Trevider, and other lands in Buryan, once belonged to their forefathers.

THE SMALL PEOPLE'S COW.

They are fairies; he that speaks to them shall die.
I'll wink and couch; no man their works must eye.

Merry Wives of Windsor.

THERE is a story connected with the Pendars which says that, when this family was on its wane, the owner of Baranhual had a fine red cow, called Rosy, which gave twice as much milk as an ordinary one. She retained her milk-yielding power all the year through, and kept in good condition, even in winter, when other cattle on better food were reduced to skin and bone. Rosy would yield all her morning's milk, but every evening when much—and that the richest—still remained in her udder, she would stop chewing her cud, cock her ears, low gently as if calling a calf, and the "shower" of milk would cease. If the maid attempted to renew her milking Molly would kick the bucket and gallop away to a remote part of the field.

Dame Pendar, thinking the milkmaid didn't shake Rosy's bag and coax her enough, tried, one evening, what she could do, but when she thought by "visting" Molly's teats to get more milk, after the cow's usual signal to cease, she up foot and smashed the wooden pail to pieces, tossed Dame Pendar over her back, and, bellowing, raced away—tail on end.

Though Rosy kept in milk when all other cows were "gone to sew" (dry), yet, because there was something strange about her and as she was always fit for the butchers, an attempt was made, soon after the dame's tossing, to get her to market; but all the people on Baranhual couldn't drive her off the farm.

Over a while Rosy had a heifer calf, and when it had sucked its fill, its dam gave her usual quantity of milk into the bucket, and then enough remained to fill another. Stranger still, in a few weeks the calf could eat herbage, and its dam weaned it gradually, but it could never be separated from her.

Everything prospered with Mr. Pendar. His cattle and crops throve wonderfully, till one Midsummer's night. His milkmaid having gone to games held at Penberth, or some place near it, only returned when the stars began to blink. Rosy, impatient to be milked, came to meet her in the field, stood still, placed back her leg, chewed her cud, and showered her milk into the bucket till she had yielded more than usual: then she stretched herself, looked around, and gently lowed whilst the maid, without rising from her milking-stool, pulled up a handful of grass, rolled it into a pad and placed it inside her hat, that she might carry her bucket the steadier. Having put on her hat she was surprised to see hundreds of "Small People" (fairies) around the cow, and on her back, neck, and head. A great number of little beings—as many as could get under Rosy's udder at once—held butter-cups, and other handy flowers or leaves, twisted into drinking vessels, to catch the shower of milk that fell among them, and some sucked it from clover-blossoms. As one set walked off satisfied, others took their places. They moved about so quickly that the milkmaid's head got almost "light" whilst she looked at them. "You should have seen," said the maid afterwards, "how pleased Rosy looked, as she tried to lick those on her neck who scratched her behind her horns, or picked ticks from her ears; whilst others, on her back smoothed down every hair of her coat. They made much of the calf, too; and, when they had their fill of milk, one and all in turn brought their little arms full of herbs to Rosy and her calf,—how they licked all up and looked for more!"

Some little folks, who came late, were mounted on hares, which they left to graze a few yards from the cow.

For a good while the milkmaid stood, with the bucket on her head, like one spell-bound, looking at the Small People; and she would have continued much longer to admire them, but, just as some came within a yard of her, Dame Pendar suddenly stood up on the field-hedge and called to know how she was so long about Rosy, and had all the rest still to milk, and how she hadn't brought in a bucket-full yet?

At the first sound of old Dame Pendar's voice, the Small People pointed their fingers and made wry faces at her; then off galloped Rosy and the troop of small folks with her—all out of sight in a wink.

The maid hastened in, and told her mistress, and master too, what she had seen.

"Ah! fax, I knowed," said Dame Pendar to her husband, "and didn't I always tell 'e something was the matter that Rosy wouldn't yield half her milk. And surely," she continued to the milkmaid, "thou must have a four-leaved-clover, about thee; give me the wad in thy hat that I may look through it."

She examined it, and sure enough, found a stem of white clover, or three-leaved grass, with four leaves on it.

The mistress asked how big the Small People were, and how dressed.

"But few of them are more than half a yard or so high," the maid replied; "the women not so tall, yet they looked beautiful, all dressed like gentry; the women wore gowns as gay as a flower-garden in summer; their flaxen hair fell, in long curls, on their necks; and the men were very smart, all like sodjers or huntsmen, so it seemed to me. But they made frightful faces at you, and glared as if they would be the death of 'e. I shouldn't like to be in your shoes."

"Our best cow is as bad as bewitched," said Dame Pendar to her husband, "and what shall we do to drive the plagues of sprites?"

Her husband told her not to be so greedy; for old folks said that the Small People always brought good luck when unmolested and their doings were not pried into by curious fools; for his part, he was content to leave well alone. She made no reply, but—determined to have her way, next morning, betimes, unknown to her good man—she trotted off to Penberth, or Treen, and consulted a red-haired woman that Mr. Pendar couldn't "abide," because she was reputed, and truly, to be a witch.

"I'll drive them from our best cow, and from Baranhual, too, if it can be done," said Dame Pendar to the hag. "Nothing easier," replied she, "for they can't endure the sea, nor anything that comes therefrom, and, above all, they abhor salt; so you have only to scatter it over your cow, wash her udder in brine or sea-water, and sprinkle it about your place."

Dame Pendar hastened home, and, without delay, powdered Rosy with salt, bathed her udder in brine and sprinkled it about the fields and town-place.

In the evening, betimes, she went herself to milk her best cow, and carried two buckets, thinking they would both be filled. Rosy, without budging, let her be seated and milk a little; but feeling her udder thumped, "visted," and roughly shaken, when she withheld her flow, she kicked the pail to shivers, laid Dame Pendar sprawling, then tossed her greedy mistress heels over head, and galloped off, "belving" like a mad thing.

All the people in Baranhual couldn't stop her in a corner, and, from that day, not a drop of milk did they get from her.

For days and nights she would roam about the farm, followed by her heifer— no hedges stopped them—and both "belving," all the time, like cows that had lost their calves. Before Christmas they became hair-pitched, lean, and lousy; and all the other cattle on Baranhual were as bad.

Mr. Pendar, being ignorant of what his wife had done, sought aid from, and brought to his farm, all the most noted conjurers, pellars, and white witches in the West Country to arrest the run of bad luck that pursued everything belonging to him. They bled his diseased cattle on straw, burned the straw and blood, carried flaming torches of a night, around the folds. Fire was also borne—with the sun's course—around sown fields. Bonfires were lit, and his cattle forced through their flame. Other rites were performed according to old usages only known to pellars. Even his finest calf was burnt alive. But all was of no avail.

To leave nothing undone, they cut down or rooted up all barberry bushes, that grew about on orchard hedges and elsewhere; but Mr. Pendar's crops were blighted all the same. In the meantime Rosy and her heifer were seldom seen, but often heard bellowing about Pednsawnack, over Porguarnon, or in other dangerous cleves and unfrequented places: they couldn't be brought into the town-place to undergo spells or counter-spells. But when more than a year had passed, and the next Buryan fair came round, Mr. Pendar made up his mind to sell Rosy and her heifer. All Baranhual men and boys, with many neighbours mustered, and after much trouble, drove them on to the church-town road. But they could neither be got to fair nor home again. After following them on horseback till night, Mr. Pendar caught a glimpse of Rosy and her heifer racing over Sennen Green toward Genvor Sands, and they were nevermore seen. Dame Pendar, from the time she got kicked and tossed, was rickety till the day of her death. The milkmaid, too, from a spanking damsel who had her choice of sweethearts, in less than a year became a doudy that no young man cared for or would look at. From that time everything went wrong with the Pendars, and, in a few generations, those of the name who remained in Buryan hadn't an inch of land to call their own.

There are two or three versions of this story, which differ but little from the above, except in locating the Small People's Cow on other farms that were dwelling-places of the Pendars in olden times.

TOM OF CHYANNOR, THE TIN-STREAMER.
A WEST-COUNTRY DROLL.

Telle us swiche thing, as may our hertes glade.
Be blithe, although thou ride upon a jade.
What though thyn horse be bothe foule and lene,
If he wol serve thee, recke thee not a bene:
Loke that thyn herte be mery evermore.
Yes, hoste, quode he, so mote I ride or go,
But I be mery, ywis I wol be blamed.
    *   *   *   *   *   *   *

But right anon thise gentiles gan to crie;
Nay, let him tell us of no ribandrie,
Tel us som moral thing, that we mow lere,
Som wit, and thanne wol we gladly here.

CHAUCER.

A LONG way back, in old times, when Parcurnow was the chief port west of Hayle, and Treene a market town, (as it had been since the castle's outer walls were built, 'tis said), there lived in a little out-of-the-way place known as Chyannor, a man called Tom, with his wife—we don't know her name, more's the pity—and their daughter Patience. When farm-work fell scant Tom streamed for tin in moors near his dwelling; but, the overburthen there being deep and tin scarce, he got sick of the job, and one day, between tilling season and harvest, knacked his bal, and took the little tin he had raised that summer down to Treen for sale. Many woollen-weavers and ropers lived there, and withe-weavers (basket-makers) who made cowals (creels) that pleased fisherwomen better than any to be got elsewhere. In Treen market-place stood a fine broad garack-zans (holy rock). It was nearly round, about four feet high, eight feet across, and level as a table, except that in its upper surface shallow pits were hollowed, and in these stream-tin, brought for sale or exchange, was piled. Tom, having placed his tin in one of the hollows of this stone, inquired the news, and asked how work was away in the East Country, of merchants from Market-jew, who brought goods in their vessels to Parcurnow, which was then clear of sand, and the tide flowed in a deep channel up to an old caunse (paved road) still to be seen. The merchants told him that streamers' work might be had in a place called Praze-an-Beeble, a short day's journey from Market-jew. Tom, having exchanged his tin for leather and other things, took a drink of cider with the merchants, went home, and told his wife what he had learned.

"One must be a fool," said he, "to stay here and starve, when two or three days' journey will take one to a land of plenty. What do'st thee think wife?"

"Well, good man," said she, "thee west (wilt) always have thy own way, whatever one may say: if thee hast a mind to go eastward, to look for work, go! I and the maid will stay and get our living here. But don't 'e go for a day or two, that I may put thy clothes in order, and bake a fuggan (heavy cake) for thee to eat on thy way. Long lanes and scant entertainment thee west find, I expect?"

"It will take me some days," replied he, "to go round and wish the neighbours well, and to get my tools to-rights before I start."

In three days Tom got his piggal (beat-axe) and visgey (pick) cossened (re-steeled), and other tools repaired, that he intended to take with him, and had said, "I wish 'e well, till I see 'e again" to every body for miles round. Tom kissed the young women, and the elderly ones kissed him, and said, "If we never see thee again we wish thee good luck for thy courage; but take care thee doesn't get kidnapped and sperritted away in Market-jew, as many a good man have been before now, and nevermore heard of."

When all was ready for Tom's journey, his tools, provisions, and clothes made a heavy load to travel with. In the morning, early, he started. His wife and daughter went many miles on the way, carrying his things, till they arrived at a public house where the roads meet in a place since called Catch-all. Here they had a drop to cheer their hearts. "Be sure, wife," said Tom, "to take care of our only child, Patience. She is but fifteen, mind." After much kissing, crying, wishes for good luck, and a speedy return, they parted.

Tom reached Market-jew before dark, and was much bewildered to see so large a place and so many people. Moes-hal was the largest town he had seen, and the farthest east he had ever been till then. As it happened to be Whitsun market, streamers in great numbers had brought their tin for sale or to exchange for clothing and other things. It was sold by measure, from a pottle to a strike (bushel). Large quantities were purchased by smelters and merchants. What with foreign traders, market-people, pilgrims to the Mount, and pleasure-seekers, there was noise and bustle enough. Tom, however, found lodgings in a quiet house, a little out of the town, and was on his road, early next day, towards a place where he was told that he might get work. Though in a strange land he went boldly on over barren hills, across deep bottoms, overgrown with thickets; and, nothing daunted, he waded streams of names unknown; and indeed he felt proud, as a traveller, to think that he was going farther east from home than but few of St. Levan had ever been. Thus trudging along he passed over Roost Common, through Colenso and Chypraze, traversed Godolphin hills, rested some time near Godolphin stepping-stones, and then pursued his way through Chywhella, and over

Crenver Downs. About sunset he passed this tract of moorland, rich in tin, and arrived at a dwelling surrounded with a court and outbuildings that showed it was a farmer's house. This he afterwards learnt was Penthoga.

He knocked at the door and said to the mistress, who opened it, "I have travelled from far away in the West Country, to seek work, and would be glad to lodge in your barn to-night."

"Come in, good man; lay down your burthen and sit at the board," said she.

"What cheer, stranger?" exclaimed the farmer; "come here beside me, and when supper is over we will hear the news from your country. And wife, bring a flagon of ale; that's better drink after a journey than milk," continued he, whilst heaping Tom's trencher from a huge steaming pie of hare, beef, and other meat.

Having made a hearty meal Tom turned his leg over the form and, looking towards the farmer, said, "This is a house of plenty, master. I wish you wanted a servant."

"Well, my son, and what work can you do?" asked the farmer.

"All sorts of husbandry or moor-work," he replied. "Give me a board like this, to keep up my strength, and I'll turn my back for no man."

After some hours' talk about Tom's country, and other matters, the farmer, finding him to be a simple, honest fellow, agreed to take him, and they bargained for two pounds a year wages. Now, as Tom didn't mind doing a trifle of work, after his day's task was done, the farmer gave him many odd pence. After supper of winters' nights master and men told old drolls and carded wool, whilst mistress and her maids kept their turns (spinning wheels) going till they had each spun their pound of yarn. The women knitted for him warm stockings, and washed and mended his clothes. All were well pleased with Tom, and he liked his place.

When the year was ended, the farmer brought two pounds from his chest, laid them on the board, and, showing them to Tom, who sat opposite, said "Here are your wages, my son; but if you will give them back to me I will teach 'e a piece of wisdom more worth than silver and gold."

"Give them here to me," said Tom, "and keep your pennyworth of wit."

"No," said his master, "give them to me, and I will tell thee."

"Well take them to thee," said Tom.

Then said his master, "*Take care never to lodge in a house where an old man is married to a young woman.*"

Then they bargained for another year, and, when that was ended, his master brought two pounds; laying them on the table, as before, he said "See, Tom, here are thy wages; but if thou wilt give them back to me I will teach thee another piece of wisdom."

"No, by dad," answered he; "hand them here to me; I don't want your pennyworth of wit."

"No," said his master, "give them to me, and I will tell thee a piece of wisdom more worth than strength."

"Take them to thee," said Tom.

Then said his master, "*Take care never to leave an old road for a new one.*"

They bargained for another year.

Tom now thought much of his wife and daughter, and made up his mind to return home when his time was up. Next year ended, his master brought the two pounds, and said, "See here are thy wages; but if thou wilt give them back again to me I will teach thee the best point of wisdom of all."

"No bring them here; I have wit enow to find my road home again."

"No," said his master, "thou wilt need it then, more than ever. Give them to me and I will tell 'e."

"Take them to thee," said he.

"Well now, as thee hast served me truly, like an honest fellow," said his master, "I will tell thee two points of wisdom. First, *never swear to any body or thing seen through glass*; second, *be thrashed twice before content once.* This is the best point of wisdom of all."

Now Tom said he would serve no longer but leave at once and go to see his wife and child. "No, don't go to-day," his master answered; "for my wife is going to bake to-morrow morning; she shall make a cake for thee to take home to thy wife, and a hoggan (a cake with meat baked on it) for thee to eat by the way."

"Very well." said Tom, "as it's Whitsuntide, I'll wait till Tuesday."

"I am very sorry thee art going to leave us, my son," said the farmer's wife; "and I should be glad if thee west thatch the hen's house and the duck's crow for me, whilst I make thee a cake and hoggan; then I will give thee a charmed stone for thy daughter, that shall be of more worth to her than gold or jewels."

In a few hours Tom thatched all the outbuildings that required it, came into the house, and his mistress gave him a smooth grey stone, about the size and shape of an acorn, with a hole drilled through it, for hanging it by a cord round the neck. "Though this appeareth only like a bit of smooth elvan (trap rock) it is a jewel of great virtue," said the mistress. "It will preserve any woman that weareth it from much trouble if she but keepeth it in her mouth, with her lips closed, that it may not drop out when her husband or any other contendeth with her. I will tie it round thy neck, that it may'nt be lost," said she; and did so.

Tuesday morning Tom took leave, with many kind wishes and promises to see them again. "Take this cake home to your wife, my son," said his master, "and eat it when you are most merry together." "And what you will find in this dinner-bag," said his mistress, "is for 'e to eat on the road. Good luck attend thee; come to see us again; thee west be right welcome always."

Tom trudged on for many miles a somewhat different road to that he went, without meeting with anybody, till, having passed St. Hillar downs, he fell in with three merchants of Treen, driving before them their pack-horses laden with wool from Helaston fair, whither they had been with cloth and other goods. "What cheer, Tom," cried they, "where hast thou been, and how hast thou fared this long time? We are glad to have the sight of thee!"

"I have been in service and am now going home to my wife; and glad I am to meet men of my parish," said he.

"Come along with us; right welcome thou shalt be," said they.

They kept together and came to Market-jew, where the merchants proposed to sup and stay over night in a house where they had formerly lodged. "And come along with us, Tom, right welcome thou shalt be," said they. And when they were come to the inn, Tom said, "I don't know about stopping here; before settling that point, I must see the host."

"The host of the house!" they exclaimed; "what cans't thou want with the host? Here is the hostess—young and buxom, as you may see. But if you must needs see the host, you will find him in the kitchen."

By the kitchen fire, sitting on a three-legged stool, Tom saw a feeble, bald-headed old man, turning the spit. "Oh! by my dearly bought wit, I see this is never the inn for me," said Tom, "I will not lodge here, but in the next house."

"Go not yet," said Treen merchants; "stay, take supper with us, thou art heartily welcome."

Soon after supper the merchants saw their horses fed, well groomed, and littered; then, being tired, they went early to bed, and Tom, on entering the next house, was told there was no spare bed, only some straw in a garret where lumber was mostly kept; he might rest there and welcome, free of charge.

"I can sleep there very well," Tom answered; and the host shewed him the place, where sweet straw was piled near a boarding that divided it from the next house, where the Treen merchants lodged. Now the mistress of the inn was very fond of a young fellow who sauntered about, and did nothing for his living but court the landladies of Market-jew. The young wife had long been tired of her old man and wished him dead, but as he never seemed inclined to die, she persuaded the young fellow to put him going that night, as it seemed to her a good opportunity for them to escape suspicion of the dark deed.

A little before daybreak she ran to the mayor's house—her hair in disorder and her clothes rent—crying when she came near it, "Vengeance! Vengeance! Do me justice my neighbours! Help me, your worship! My sweet handsome man, don't delay," cried she, when under his chamber window. "I have been foully dishonoured. My money is stolen, and my dear husband murdered, by three West Country villains, who lodged in our house last night. They are now getting ready to start in haste."

The mayor called from his chamber window, "Go, tell the crier to sound his trumpet through the streets, and summon the town folk to meet me in the market place."

In a short time the townspeople assembled in the market square, where their mayor and the hostess awaited them. Said the mayor to his constables, "Go to this good woman's house, and bring hither three men you will find there." Turning to the town's people he continued, "My honest neighbours, choose a jury among ye, that we may try these West Country rascals, right away, for robbery and murder, and hang them before breakfast—no doubt they are guilty—and the urgency of our own business will not admit of our wasting much time on such matters. And, thank God, we have no lawyers in Market-jew to confound us with their quibbles, to embarrass justice, and to hinder speedy punishment."

Before the mayor had finished speaking the three Treen merchants were brought, handcuffed, into his presence. When they had all entered the townhall (where the mayor, even in those days, sat with his back towards the one window) his worship said, "Good woman, state your case."

When she stood up one might see that she was one of those who never looked a person fairly in the face, but take one's measure with stealthy glances. She put on a sanctified look; groaned; sighed; turned up her eyes; and exclaimed, "Oh, blessed Saint Mary, help me to declare the troubles I endured last night! Know, your worship and kind neighbours all," said she, glancing round, "that, towards the morning part of the night, these three villains came into my chamber, where my blessed husband—God rest him!—and myself were in bed. One of them broke open our money-chest, whilst another did a deed my modesty forbids me to name. My dear man, in trying to defend my virtue and his money, struggled hard. The third blackguard, to keep him quiet, grasped his dear throat with both hands and strangled him. Then they gave me more ill usage all three."

"That will do," said the mayor, "the case seems clear to me. Gentlemen of the jury, what say ye?"

"We are all agreed to hang them," replied the foreman; "but our doctor, who saw the body, has some doubts of what the woman sayeth."

"You," said the mayor, in an angry voice, "you, with your crotchets, fears, and doubts, are always causing inconvenient delay. Yet be quick and we will hear what you have to say."

"The old man has been strangled many hours," said the doctor, "for the body is stiff and cold, and I want to know how the woman did not make an alarm before."

"Woman, what hast thou to say to that?" demanded his worship.

Without hesitation she replied, "After these three black West Country rascals, robbers, and ravishers had misused me I fainted, and remained in a fit. I don't know how long before I awoke to my trouble and ran to seek your worship's aid."

"Now, doth that clear your doubts?" said the mayor: "and you villains," speaking to the merchants, "what can ye say for yourselves that ye should not be hanged and your heads fixed on spikes over the prison-gate, as a warning to such as you not to murder, rob, and ravish the virtuous people of Market-jew?"

"We are innocent," said they, "and we never saw the old man but once, in the kitchen, where he was turning the spit. A tinner, who came with us from St. Hillar downs, knoweth us to be men of good repute, but we know not where to find him, and can only declare our innocence each for the others."

"That's a kind of evidence that won't stand here," replied the mayor, "and, not to waste more time, I sentence you to be hanged all three. Officers," he continued, "see it done immediately, and seize their horses and merchandise to pay costs."

Whilst the mayor of Market-jew was pronouncing sentence, Tom, in haste, entered the court. "Hold," cried he, "and don't ye murder three innocent men. That woman caused the death of her husband, and a long-legged-red-haired fellow, with a pimply face, who weareth a coat of this colour," said he, holding aloft a piece of grey cloth, "did the foul deed."

"What can you know of this matter?" demanded the mayor.

"Give time to draw breath, and I will tell 'e," said Tom. "I was fellow traveller with these three merchants of Treen. They asked me to lodge in the same house with them, but having bought a piece of wit that teacheth me to avoid the house where a young woman is wedded to an old man, I went next door. There was no room to spare but in the garret, where I found a pile of straw against a screen of boards between that house and the one in which the merchants lodged. On the straw I made my bed. Though tired, I didn't sleep, because music, singing, and dancing, below, kept me awake. About midnight, when all was quiet, I saw, through a hole in the screen, a light in the next house, and that woman (I know her by her purple nose and splatty face) talking to a tall red-haired man. Both stood near the screen. Then she said to him, 'I am heartily sick and tired of my old fool. All he's good for is to turn the spit, and a small dog would do that better. To-night would be a capital time to stop his wheezing. Here's what you might do it with,' said she, giving him a nackan (handkerchief). 'Draw it tight around his scraggy throat; give it a good twist, just so (said she showing him how), and we shall be no more troubled with his jealousy. Don't fear the consequences; leave them to me; I know how to get these three jeering West Country fellows into the scrape. If they are hanged for it, it will be good fun for us.' The man seemed unwilling till, putting her arms round his waist, she said, 'With all the love I have for thee, cans't thou stick at such a trifle, my dearest Honney (Hannibal), that will make the way clear for thee to be master here, with me and all the old fool's money. And there it is, in the bags by the screen—all the best of it,' said she, pointing to them; 'what's left in the chest is only copper coins and old tokens, and his claws are too stiff and crum (crooked) to untie the bags and see what's in them. And here, faint heart,' said she, taking up a bottle and pouring out a cup of liquor, 'drink this brandy; go down; be quick; and do it quietly, that Treen men, in the next room, may'nt hear thee.' The man went down with the nackan in his hand, and in two minutes or less returned. 'Well! is all right?' she asked. 'That it is,' he replied, 'I quickly wound the nackan round his neck; he moved a little and murmured in his sleep, 'Don't 'e hug me so close, my dear.' I then drew it tight, and gave it a wrench; he made but one squeak and all was over. And now I'll take the money and go.' 'Don't be in such a hurry,' said she, 'one or two bags are enough for 'e now.' 'No,' said he, getting from her and approaching the screen, 'all isn't enough for the deed I've done to please thee.' Then he handled the bags, took two, and went away.

I know it was about midnight" (said Tom in reply to the doctor's query) "because, while the man was below I heard the bell that shaven crowns on the Mount toll at the dead of night."

"Well, and what next?" demanded the mayor; "if thou hast anything more to say, be quick, and out with it."

"I have only to state," resumed Tom, "that when he stooped to pease (weigh) the bags of money, his skirt came against the hole in the screen. With my left hand I caught hold of the cloth; with my other unsheathed my knife, and cut off this piece. I tried to keep awake, knowing these men were in danger from that false woman, but I fell asleep, I don't know how, and only waked just in time to learn they were brought here to be tried for their lives."

"It's provoking," said the mayor, "yet this man's story may be as true as the woman's; or truer, my men," continued he speaking to the officers; "You know the long-legged scamp, that haunts this woman's house and all the others in the town, where liquor and victuals can be got for his bladder-dash. Hunt him up and bring him hither; he is likely to be at the St. Michael's or some other public house. Get the money he took away, and all you can find in this woman's house; bring it all here to pay the cost."

In a short time the officers returned, dragging in the man Tom had spoken of. They turned him round, held up his skirt, and there saw a hole that the piece Tom held fitted exactly, and in his pockets were found two bags of gold.

"It's a clear case now then," said the mayor, "so string them up at once—the man and woman, I mean, ye fools. You Treen men go about your business, and thank your luck that this tinner is as wise as a St. Levan witch to get 'e out of the hobble."

Tom and the merchants took a hasty breakfast, loaded their pack-horses, and started homewards, about sunrise. In passing the jail they saw the woman and her long-legged Honney strung up. They went quickly on to avoid the ugly sight, and the merchants made much of Tom, you may be sure.

Two hours or so before noon, they arrived at a public house, tied their horses to a hedge, gave them their nose-bags of corn, and eased their backs by propping up their loads with sticks, such as were then kept at road-side inns for that purpose. "You will dine with us, Tom, and we will treat you to the best the house affords," said the merchants; "we shall at least get good malt liquor and wholesome fare. We may as well rest a few hours, now that we are just as good as home and in a part where honest folks dwell."

The merchants being cheered with good ale said to Tom, "Comrade, we will one and all give thee something to show how we value the good turn thou hast done us in Market-jew. But for thee, my son, we should never more have seen our wives and children dear, or the castle and good old town of Treen."

"Hold your clack, my masters," Tom replied, "I am vexed with myself to think that I should have slept and left 'e in such danger; it's only by a mere cat's jump that you arn't hanged. But who would ever think the mayor of Market-jew is the man to try a case so quick? Come, let us be going. I am thinking, too, about my wife and cheeld; it was here we parted, and I wonder how they have got on, poor dears, since I've been far away."

"Well then, as you are so hastes we will pay the shot," replied they, "and jog along again, and be home before sunset, if all be well." Driving their horses at a quick pace, they went on with great glee and arrived at the foot of Trelew Hill.

Here, since Tom went eastward, a new road had been made, that took another direction to reach the hill-top, where it re-entered the old one. The merchants were for going by the new road, because it was easier for their horses.

"Friend Tom, you had better come along with us," said they, "than scramble up the steep hill through that rocky lane."

"No, my friends, though I am loath to leave your pleasant company," replied he, "I shall take the old road, for I have bought another piece of wit that telleth me never to leave an old road for a new one. Choose for yourselves. A short way hence, where the two roads join, the first that arrives can await the others."

The merchants went on, saying, "We shall soon meet again."

When Tom came to where the roads joined, he saw the horses jogging homewards, without their owners. He looked along the road both ways, but saw no merchants. Then getting on a high bank, in a minute or two he beheld one of them coming across the downs stripped of his coat, hat, and wallet. He saw soon afterwards the two others, coming from different directions, almost naked.

"Halloo, my masters," said Tom, when they came near, "however are ye in this sad plight?"

"Ah, comrade," answered they, "we wish we had been so wise as thou. Half-ways up the hill robbers fell on us and stripped us, as you see."

"How many were they?" Tom asked.

In their confusion each merchant answering, "Three attacked me;" they counted the robbers nine, till considering how they had separated at the onset, each one trying to save himself, they saw that the same men, having fallen on each one of them in turn, they were only three robbers after all. Tom remarked, in angry tones, "One wouldn't take you for West Country men, yet I should think it's hard to find three stouter than you, this side of Hayle. But you forgot *One and All*; so I havn't much pity for 'e; each one trying to save himself took to his heels and left his comrades in the lurch; that's the way you are beaten; and serve 'e right. My old dad always said to me, "Tom, my boy, mind *One and All*. Fall fair, fall foul, stand by thy comrades, and in misfortune, stick all the closer, my son." But we have no time to lose," he continued, "we are four of us together now; they can't be gone far, and, dash my buttons, if we don't beat them yet. You have lost your sticks, I see, but here's what will serve your needs," said he taking up his threshal (flail), undoing it, and putting the keveran (connecting piece of leather) in his pocket. "One take the slash-staff, another the hand-staff, the other of 'e take my threshal-strings, and bind the rascals hand and foot as we knock them down. Now come on, boys! *One and All* mind; or the devil take the first to run."

The merchants, wishing to recover their clothes and money, readily agreed to return with Tom in pursuit. They ran down the rocky lane. At the bottom, near where the roads separated, they saw, on a rock, by the side of the new road, bundles of clothes and the merchants' wallets. Going on softly a few paces farther, they beheld the three robbers stretched on the grass, a little off the road, counting the stolen money and dividing their spoil. They sprang to their legs, but were scarcely up when Tom and the two merchants knocked them down and the other secured them.

"Ah!" said Tom, with a satisfied look, when he saw the robbers laid low, "the buff coat and new boots on that big fellow, who looks like their captain, will suit me, and I will take them for my Sunday's wear."

No sooner said than done with Tom. Whilst the merchants gathered up their money, he pulled off the captain's boots and stripped him of his buff; saying, "Now, my fine fellow, you won't be able to run very fast over furze and stones, if you should be inclined to give chase when you come round again."

The merchants, having well thrashed the robbers, left them stretched on the ground, half-killed, took their own clothes, and proceeded homewards, giving Tom much praise for his wit and valour.

They soon overtook their horses, and, without stopping, arrived at Coet-ny-whilly. Here the nearest road to Chyannor strikes off to the right of that leading to Treen. The merchants pressed Tom to go home and sup with them.

"No, thank 'e, not now, some other time," he answered.

"Come along," they again urged, all three; saying, "thou art right welcome, and we will treat thee well."

"No, not now," replied he, "but I don't doubt your welcome, though, as my master used to say, 'It is often good manners to ask, but not always to take.' Besides," continued he, "I am longing to get home quickly and see my wife and cheeld."

Each party proceeded their separate ways. When Tom had passed a place called the Crean, and was within half a mile of his dwelling, he sat down on a bank and lingered there till dusk, that he might get home about dark, and have a chance to look round unperceived, and thus find out if his wife had attended to her duty. Tom had learned but little about his family from the merchants. They merely told him that his wife had often been to Treen with yarn to sell, and, as she was a good spinster, they supposed the weavers gave her plenty of work. They knew nothing of either his wife or his daughter.

When it was all but dark Tom again went on slowly, and quickened his pace in going up the Bottom, till he approached within a stone's-cast of his dwelling. Here he paused a moment, on hearing a man's voice inside. Then he went softly on to a little glass window—the only one glazed in his house— and peeped in.

On the chimney-stool he espied, by the fire-light, a man and a woman, hugging, kissing, and seeming very fond of each other.

"Oh! but this is double damnation," groaned Tom to himself, "that I should ever come home, after working for years far away, to be greeted with such a sight. Where can the cheeld be? 'Tis enough to make one mad to see her faggot of a mother there, showing more love for that black-looking fellow than she did for me, except in our courting times and a week or so after marriage. I'll kill the villain, and drive the old huzzey to doors, that I will."

Whilst such thoughts of vengeance passed through Tom's mind, he recollected his last two pounds' worth of wit, and hesitated a minute at the door; but he was sure of what he saw; and now, hearing them laughing and couranting (romping) in their loving play, that aggravated him all the more. He grasped his stick and looked again to be certain, when a voice close behind him called out to him in tones like his wife's, "Halloo, eaves-dropper! Who art thou, and what dost thee want there spying and listening? Thee west hear no good of thyself, I'll be bound!"

Tom looking round, saw his wife close by, with a 'burn' of ferns on her back.

"That can never be thee, wife," said he, "unless thee art a witch; for this instant thou wert sitting on the chimney-stool with a strange man, and behaving in a way that don't become thee."

"Art thou come home such a fool as not to know thy own cheeld?" she replied. "Who else should be in but our Patience and her sweetheart Jan the cobbler. I left them there half an hour ago, when I went down in the moors for a 'burn' of fuel. Come in, quick, and let's see how thee art looking, after being so long away. Wherever hast a been to? We didn't know if thee wert alive or dead. If I had been married again nobody could blame me."

Patience, hearing her father's voice, ran out, and great was her joy to find him come home. Tom shook hands with her sweetheart, saying, "I could never have believed when I left thee, Jan, a mere hobble-de-hoy, I should come back and find thee such a stout man, and the cheeld too, grown a woman— taller than her mother."

Tom having taken his accustomed place on the bench, his wife said, "I see thee hast got a buff coat and a pair of new high boots, fit for any gentleman or a lord of the land to wear on Sundays and high holidays, and I suppose you have brought home something new for me and the maid to wear that you mayn't be ashamed of us, when rigged in your boots and buff. Come now, Tom dear," continued she, over a bit, when they had admired what Tom didn't tell them he took from the robber; "Come, love, let's see what have 'e got for us?"

"I have brought 'e home myself," Tom replied, "and a charm-stone for Patience to wear when she is married, that will be better than a fortune of gold and lands for her and her husband. Besides, I have brought 'e a cake," continued he, in placing it on the board.

"And is that all?" demanded his wife, looking as black as thunder at him; "and tell us what's become of thy wages then," continued she with increasing anger.

"I gave my two pounds a year wages," he replied, "back again to my master for six pounds' worth of wit, and he gave me that cake for thee."

"Ay, forsooth," said she in a rage. "Thee art a wise man from the East, that lacked wit to know his own cheeld after being three years from home. Go the way'st away again, and take thy fuggan along with thee." Saying this she snatched up the cake and fired it at her husband, aiming for his head; but Tom ducked quick, the cake went smash against the wall, broke in pieces, and out of it fell a lot of money. Silver and gold ringled on the floor! When all was picked up and counted they found Tom's three years' wages and many shillings over.

"Oh, my dear Tom," said his wife, "no tongue can tell how glad I am to see thee home again, safe and sound, after being so long away in strange countries one didn't know where. And thou didst know well enow about the money, and only played the trick to try me."

"The devil a bit," said Tom, "but I forgive thee, and let's have supper."

The wife gave Patience a large bottle, telling her to run quick over to Trebeor and have it filled with the best she could get, to drink her father's health and welcome home. Turning to Tom she said, "The sand will soon be down in the hour-glass, and then a leek-and-pilchard pie, put down to bake before I went out for fuel, will be ready; meanwhile let's have a piece of thy cake; it seems very good."

When Patience and Jan had gone away for liquor, Tom's wife seated herself on the chimney-stool, with a piece of the cake in her hand, and said quite coaxing like, "Take thy piece of cake in thy hand, my son, and come the way'st here alongside of me; I have something to tell thee."

When both of them were seated on the chimney-stool, very lovingly, eating their cake together, she continued to say, "I hope thee wesent be vexed, Tom dear, to hear me confess the truth; and if thee art it can't be helped now; so listen, and don't leave thy temper get the upper hand of all thy wisdom, for I have had a young fellow living in the house more than two years and we have slept in the same bed lately every night. Why thee art looking very black good man, but he is very innocent and handsome and so thee west say; he is in my bed asleep now! Come the way'st down in the 'hale' and see him. One may see by thy looks that thee hast a mind to murder the youngster, but have patience and come along."

Tom sprang up, like one amazed, and followed his wife when she took the chill (lamp) and entered the other room.

"Come softly, Tom," said his wife, as she approached the bed, turned down the bedclothes, and showed her husband, to his great surprise, a fine boy nearly three years old. She then told Tom how, after being many years without children, when he left her for the East she found reason to expect an increase to their limited family. Tom's joy was now past all bounds. He had always wished for a boy, and hadn't satisfied himself with kissing the child, and admiring his big-boned limbs (for one of his age) when Patience and her sweetheart entered. Tom and the rest drank to the boy's health, and all was now joy and content.

News of Tom's return having been quickly carried from house to house, supper was scarcely put aside, when in came a number of neighbours. All brought wherewith to drink his welcome home, and the night sped jovially in hearing him recount his adventures in the East Country.

Next day, Tom and his wife, being alone together, she said to him, "Now, whilst the maid is out, tell me, my son, what dost thee think of her sweetheart and of their being married soon?"

"Well, wife, from what I saw when I looked through the window last night," Tom replied, "I should say that she wouldn't break her heart, any more than her mother before her, if she were to be married to-morrow; but is Jan a fool, like I was, to give up a young man's life of pleasure and wed in haste, like I did, thou knowest, that he may repent at leisure? Yet thee wert very good looking then, just like our Patience is now, and, with thy deceiving ways, I didn't stop to consider that beauty is only skin deep. Jan the cobbler," Tom continued, nodding his head very knowingly, "is hale and strong, and come of an honest 'havage' enow. I am loath to lose the maid so soon; yet my wise master used to say to his wife, 'One that will not when he may, when he will he shall have nay;' and it is better to have a daughter but indifferently married than well kept; though the charm I have for Patience will make her a prize for a lord, yet a cobbler isn't to be despised, and a good trade is often more worth than money that may be spent; so, with all my heart, let them be wedded when they will."

A few days after Tom's return, he and Patience went down to Treen. Whilst they were away, his wife, curious (like most women are), took it into her head to examine the coat Tom took from the robber. She wondered how it was so heavy, and noticed that the body-lining of serge was worked over very closely. She undid the cloth, and found that gold coins were quilted in all over it, two-deep in some places, between the woollen stuff and an inner lining. Before Tom returned she took out more money, all in gold, than filled a pewter quart, and then there was a good portion left untouched, for fear Tom might come home and see the nest she had found; all in good time, the money and coat were put in an old oak chest, of which she kept the key. When Tom and Patience came in she could hardly conceal her joy. They wondered at her sprightly humour yet, for a great marvel, she kept her counsel, though Tom said more than once that evening. "I can't think, old woman, what can be the matter, that thee art going about cackling to thyself like an old hen shot in the head, and with as much fuss and consequence, too, as a mabyer (young hen) searching for a nest, days before it is wanted, and finding none to her mind, good enow to drop her first egg in. And look at her, tossing her head," he continued, "don't she look proud, like the lightheaded mabyer, after laying her egg?"

As Tom knew nothing of his good fortune he continued to work on diligently, as usual.

When Feasten Monday came round Jan the cobbler and Patience were married. Her father gave her the charm-stone privately, with instructions for its use, as his old mistress had directed. Strangers were not let into the secret, because all charms lose their virtue when known to others than the charmers, who, if they give or tell it, lose its use for ever.

When the honey-moon waned Jan would sometimes get into an angry mood. Then his wife would, unobserved, slip the charm-stone into her mouth, and (let him talk or fume) keep quietly about her work. In a short time with good humour, like sunshine returned, he would again be heard ringing his lap-stone to the measure of some lively old tune. The quiet ways of Patience and her gentle bearing, kept love and content, with peace and plenty, in their happy dwelling; and her charm had such power that, over a while, she had seldom occasion to use it. Yet, indeed, some women, living near, who liked to let their crabbed tongues run like the clapper of a mill, would say that Patience was a poor quiet fool, and that the more one let blockheads of husbands have their own way the more they will take till they go to the dogs, or the devil, at last. Jan would tell these idle cacklers, who stuck up for woman's misrule, to mind their own affairs and that for such 'tungtavusses' as they were the old saying held good—that "a woman, a dog, and a walnut tree, the more you beat them the better they be." But gentle Patience, heedless of their prate, kept on in the even tenor of her life, and retained her husband's unabated love till the peaceful close of her days.

Now it happened about three years after Tom had returned from the East Country, there was a large farm in St. Levan for sale. "Ah, poor me," said Tom one night, after a hard day's work, "I have been toiling and moiling, like a slave, all my life long, but we shall never have an inch of land to call our own till laid in the church-hay. Yet here are our hunting gentry, who have more than they can make good use of, and they can't live on that. If we could but scrape together enough to buy an acre or two of fee, or only the corner of a croft, where one might have a hut and a gar'n for herbs, with the run of a common for a cow or anything else, and none to say us nay, how happy we should be. But now," he continued, "it is only by the lord's leave, and that I don't like to ask of any man; and why should one who hath hands to work when there is so much land in waste untilled?"

"Tom, my son, cheer up," his wife replied; "there are many worse off than we are, with our few pounds laid by for a rainy day, and health and strength to get more. Why I am afraid," said she, "that thou would'st go crazy, or die for joy, if any one gave thee enough to buy a few acres."

"I wish to gracious somebody would but try me," Tom replied.

"Well now, suppose I were to tell thee," said she, "that we have saved enough to buy good part, if not all, of the land for sale, as you shall soon see."

She then brought from the chest a quart measure of gold coins, and poured them out on the board. At the sight of the glittering gold Tom sprung up in a fright and exclaimed, "Now I know, for certain, that thee art a witch! I had often thought so. That money is the Old One's coinage; don't think that I'll have any dealings with him; I wouldn't touch with a tongs a piece of the devil's gold."

"Hold thy clack, cheeld vean, if I'm a witch thou art no conjuror, that's clear," replied she. "Now listen, and learn that the coat taken by thee from the robber-captain was all lined with gold, quilted in between the serge and the leather, and what thou seest on the board isn't all I found in it."

When Tom's surprise had somewhat abated, he counted the money and found more than was required to purchase and stock two such farms as the one then for sale. Over a while Tom bought a great quantity of land—many acres might be had for a few pounds in Tom's time, when a very small part of the land was enclosed, and much less cultivated. In a few years he was regarded as a rich yeoman, and his sons and grandsons became substantial farmers.

Tom's posterity may still be flourishing in St. Levan, or some place near, for what any body can tell, as no one knows what name they took when surnames came into use, long after Tom lived in Chyannor.

THE FAIRY DWELLING ON SELENA MOOR.[3]

"Merry elves, their morrice pacing,
To aërial minstrelsy,
Emerald rings on brown heath tracing,
Trip it deft and merrily."

SCOTT.

WHEN the ancient family of Noy flourished in Buryan there was a large tract of unenclosed common, belonging to the farms of Pendrea, Selena, and Tresidder, which extended from Cotnewilly to Baranhual, and branched off in other directions. Great part of this ground was swampy and produced a rank growth of rushes, water-flags, and coarse herbage. Many acres were gay in summer with cotton-grass, bog-beans, cucco-flowers, and other plants usually found in such soil. In some places were dry rocky banks overgrown with sloe-trees, moor-withey, furze, and brambles; these patches being surrounded by a broad extent of quaking bog or muddy soil appeared like islands in a marsh. There were also many springs, rivulets, and pools, that seldom froze, much frequented by wild-fowl in winter. Great part of this moorland was then impassable; horse-tracks leading to Baranhual, Selena, and other farms, passed over the dryest places, and were continued by rough causeways through swamps;—they were very bad roads at all seasons.

Most of this wilderness has long been enclosed and drained; Pendrea portion of it is now a separate tenement called Westmoor. Near Cotnewilly were the scattered remains of an ancient grove which, in very remote times, extended thence to Alsia-mill.

One afternoon in harvest, Mr. Noy, with some of his men, were over to Baranhual helping his kinsfolks, the Pendars. As more hands were required for the next day, which was to be the gulthise (harvest home), soon after 'croust' time he rode up to Church-town to get them, and to invite the parson, clerk, and sexton—the latter was particularly welcome to the harvest folk as he was generally a good fiddler and droll-teller. With these, according to old usage, were asked the crafts-men and others who had lent hand about the harvest work, and aged inmates of the poor house; one and all were welcome to the gulthise supper.

Soon after 'day-down' Mr. Noy, followed by his dogs, left the public-house intending to return to Baranhual, but he didn't arrive there that night nor the next. The Pendars and their people thought he might have enjoyed himself at the *Ship* Inn till late, and then have gone home to Pendrea. Mr. Noy had no wife nor anybody else to be much alarmed about him, as he was a middle-aged or rather elderly bachelor. But next day when people from Church-town, Pendrea, and scores of neighbours from other farms, came with their horses to help and to feast at the gulthise, and nobody among them had seen or heard of Mr. Noy from the time he left the inn, they got somewhat uneasy; yet they still supposed he might have gone to some corn-carrying down the lower side of Buryan, as was likely enow, for all the neighbours round about were just like one family then.

As usual there was a great chase bringing home the corn in trusses; leaders and other helpers took their flowery-milk (hasty pudding) for breakfast, apple pies for dinner, just when and how they could, with beer and cider whenever they felt inclined, so they might keep the mowers always building, to have the corn under thatch before supper time. All being secured in the mowhay scores of all ages enjoyed roast and boiled beef, mutton, squab pies, rabbit and hare pies, pudding, and other substantial fare, usually found at a bountiful gulthise supper; then drinking, singing, dancing, and other pastimes, were kept up till late. In the meantime Dame Pendar had sent messengers round to all places where she thought Mr. Noy might have gone, and they returned, just as the feast was breaking up, without any tidings of him.

Then everyone became anxious, and as it was near daybreak they volunteered to disperse and search in every place they could think of before going to bed.

So away they went, some on horseback, others afoot, to examine mill-pools, stream-works, cliffs, and other dangerous places, near and far away. They returned at night, but nobody had seen or heard of the missing gentleman. Next morning horsemen were despatched to other parishes, and as Mr. Noy was well known and liked there was a general turn out to hunt for him; but this day, too, was passed in a like fruitless search miles away.

On the third day, however, in the grey of the morning, a horse was heard to neigh, and dogs were heard barking among thickets on a piece of dry ground almost surrounded with bogs and pools, on Pendrea side of Selena moor.

Now it happened that no one had thought of looking for Mr. Noy in this place so near home, but when with much ado, a score or so of men discovered a passable road into this sort of island in the bogs, there they saw Mr. Noy's horse and hounds; the horse had found plenty of pasture there, but the dogs, poor things, were half-starved. Horse and dogs showed their joy, and led the way through thorns, furze, and brambles—that might have grown there hundreds of years—till they came to large 'skaw' trees and the ruins of an old bowjey or some such building that no one knew of. Hunters never attempted in winter to cross the boggy ground that nearly surrounded these two or three acres of dry land, and in summer no one was curious enough to penetrate this wilderness of thickets which, like all such places, was then swarming with adders.

The horse stopped at what had been a doorway, pawed on the 'drussal,' looked around and winneyd; the dogs, followed by several people, pushed through the brambles that choked the entrance, and within they found Mr. Noy lying on the ground fast asleep. It was a difficult matter to arouse him; at last he awoke, stretched himself, rubbed his eyes, and said, "Why you are Baranhual and Pendrea folks; however are ye all come here? To-day is to be the gulthise, and I am miles and miles away from home. What parish am I in? How could 'e have found me? Have my dogs been home and brought 'e here?" Mr. Noy seemed like one dazed as we say, and all benumed as stiff as a stake, so without staying to answer his questions, they gave him some brandy, lifted him on horseback, and left his steed to pick its way out, which it did readily enow, and a shorter one than they discovered.

Though told he was on his own ground, and less than half a mile from Baranhual, he couldn't make out the country as he said, till he crossed the running water that divides the farms. "But I am glad," said he "however it came to pass, to have got back in time for the gulthise." When they told him how the corn was all carried three days ago, he said they were joking, and wouldn't believe it till he had seen all in the mowhay under thatch and roped down; that the loose straw was raked up, and all harvest implements put away till next season.

Then whilst breakfast was getting ready, seated on a chimney-stool by a blazing fire, he told his neighbours that when he came to Cotnewilly, the night being clear, he thought he might as well make a short cut across the moor and save nearly a mile—as he had often done before in summer time—instead of going round by the stony bridle-path; but his horse, that was pretty much used to finding his own way when his master was tipsy, wanted to keep the usual road, and his rider, to baulk him, pulled farther off towards Pendrea side of the common than he would otherwise have done, and went on till he found himself in a part that was unknown to him; though he had been, as he thought, over every inch of it that man or beast could tread on, both in winter and summer. Getting alarmed at the strange appearance of everything around him, he tried in vain to retrace his steps, then gave the horse its head, and let it take its own course.

Yet instead of proceeding homeward, as was dobbin's wont, it bore Mr. Noy to a land so crowded with trees that he had to alight and lead his steed. After wandering miles and miles, sometimes riding but oftener afoot, without seeing any habitation in this strange place, which he believed must be out of Buryan but in what parish he couldn't tell, he at last heard strains of lively music, and spied lights glimmering through the trees and people moving about, which made him hope that he had arrived at some farm where they had a gulthise, and the harvest-folks were out, after supper, dancing in the town-place.

His dogs slunk back, and the horse wasn't willing to go on, so he tied him to a tree, took his course through an orchard towards the lights, and came to a meadow where he saw hundreds of people, some seated at tables eating and drinking with great enjoyment apparently, and others dancing reels to the music of a crowd or tambourine—they are much the same thing—this was played by a damsel dressed in white, who stood on a heaping-stock just beside the house door, which was only a few paces from him.

The revelers, farther off, were all very smartly decked out, but they seemed to him, at least most of them, to be a set of undersized mortals; yet the forms and tables, with the drinking-vessels on them, were all in proportion to the little people. The dancers moved so fast that he couldn't count the number of those that footed jigs and reels together, it almost made his head giddy only to look at their quick and intricate whirling movements.

He noticed that the damsel who played the music was more like ordinary folks for stature, and he took her to be the master's daughter, as, when one dance was ended, she gave the crowd to a little old fellow that stood near her, entered the house, fetched therefrom a black-jack, went round the tables and filled the cups and tankards that those seated, and others, handed to be replenished. Then, whilst she beat up a new tune for another set of dancers, Mr. Noy thought she cast a side-glance towards him; the music, he said, was so charming and lively that to save his soul he couldn't refrain from going to join the dancers in a three-handed reel, but the girl with a frown and look of alarm, made a motion with her head for him to withdraw round a corner of the house out of sight. He remained gazing, however, and still advancing till she beckoned to the same little old man, to whom she spoke a few words, gave him the crowd to play, and leaving the company, went towards the orchard signaling to Mr. Noy to follow her, which he did. When out of the candle-glare and in a clear spot where moonlight shone, she waited for him. He approached and was surprised to see that the damsel was no other than a farmer's daughter of Selena, one Grace Hutchens, who had been his sweetheart for a long while, until she died, three or four years agone; at least he had mourned her as dead, and she had been buried in Buryan Churchyard as such.

When Mr. Noy came within a yard or so, turning towards him, she said, "thank the stars, my dear William, that I was on the look-out to stop ye, or you would this minute be changed into the small people's state like I am,— woe is me."

He was about to kiss her, "Oh, beware!" she exclaimed, "embrace me not, nor touch flower nor fruit; for eating a tempting plum in this enchanted orchard was my undoing. You may think it strange, yet it was all through my love for you that I am come to this.

"People believed, and so it seemed, that I was found on the moor dead; it was also supposed that I must have dropped there in a trance, as I was subject to it. What was buried for me, however, was only a changeling, or sham body, never mine I should think, for it seems to me that I feel much the same still as when I lived to be your sweetheart."

As she said this several little voices squeaked, "Grace, Grace, bring us more beer and cider, be quick!"

"Follow me into the garden, and remain there behind the house; be sure you keep out of sight, and don't for your life, touch fruit or flower," said she, in conducting out Mr. Noy, who desired her to bring him a tankard of cider too. "No, my love, not for the world," she replied, "await me here, I'll soon return. Sad is my lot to be stolen from the living and made housekeeper to these sprites," murmured Grace, in quitting the garden.

Over a few minutes she returned to Mr. Noy, led him into a bowery walk, where the music and noise of merriment didn't overpower their voices, and said, "you know, my dear Willy, that I loved you much, but you can never know how dearly."

"Rest yourself," she continued pointing to a stone, "on that seat, whilst I tell ye what you never dreamt of." Mr. Noy seated himself as desired, and Grace related how one evening, about dusk, she was out on Selena Moor in quest of strayed sheep, when hearing him, in Pendrea ground, halloo and whistle to his dogs, she crossed over towards the sound in hopes of falling in with him, but missed her way among ferns higher than her head, and wandered on for hours amidst pools and shaking bogs without knowing whither.

After rambling many miles, as it seemed to her, she waded a brook and entered an orchard, then she heard music at a distance, and proceeding towards it, passed into a beautiful garden with alleys all bordered by roses and many sweet flowers, that she had never seen the like of. Apples and other tempting fruit dropped in the walks and hung over head, bursting ripe.

This garden was so surrounded with trees and water—coming in every here and there among them—that, like one 'piskey-led,' all her endeavours to find a way out of it were in vain. The music, too, seemed very near at times, but she could see nobody. Feeling weary and athirst, she plucked a plum, that looked like gold in the clear starlight; her lips no sooner closed on the fruit than it dissolved to bitter water which made her sick and faint. She then fell on the ground in a fit, and remained insensible, she couldn't say how long, ere she awoke to find herself surrounded by hundreds of small people, who made great rejoicing to get her amongst them, as they very much wanted a tidy girl who knew how to bake and brew, one that would keep their habitation decent, nurse the changed-children, that wern't so strongly made as they used to be, for want of more beef and good malt liquor, so they said.

At first she felt like one entranced and hardly knew how to 'find herself' in such strange company; even then, after many years' experience, their mode of life seemed somewhat unnatural to her, for all among them is mere illusion or acting and sham. They have no hearts, she believed, and but little sense or feeling; what serves them, in a way, as such, is merely the remembrance of whatever pleased them when they lived as mortals,—may be thousands of years ago.

What appear like ruddy apples and other delicious fruit, are only sloes, hoggans, (haws) and blackberries. The sweet scented and rare flowers are no other than such as grow wild on every moor.

In answer to Mr. Noy's enquiries about small people's dietry, Grace told him how she sickened, at first, on their washy food of honey-dew and berries—their ordinary sustenance—and how her stomach felt so waterish that she often longed for a bit of salt fish.

The only thing she relished was goat's milk, "for you must have often heard," said she, "that these animals are frequently seen on moors, or among carns and in other out-of-the-way places, miles from their homes. They are enticed away by small people to nourish their babes and changelings. There's a score or more of goats here at times. Those cunning old he-ones that often come among a flock—no one knows whence—and disappear with the best milkers, are the decoys, being small people in such shapes. One may often notice in these venerable long-beards, when seen reposing on a rock, chewing their cuds, a look of more than human craftiness and a sly witch-like glance cast from the corner of their eyes."

Looking at Mr. Noy for a moment with a melancholy expression, she sighed and continued, "I am now getting used to this sort of life and find it tolerable, the more so because the whole tribe behave to me with great kindness, the elderly men above all; you observed that little fellow to whom I spoke and who now plays the tambourine, I desired him to tell the rest, in case they inquired for me, that I was gone to look after the children, and he is so much attached to me as to do or say anything I request." Seeing Mr. Noy look somewhat lowering, Grace exclaimed, "Oh! my dear Willy, don't be such a noddy as to be jealous, for he's no other than vapour, and what he is pleased to think love, is no more substantial than fancy."

Mr. Noy asked if there were any children among them besides those they stole and replaced with changelings?

"Very few indeed," she replied, "though they are fond of babies, and make great rejoicing when one happens to be born amongst them; and then every little man, however old, is proud to be thought the father. For you must remember they are not of our religion," said she, in answer to his surprised look, "but star-worshippers. They don't always live together like Christians and turtle-doves; considering their long existence such constancy would be tiresome for them, anyhow the small tribe seem to think so. And the old withered 'kiskeys' of men that one can almost see through, like puffs of smoke, are vainer than the young ones. May the Powers deliver them from their weakly frames! And indeed they often long for the time when they will be altogether dissolved in air, and so end their wearisome state of existence without an object or hope."

She also told him—but he didn't remember exactly the words she spoke—that she was the more content with her condition since she was enabled to take the form of any bird she pleased, and thus gratify her desire to be near him, so that when he thought of her but little suspected her presence; she was mostly hovering round and watching him in the shape of some common small bird. Grace assured Mr. Noy of her everlasting love, yet as long as nature would permit him to retain his mortal form she would rather behold him in flesh and blood, than see him changed to her state. She also told him, that when he died, if he wished to join her, they would then be united and dwell in this fairy-land of the moors.

Mr. Noy wanted to know much more about these strange beings, and was about to enquire, when they again called, "Grace, Grace, where art thou so long? Bring us some drink quickly." She hastily entered the house, and that moment it came into his head that he, too, would have some liquor, disperse the small tribe, and save Grace.

Knowing that any garment turned inside out and cast among such sprites would make them flee, and happening to put his hand into his coat pocket, he felt there the gloves that he had worn for binding in the afternoon; quick as thought, he turned one inside out, put into it a small stone, and threw it among them; in an instant they all vanished with the house, Grace, and all the furniture. He just had time to glance round, and saw nothing but thickets and the roofless house of an old bowjey, when he received a blow on his forehead that knocked him down, yet he soon fell asleep and dozed away an hour or two he thought.

Those to whom Mr. Noy related his story, said that he had learnt nothing new from Grace, for old folks always believed of the fair people such things as she told him, and they disliked to be seen, above all by daylight, because they then looked aged and grim. It was said, too, that those who take animal forms get smaller and smaller with every change, till they are finally lost in the earth as muryans (ants), and that they passed winter, for the most part, in underground habitations, entered from cleves or carns. And it is held that many persons who appear to have died entranced, are not really dead, but changed into the fairy state.

The recovered gentleman farther informed them that he had remarked amongst the small folks, many who bore a sort of family-likeness to people he knew, and he had no doubt but some of them were changelings of recent date, and others their forefathers who died in days of yore, when they were not good enow to be admitted into heaven, nor so wicked as to be doomed to the worst of all places. Over a while, it is supposed they cease to exist as living beings, for which reason fewer of them are now beheld than were seen in old times.

From the night that Mr. Noy strayed into the small people's habitation, he seemed to be a changed man; he talked of little else but what he saw and heard there, and fancied that every redbreast, yellow-hammer, tinner (wag-tail), or other familiar small bird that came near him, might be the fairy-form of his departed love.

Often at dusk of eve and moonlight nights, he wandered round the moors in hopes to meet Grace, and when he found his search was all in vain he became melancholy, neglected his farm, tired of hunting, and departed this life before the next harvest. Whether he truly died or passed into fairy-land, no one knows.

A story, much like the foregoing, is related of a young farmer called Richard Vingoe, who was 'piskey-led' in Treville Cliffs. After wandering for hours over places which appeared strange to him, he followed a path through a rocky 'bottom' or glen into an underground passage or cavern, from which, on emerging, he found himself in a pleasant looking country. Walking on he heard sounds of merry-making, and came to a place where people appeared to be keeping feast. He noticed a great number of persons hurling, and being fond of that game, he was about to run and seize the silver ball, as it fell near him, when a female darted from behind a rock—which screened her from view—and made eager signs for him to desist and follow her, as she withdrew into an orchard near at hand. He approached and saw that she was a damsel who had been dead a few years. She told him how she was changed into the fairy-state by having trespassed on the small people's domain, and that he had narrowly escaped the same fate. She also informed him of their mode of life, and that she was disposed to save him for the sake of their former attachment, as in the above story.

When the hurlers and spectators of the game had all gone out of sight, she conducted her former lover to the upper world by a shorter road than that by which he entered; on the way she told him that as he had engaged to be married within a few weeks, she had no desire to detain him. She advised him, however, to defer his wedding three years, that he might be sure he knew his own mind. When Vingoe promised to follow her advice, they passed through an opening in a carn, and he saw Nanjizel; his conductress then said good-bye, and vanished. Being fatigued with his journey he lay on the grass, near the spot where he again saw the light of day, and there he was found asleep nearly a week after. Vingoe was never like the same man again, for he took to hard drinking and died unmarried.

The details of both stories are so similar that they appear to be mere versions of the same fairy-tale.

The I'an's House of Treen.

All within is dark as night;
In the windows is no light;
And no murmur at the door,
So frequent on its hinge before.

Come away: no more of mirth
Is here, or merry-making sound.
The house was builded of the earth,
And shall fall again to ground.

TENNYSON.

SOME few years ago, there might have been seen on rising ground, west of the road which passes through Treen, the remains of a very old dwelling, formerly known in that neighbourhood as the I'an's (pro Jan's) house. Though neglected and ruinous it still retained some signs of its former consequence when it was regarded as a mansion. Visitors to the Logan Rock often stopped to look at this forlorn-looking old house, with great part of its mullioned windows and a doorway, that had once been its grand entrance, walled up. Its peculiar old style of masonry, the massiveness and irregularity of the rough granite blocks with which it was constructed, and its high-pitched thatched roof, made this old building an object of interest, though it was neither beautiful nor picturesque. And a few casements, still retaining their old lead-lights of small panes in various patterns, to which age had imparted purple or rather prismatic hues, glimmered and glanced with changing lights that gave to the habitation a very ghostly look.

What remained had long been divided into three or four dwellings; but one wing was mostly unoccupied, because few persons could be found so courageous or necessitous as to live in it and have their rest disturbed every night, and often by day, with the rumbling of a turn (spinning-wheel) varied by wild shrieks, unearthly laughter, and other frightful noises. There was also beyond the kitchen-court (and entered from it) a garden, surrounded by high walls, which rendered it as secluded as any room of the mansion. This ground was long called Beaton's garden, even after, denuded of herbs and flowers, it was turned into a pig's-court. This place was haunted too. In this state the old house and appurtenances remained until destroyed by fire, about ten years since, and it always retained the name of a family that built it and resided there for generations, in the style of gentry, though never very rich nor persons of much note beyond that locality.

Three or four centuries ago, from their extravagance and a run of bad luck, the I'ans were reduced to comparative poverty. It was said that ill fortune ever followed them from the time they broke up and removed to Garrack-zans (holy rock) that stood in front of their mansion, and around which a market was held in old times when Treen was an important trading-place. However, that may have been, shortly after all the family remaining in Treen were John I'an (or Ivan) and his sister Beatrice, usually called Beaton, who had lost their parents when children. Young I'an from having much family pride and but little property to support its dignity, led a very unsettled life— mostly at sea, with a company of reckless young men, who carried on a hazardous trade in importing liquors, silks, salt, and other contraband goods from Roscroff; making Penberth, or some other cove, near it, their usual landing-place. Both brother and sister are said to have been remarkable for their tall stature and good looks, though of very dark complexion.

They might, now and then, be seen at church—the former dressed in a long bottle-green coat of cut velvet, and dusky crimson waistcoat (both overlaid with tarnished gold lace,) a plush breeches, and diamond-buckled shoes. These everlasting garments, that might have been worn by his grandfather, were only changed in winter for home spun; and his sturdy legs were then encased in long funnel-topped boots of French make; and his jet black hair, that hung in curls on his shoulders, was surmounted by a laced hat and plume. Though young I'an's state dress appeared much the worse for wear he looked every inch a gentleman, when, with old-fashioned courtesy, he led into church his sister, arrayed in silks or samite, a century old or more, yet still looking rich with their brilliant sheen, and thick enough to stand on end; point-lace ruffles, yellow with age, hanging from her elbows, were met by embroidered silk gloves; her hair, of darkest chestnut hue, turned back over cushions, hung in ringlets down her neck; and a little hat was fastened by jewel-headed pins to her high head-dress. These remnants of old finery, contrasted with homely articles of dress that had to sustain more wear and tear, made the I'an's poverty only too apparent; the more so because, at that time, several well-to-do families resided in St. Levan, and at church their old bravery and newest fashions were all displayed and duly criticised. Beaton showed, however, what her brother thought becoming pride, in treating with coolness or contempt all attentions offered by such rural beaux as he thought beneath her, though she had but slight chance, poor girl, of becoming acquainted with any of higher rank.

I'an being seldom at home during the summer, his sister and two or three old servants managed the farm—then but a few acres of arable land, and a great run of common—and were sole occupants of their gloomy mansion. The poor young lady's dreary existence was partially relieved by her brother's presence during winter. Then, too, he often brought home with him many of his sea-mates or hunting companions, and the old house resounded with their reckless drunken revelry for days and nights together.

Among I'an's comrades his favourite was an able seaman called Willy Taskes or Trevaskes, who was a few years older than I'an—a courageous smuggler, and mate of his fair-trader the *Mur*. Taskes was remarkably strong built, the best wrestler and boxer in the western parishes. With much practice he taught I'an these arts of self-defence, and trained him to be just as good a seaman as himself. I'an, when overloaded with drink, was often quarrelsome or rather fond of fighting, without reason, both at home and abroad. Taskes as often belaboured him soundly to divert his combative inclinations from dangerous antagonists; often also, he got himself thrashed black and blue in taking I'an's part, which he was ever ready to do against any odds. From Willy being frequently in Beaton's company, and from the favour shown him by her brother, she was less reserved with him than others of his crew whom she kept at due distance.

Of an evening when he often came alone, Beaton would ask him to card the wool that she passed great part of her time in spinning, and no one more ready than Willy Taskes to please her. I'an frequently left them together, little deeming that his sister—of gentle blood, poor as she might be—could have a thought of the handsome young sailor as a lover. Ere long, however, I'an was informed by his ugly old female domestic—one who ever longed for but never had a lover—that her young mistress often met Willy Taskes by night in the walled garden, Caercreis barn, or among the Castle carns. I'an, enraged, entered his sister's apartments—she had three rooms at her sole disposal in that portion of the mansion known as Beaton's wing—and, after much upbraiding, threatened to shoot Taskes if he came near the house any more, and both of them if he caught them together. Beaton defied her brother, and answered that if she could not see Willy Taskes there she would meet him elsewhere, and that it only depended on Willy as to whether she should be his wife or not. Warned of what had taken place, the lover kept aloof, and I'an, discarding his jovial companions, remained much within doors, moody and discontented, wishing for the company of his former comrade, but pride forbade his making friendly overtures; and his ill-humour was aggravated all the more because his sister had the policy to persuade him that, after all, she didn't care anything for Willy Taskes, nor any of his crew, and that his chagrin was all for nought. The dreary winter past, and corn tilled, I'an and his crew prepared for an early trip to Roscroff. Their former mate, from his quarrel with the captain, or rather from the coolness between them, having gone to work on land, they selected a new one and made sail.

I'an left on good terms with his sister, thinking that, though she might have had an unbecoming affection for Taskes, yet her self-respect and regard for the dignity of their family—which he had awakened—had enabled her to subdue her misplaced love.

In a few weeks the *Mur*, as I'an's craft was called, returned with the usual goods, which were soon landed and disposed of, as the most valuable liquors, silks, lace, &c., were bespoke by the neighbouring gentry. Farmers, and others who assisted to land and secure the cargo soon took off what remained. There was then little or no interference from any government officials; indeed in more recent times those paid to check "fair-trade" were often the smugglers' friends, because they durst not interrupt their proceedings with anything but well-understood shams of activity, and they were always rewarded with a share of the goods if they conducted themselves with discretion. Old smugglers say they often wished to fall in with the revenue-cutter that their trip might be the more exciting—they answered her shots by a loud hurrah, and a blaze from their own swivel-gun. As for the riding-officer they didn't mind him a straw, and of other coast-guards there were none.

All hands being ready for another trip, the evening before they intended to start I'an told his sister he was going to meet his crew at the *Skaw Tree*—the inn at St. Levan Church-town,—have a carouse, and sail in the morning early. Wishing to become friends with his old mate, I'an had requested one of his crew to tell Taskes that he would be glad of his company at the public-house and to let all past unpleasantness be forgotten. In I'an's happier moods a lingering regard for his former comrade and staunch friend would get the upper hand of his prejudice and family pride, and then he would even think of Taskes as his brother-in-law with complacency.

From jealousy on the part of his new mate and others, his friendly message was not delivered. I'an not guessing the reason why Taskes didn't join them, and only thinking his offers of renewed friendship were slighted, was in ill-humour, and what was intended to have been a jovial night, passed unpleasantly. At length some of the fuddled crew, vexed because of their captain's preference for his former mate, hinted that he might be in Caercreis barn, in company he better liked, and that, by all accounts, his sister and Willy had always been on very good terms. I'an, tipsy as he was, understood their meaning, made imprudent threats of the way he would be revenged on Taskes; and left the company much earlier than was his wont on such occasions.

Very mixed feelings, and all of an irritating nature, spurred him on his way towards an old solitary 'bowjey,' or field barn, where a cottage now stands— five minutes' walk from Castle Treen; and he had only gone a few yards beyond Pedny-vounder lane, when, by the dim moonlight, he spied two persons sauntering along a sheep-track that wound among rocks and carns below him. Approaching and seeing they were his sister and her lover he assailed them with angry words, which soon came to blows between the men. Taskes, finding that I'an was the worse for drink, merely defended himself and received his blows that he might expend his fury on him, as he had often done when they were the best of friends. But, as bad luck would have it, Taskes, in going back, to avoid what might have been ugly strokes, fell over a shelving rock on to a ledge (or shelf, as we say), many feet below.

When I'an saw the young man he had once loved as a brother lying prostrate and apparently dead, his pride and anger gave place to bitter sorrow. He raised the wounded man, who moaned, and gasped for breath for some minutes; then hearing I'an crying like a child, begging him to forget and forgive the past and be friends, "I have nothing to forgive thee, my son," Taskes replied; "it was my bad luck, and, whether I die or live a cripple, I would rather for it to be my case than thine."

Over a while I'an and his sister helped him to stand, and one on either side of Taskes, with his arm round the neck of each, they slowly reached their house and placed him on I'an's bed. The servant-man was summoned, and told to ride with all speed for a doctor. Taskes tried to speak, and signed that he might be lifted up in bed. Supported on I'an's breast, and holding the brother's and sister's hands, he said "I know, dear John, a doctor can do me no good." And, looking towards Beaton, he told her to bring the man close to the bedside, for he had something to say before it might be too late.

The old servant approached. Taskes called him by name, and continued, "I am dying. None but ourselves know how I came by my end. You must bear witness for John, your master, that I declare it was all by my own mischance that I fell over a rock, and received my deadly hurt." He hadn't strength to say more. I'an wiped the bloody froth from the sinking man's lips, and tried to cheer him by saying, "Thou shalt live yet, my dear Willy, and be my brother."

Beaton, like one in a terrible dream, was unconscious of most that passed, till Taskes, awakening from a long swoon, grasped her hand and moaned in sad accents, "Beaton, dear Beaton; if I could but live till we might be married, I should die more content. And my dear John," he continued, directing his gaze towards I'an, "promise me, for all the years we have been like brothers, to be ever kind to Beaton and to my—to our"—he gasped for breath—with a gurgling in his throat, blood oozed from his lips. Looking wistfully at Beaton, he grasped brother's and sister's joined hands with a death-grip; his head sunk on I'an's breast; and thus Willy Taskes passed away in his prime.

Beaton, distracted by sorrow, had to be forcibly taken from her lover's bedside, and for weeks she seemed to be on the verge of madness. Her brother scarcely less grieved, tried to find some solace for his anguish in ordering that, in all respects, the funeral should be conducted as for one of his kindred. It was a custom with the I'ans, and a few other West Country families, to have their burials at night. So, a week after the fatal encounter, and in the summer evening's twilight, Willy Taskes was borne out of the old mansion, carried by his former comrades, followed by I'an and by many neighbours to his last resting-place in St. Levan Churchyard.

THE I'ANS QUIT TREEN.

She woke at length, but not as sleepers wake,
Rather the dead, for life seem'd something new,
A strange sensation which she must partake
Perforce, since whatsoever met her view,
Struck not her memory, though a heavy ache
Lay at her heart, whose earliest beat, still true,
Brought back the sense of pain without the cause,
For, for a while, the furies made a pause.

BYRON.

I'an being reluctant to leave his sister all alone with her sorrow, procured a good seaman to command the *Mur* for her next run. Fears were entertained that Beaton's mind might become permanently deranged from excessive grief. She could seldom be induced to leave the room in which her lover died, and I'an, feeling a repugnance to sleep there, she took it for a bed-room, saying she intended to keep it because that apartment, with two or three others adjoining it, were bequeathed to her (as indeed they were, with their furniture), for her lifetime. For many days together she was never seen except by the aged servant, who, at the usual meal-times, took to the gloomy chamber food that was often removed untasted. Her spinning-wheel was thrown aside; yet she seemed occupied in some quiet mysterious way; and I'an, getting alarmed for the probable result of her sad seclusion, consulted a doctor, who, being an old friend of the family, came to visit Beaton without delay, and requested to be taken to her room without being announced. I'an entered, followed by the doctor, and saw Beaton in a window-recess, busily sewing; at the same time, so absorbed was she in singing a baby's lullaby and rocking a cradle—in which there was no child, but a christening-dress with other articles of her infantile wardrobe—that she did not perceive her visitors. They noted, too, that the bed was covered with old dresses, in various beautiful fabrics, and that Beaton had been cutting them up, seemingly to waste. I'an annoyed to see this destruction of gay and costly gowns, said, "Sister dear, art thou going crazy to be cutting up thy best clothes?" "No, John," she replied, without looking up from her work; "yet methinks you are very rude thus to enter a lady's bedchamber with so little ceremony. But men understand so little of women's hearts," she continued, as if speaking to herself and taking no further notice of her brother; "little do they know that, when damsels don their gayest robes, they long for the time when they may cut them up for their babies' clothes. But is it to-morrow that is to be my wedding-day?" demanded she. "Oh, dear Willy, where art thou? Do tell me. It was to have been some time before brother John came back. The banns called thrice, we are to be wedded before he returns; then he will love my Willy like he used to, and all will be right well."

Unconscious, seeming, of any presence save what her crazed fancy imaged, she looked towards her brother and the doctor, who now advanced and noticed there was no intelligence in her fixed gaze. She appeared to be looking within rather than at anything external, when she went on to say, "Our child, if a boy, shall be named William, after you, my love; but if a girl, it shall never be called Beatrice for me. I have often been told that the name, though a favourite one, has always been ill-starred in our family. Shall we call her Mary for your mother, or Agnes for mine? Any names of those we love sound sweet, like a dear mother's. That I remember, and how she rocked me singing, 'Lullaby, lullaby, littly maid Beatrice; angels protect thee, my darling.'"

I'an, cut to the heart to see her thus, took her hand and said, "Sister, you are ill, dear, and our good friend, the doctor, is come to visit you." "Oh, how foolish people are," she replied, "I was never better in my life, yet our old Betty will have it that I don't eat enough, what next I wonder? I am glad, however, he is come to visit us; our house seems lonely now, and he is a dear man—so kind, true, and hearty, I always liked him from a child, and how he enjoys his pipe and glass, dear man! I'll leave my work now, and see that he be entertained with the best our house will afford."

Beaton folded her work, rose, passed near their friend without recognition, and descended to the kitchen, where she gave orders for a sumptuous repast, though there was nothing in her house to furnish it. She then returned to her work, saying that it would be time enough to dress for dinner in an hour or more, meanwhile her brother would entertain their guest, and the doctor would excuse her; for indeed she was very busy. Then she wailed, rather than sung,

'Twas down in the garden green, sweetheart,
Where you and I did walk;
But the fairest flower that in my garden grew
Is withered to a stalk.

The doctor, perceiving her pitiably distracted state, advised I'an to remove her to a change of scene—far away if he could—and trust to an occurrence that might soon take place to do more to restore her reason than anything in his power. "Nature," he observed, "beats all doctors, and maternal instinct supplies the place of reason, now happily dormant for the assuagement of her bleeding heart, poor dove."

The old servant, being called and questioned, she confirmed what the doctor surmised, and further informed him that she was aware of the intention of William and Beaton to be married during her master's absence, trusting to have his forgiveness, when all was done; then possible to make amends for the thoughtlessness of youth and love.

The doctor's advice tallied with I'an's inclination. He had often thought, and at length determined, to leave the wreck of his property for his creditors, as it was deeply mortgaged, and the accumulated interest of many years unpaid. He would seek a home for himself and his sister in Brittany, where he had formed acquaintances, and where no fancied requirements of sham gentility and beggarly state would impede his endeavours to push his fortune by land or sea. Being assured that a trip across the Channel was likely to prove beneficial to Beaton, who had often been to sea and enjoyed life on the waves like the sea-bird after which the smuggler's craft was named; wearing apparel, bedding, and a few heirlooms, of no great value, were soon packed so that they might be ready to leave when the *Mur* next made sail for France. Their moveable furniture was placed in Beaton's portion of the house, where two old servants were installed to keep possession for her of that, and also of some garden ground and pasture land in which she had a life interest. It was feared there might be some difficulty in persuading the poor demented woman to embark; yet, when the vessel was ready, by a harmless deception she was led to connect the proposed voyage, somehow, with going to meet her lover and hastening her bridal. So, one day, about a month after Willy was laid beneath the turf, I'an had a stone placed to mark the spot, and— following a very ancient custom in St. Levan—planted rosemary, box, lillies, and other garden flowers on the grave, over which he and his crew shed many tears. The following night I'an, with his sister, bade farewell to the ancient home of their forefathers, now rendered doubly sad to him by the remembrance of Taskes's ill-fated death, and his sister's melancholy plight.

Little more was then heard of either brother or sister. Penberth men, belonging to I'an's crew, purchased his share of their vessel, and before they left port, Beaton was lodged at a farm house, where she was kindly nursed; and it was hoped that, ere long, maternal cares might tend to restore her reason and somewhat relieve her anguish for her lover's untimely death. I'an was well known at the port, where they had long traded, as an expert seaman and good navigator, and he soon obtained the command of a ship. For a long while the old servants lived in Beaton's part of the house, hoping for her return, and cultivated the small quantity of ground that belonged to her. But no tidings ever reached them of either sister or brother; and when the two old servants died—it being supposed that their mistress was also dead, and her portion fallen in hand—I'an's creditors took possession of it.

UNEXPECTED VISITORS.

With fairest flowers,
Whilst summer lasts, and I live here, Fidele,
I'll sweeten thy sad grave.

Cymbeline.

A little above Penberth Cove, and near the Green, there is an ancient cottage in an orchard. In this dwelling lived an old dame called Joan Taskes, who kept a kind of public-house, as liquors and other goods were entrusted to her, by smugglers, for sale.

One afternoon, about nineteen or twenty years after Willy's death—when he and the I'ans were almost forgotten—An' Joan, whilst busy spinning flax with a treadle-turn heard a knock at her open door, and, thinking it was somebody come to buy liquor, or "honey-pins"—a sweet apple for which her orchard was noted—without rising she called out, "Come 'e in cheeld, and don't 'e stay knacking at the door." But An' Joan was rather startled when, on looking round, she saw two ladies standing near her. They were both tall. One appeared about fifty and the other near twenty years of age. Their dresses made her think they must be foreigners. The elder was clad in some kind of white woollen stuff, by whatever name one might call her garb: it had loose, hanging sleeves, and its ample folds were confined by a girdle to her waist. Over her head she wore a square of black serge; its ends hanging on her shoulders, and shading her face, gave it a pallid appearance, which was rendered somewhat ghastly by a white linen band across her forehead. The younger wore a silver-grey dress of more ordinary mode, and for head-dress a lace veil that covered, without concealing, her braided dark brown hair.

An' Joan, rising, drew out her form and said, "Pray be seated, ladies, and excuse me, as I thought you might have been some neighbours' children knocking at the door."

"We called," the elder lady replied, "to enquire if there be any small dwelling unoccupied in Penberth, or Treen, or in any place near."

"Be pleased to sit, ladies, and leave me think a moment," said the dame; "but I havn't heard of any place that would be good enough for you, and the only one I know of, close at hand, is Chynance. Why it seems to me," she continued, "as if I had heard the sound of your voice, years agone, somewhere, but can't call 'e to mind."

"Look at me well, Aunt Joan," the lady rejoined, "and tell me if you can think of anyone you ever saw like me."

The dame having adjusted her barnacles, peered at the lady's face and at length said in tremulous tones, "You can't be a spirit to come here high by day! Yet now I look at 'e again there's the dark brown eyes, straight nose, small mouth, and pitted chin of our poor lost Beatie! You can't be she? But with that white band across your forehead one can't see a lock of your hair; her's was of the darkest chesnut colour; besides the black kerchief or scarf, over your head, shades your face."

"If you saw my hair, now nearly as white as your own, you wouldn't know me by that," the lady answered. "But don't be frightened, dear An' Joan," continued she, in folding back her veil, "look again and you will see Beatrice I'an, and this dear girl is my daughter Mary."

An' Joan sprung from her seat, kissed Mary, clasped Beaton to her breast, and wept aloud for joy. She then took from her cupboard a bottle of brandy and another of sweet-drink (mead), filled two rummers with a mixture of the strong and sweet, saying, "Here, dears, drink this, and help yourselves to more while I get something for 'e to eat before I hear another word."

The old dame skipped about as if the sight of Beaton and her daughter had made her twenty years younger.

In a few minutes An' Joan fried fish, boiled eggs, and placed on the board milk, cream, and butter, with bread and honey, apple pasties, a jug of beer, and more bottles of her choice cordials. When all three had done ample justice to the repast, Beaton, looking round the dwelling, said, "Now Aunt Joan, I am again at home and as happy as I can ever hope to be, but I always felt like one banished for all the years I dwelt in the land where Mary was born and bred. Everything here looks the same as long ago, when my delight was to run down for some of your choice fruit and sweet flowers, and to play with your turns till you learnt me to spin just as well as yourself." Seeing Mary's gaze fixed on the dresser, she continued, "You may well admire that, dear, and all its shelves contain; a dresser is the crowning glory of every Cornish cottage. You have never seen such quaint looking old jugs, ornamented with queer figures and wry faces, grinning amidst flowers and fruit, as those on the upper shelf; see on the next there are bright coloured glasses with long threaded or twisted stems, and scores of rare pretty things besides, brought from over sea or saved from wrecks; the dresser-bed is covered with a cloth as white as snow, and many ladies would covet the bowls and other vessels of old china that rest on it; and one might take the bright pewter flagons and platters for silver. A brass warming-pan, such as you see on the other side, is an article for ornament rather than use, but every couple here, however poor, think they must get one before they be married. And that shelf of wooden trenches, butter-prints, mustard-bowls, and other 'temberan things,' scoured with 'gard,' have a look of cleanliness not to be surpassed by more costly furniture."

On the chimney-piece they might have noticed an hour-glass between tall brass candlesticks, branches of coral, sea-birds' eggs, sea-urchins, and foreign shells. Turning to An' Joan, Beaton remarked as if delighted, "there, too, beside the door is the same sweet-brier; rosemary, thyme, and other sweet flowers, blooming all over the garden; and the house swarming with bees, as of old, coming and going through the open window, and alighting on your cap as if to tell 'e they were going on well, and to see how you were looking."

"I hope, dears, you are now come home to live for the rest of your days," said Joan. "Your grand old house is cut to pieces, and three families dwelling in it; but most of your furniture is still there, packed away in the best chamber, all in that room as you left it, and the door hasn't been unlocked for many years,—scarcely opened, indeed, since you last slept there." Beaton replied to the effect that during all the time she lived abroad, her greatest desire was to return and end her days where she was born, and to be buried beside the one she loved above all the world; and that she intended, after a short rest, to go along the cliff to church-town to see his grave, and that she wished to go alone.

"Poor dear Willy, the Lord rest with him," said An' Joan, "you will see by his grave that he hasn't been forgotten. On his breast there's a rosemary, the pride of my heart, grown to a bush that overtops his tombstone; a box-tree grows at the foot, and betwixt them sweet-brier, tansy, herb-of-grace, and such other long-lived and evergreen plants as are good for remembrance, besides a border of pinks and lillies. You'll see that none in the church-hay have been more lovingly tended, for I and others have planted on his grave fresh flowers when old ones died."

When Cribba Head threw its shadow over the water, Beaton started on her sad pilgrimage, saying to her daughter, who wished to accompany her, "Remain, dear, with our old friend; tell her all about your uncle John, and how we lived in Brittany; she is longing to know but don't like to ask."

The kind dame took Mary round her garden, well stocked with sweet old-fashioned flowers and many hives of bees; then passing through her orchard from one tree of choice fruit to another, equally good, they came to a clear brook, overhung by branches weighed down by their load of apples, pears, and plums that often fell in the stream and floated out to sea, unless found on their passage by children who often watched the water, gurgling among reeds and rocks below the orchard, for An' Joan's apples and plums.

Milking time being come, Joan took her bucket, and they went up to Penberth Green, where the old dame's cow—little and good—was waiting to be milked. At that time, and long after, almost every cotter kept a cow, which found sufficient pasture in green lanes, and commons. An' Joan, having finished her out-door evening work, made a mullet-and-parsley pie, as that was a favourite supper dish. When placed on the hearth to bake, she said, "I have, for many years, been longing to know how it fared with your mother and uncle, and had given up all hopes of ever again seeing them, not knowing if they were alive or dead; and you, poor lonely flower, have no other relations on your mother's side that I know of."

"I have a good many cousins in Brittany," replied Mary, "as my uncle has a large family." She then related what she had heard from her mother, and what she remembered, to the effect that when I'an settled in Brittany he hired a small farm, and soon after married a person of good property. For a short time, he cultivated the land acquired by his marriage, but he soon tired of a farmer's life, and went to sea as captain of a large ship; he was often away for years together. Mary seldom saw him, as there appeared to be little desire, on the part of brother or sister, for much intimacy. Yet, on his return from a voyage, he always sent them money and goods, which they didn't require, because Beaton, by her spinning, and Mary, by her lace-work and embroidery, gained more than sufficed for their needs. Her uncle often took her lace-work abroad, where he traded, and brought her more for it than its weight in gold.

Although they wanted for nothing, and everybody was kind to them, Beaton was always pining to return; and in spite of I'an's wishes for them to remain, she made a vow that before Mary became of age, she would go home and pass the rest of her life in the practice of some devotion for the repose of Mary's father. About a week ago, Beaton having heard there was a smuggling craft from Cornwall in a cove near their dwelling, she packed up all her household goods that she cared about, and they left, bag and baggage, in the boat which landed them in Mousal that morning. When Mary had just ended her recital, her mother silently glided in, kissed her, and placed in her bosom a few flowers, saying, "Cherish these from a garden I prize above all others, and we will soon plant it with choicest flowers." "And now," she continued, "we must bid dear Aunt Joan good-bye, and proceed to Buryan Church-town, where we can remain for the night." "No, my dears," An' Joan interposed, "there's a pie baking for your supper, and a spare bed on the talfat as good as any in Church-town, though I say it; remain with me till you have found a better place, or hired Chynance for a time, as there may be more delay than you calculate before your house in Treen will be ready for 'e."

Both ladies gladly accepted the kind dame's hearty welcome, and enjoyed her savoury pie and good ale, of her own brewing; no woman then expected to get a husband, unless she knew how to make a good barley-brew, and they say that people of that day, who drank good beer as their ordinary beverage, were stronger by far than their descendants, raised on tea-wash.

Beaton hired Chynance, procured a few articles of furniture—in addition to what she brought from over sea—also a cow and poultry; had the garden planted, the house thatched, and comfortably arranged for winter. Owing to delay in getting possession of Beaton's property in Treen they lived here a year or more, and, when all was ready for their removal, Mary would have much preferred to remain in that sunny sheltered cot, nestled at the foot of Buryan Hill; but her mother got into a restless fidgetty state that caused An' Joan to look more grave than was her wont. She had heard that as far back as there was any record, many of the I'an family—particularly the women—when between forty-five and fifty years of age, either went mad or died; and she feared that the gloomy grandeur of Beaton's old home, with the sad remembrances, likely to be renewed thereby, would tend to bring on this family infirmity. It was all in vain, however, for Mary to say, "Dear mother let us remain here in this sunny nook, where flowers grow all the year; spotted trout sport in the stream; and our goats, lambs, and poultry can range at their own sweet will." When all was arranged in Beaton's part of the mansion, so as to give it an air of its former state, thither they removed, but still retained Chynance for the sake of having pasture for their cow, and to please Mary, who took a great fancy to it.

Beaton was not in her old habitation many days when she had her 'turn' and other spinning utensils taken into the chamber where Taskes breathed his last. There she passed most of her time, and often kept all night at her work; the rumble of her spinning-wheel and doleful noises that she frequently made, soon caused those living in parts of the house, not in her possession, to quit rather than have their rest nightly disturbed; and she rejoiced that the house was cleared of all strangers and interlopers, as she styled its other occupants. Often she would be away to St. Levan churchyard at dead of night—unknown to Mary and their servant—pass hours, in prayer it was supposed, beside Willy's grave; and bring thence flowers, wet with morning dew, to be kept in her chamber, and when withered all were laid by in her chest. This penance, as much inspired by love as enjoined by her faith, was duly observed, in spite of her failing health. On dark, stormy nights, she would often be met wandering along the cliffs between Church-town and Treen; or seen kneeling on the rock where her lover received his fatal hurt.

Many persons were startled by encountering, at unexpected times, her phantom-like figure, gliding along the cleves or amongst the carns of Castle-Treen, in her strange dress of white robe, black veil, and ghastly linen band across her forehead, that made her look like one escaped from a grave in a winding-sheet and shroud. It was evident that Beaton was at times insane; yet, sad as such a state seems, it may not have been the most melancholy portion of this poor soul's destiny; for when her mind was burthened with more grief than it could bear, her reason became unsettled, and her memory infolded with clouds that were often of roseate hue. Old crones whispered that they had heard of more than one Beatrice I'an, and men of that family as well, who went crazy; and that their madness began in melancholy seclusion, and the practice of old-fashioned devotions that few cared about since they were declared Popish and unlawful. Yet, the same old dames took good care to preserve many charms for the cure of diseases, and to use them as in Catholic times, and the same are retained and practised by their descendants to this day, with others that are probably transmitted from an age when sun-worship was in vogue.

As Penberth and Mousal fair-traders maintained a constant intercourse with Roscroff, I'an's family often sent Beaton presents of flax, clothing, and other goods; they did not require them, however, for Mary, like her mother, was an excellent spinster and skilful in embroidery and lace-work. Treen being a noted place for good weavers, they provided them with plenty of spinning-work; and when Mary showed her rare lace to An' Joan, she assured her that ladies, within a short distance, paid large sums to smugglers for what was no better. The old dame took it round to gentlemen's seats, and soon returned with much more money than Mary expected for her wares; and with orders for more lace-work than she could execute in a long time.

Beaton's lucid intervals became less and less frequent. When crazy fits prevailed, she seemed happy, nay joyful; but when reason,—such as it was,— or more sober moods intervened, she would talk regretfully, often moaning to herself, "The Lord help me, alas it was all my fault, I brought blood on my brother's head, he can never have rest, nor I, no, nevermore, not even in the grave." One of her strange freaks was to sleep by day and to visit the churchyard or spin by night. Sometimes she knitted stockings and other things for her Willy; these were to be put in her coffin. She would often say, "Willy, dear, I am working for thee, love, and will soon fetch thee back; we will live here, nobody shall ever put us out of this chamber. Oh! what delight I took in spinning years ago, when thou didst card the wool of winter's nights. I can never pass the time in singing, for ever singing. I should be weary in a day, and would rather spin the time away with thee to card the wool; and as of old thou shalt give me a kiss, such a long sweet kiss, with every rull I take from the cards."

Her last whim was to spin and knit herself a shroud, which she called her wedding-dress. This was made of the whitest and finest lamb's-wool she could procure. Mary, to please her, had to give much of her best lace for trimming this 'wisht' garment; and at length after much alteration, she had it to her mind, and repeated to her daughter and An' Joan all her whimsical fancies about her bridal arrangements, as she called her funeral ceremonies. The following night she walked alone to the churchyard, and returned late.

About midnight Mary, as was her custom, looked into her mother's room, and saw by the glimmering light of a chill (iron lamp), hanging on the wall, her mother sitting in a high-backed chair, apparently in a sweet sleep, with a placid smile on her countenance; as she sometimes dosed in her chair, Mary, loath to disturb her, stepped quietly back to her own room; but feeling uneasy from her mother's unusual silence she lay awake till daybreak and then returned to her mother. On approaching her, Mary noticed that over a fine white dress she wore her shroud, with its face-cloth turned back on her head. Mary took her hand, and feeling it cold and stiff, the truth struck her that her mother was dead. Yet she hoped that it might only be a trance, as she looked so life-like and pleasant, as when asleep, in her happiest moods. But a neighbour, who was called in, assured Mary that her mother had been dead some hours. "Yet to behold her thus," said the dame, "sitting in her chair, with fresh flowers in her bosom, the hour-glass beside her, and beads in her hand, one would think she had only fallen asleep whilst saying her prayers; the Lord rest her poor soul." On looking round, when the rising sun-beams streamed in through an open window, they saw that her best quilt was spread on the bed, and on that the clothes Taskes wore on that unlucky night when he received his death-wound, and other things that belonged to him. Where, or how, Beaton could have kept them so long no one knew. An' Joan had these, and withered flowers, with other things that Beaton prized, put into her coffin, in hopes to give her spirit rest; and Beatrice I'an, according to her oft-repeated request, was laid in St. Levan churchyard, beside the dust of Willy Taskes.

"And we Treen people," said the old man who related her story, "would have been glad if she had stayed there, but she hadn't been under the turf three days when she was back again and spinning, as she always said she would, in the chamber that was locked up with everything in it as it stood when she was carried out; and it was supposed that other spirits came back with her, by the capperouse they often made." We will leave them, however, and their ghostly doings, for a while, to follow Mary's destiny.

THE PROUD PENDARS.

O it is sad! O it is sad
To think of the joys that once I had:

To wander lone over land and sea,
And know that she waits no more for me.
This tress of her fair, soft, chestnut hair,
Is all the cruel grave would spare.

MORTIMER COLLINS.

At Beaton's death what had been her portion of the property fell in hand, and Mary removed to Chynance, taking with her a few such articles of the old furniture as were not too cumbersome for her small dwelling; but everything in "Beaton's chamber" was left there for the time, as it stood when she was carried out. Mary's life had been anything but a cheerful one for the past year or two, but after her mother's decease she felt very desolate. Her uncle's family urged her to return and live with them, which she was inclined to do, as she often said that Brittany seemed less gloomy to her than this country; because in the Cornuaille over the water young and old met, every Sunday at least, at their parish church, and joined in a dance after service; besides there were yearly feasts, in neighbouring parishes on their patron saints' days, to which people flocked from miles away; they were hospitably entertained, without regard to rank, at the feasten board; and all regarded it as a sort of religious duty to take part in dancing, hurling, wrestling, and other games that were continued several days of the feasten week.

"It seems to me like forsaking my poor mother to leave this place," Mary would say to An' Joan, "but over sea my cousins are always happy together, and they knew no difference between me and their sisters; but here I feel as desolate as a forsaken bird, though Chynance is a pleasant sunny spot, and nobody can be kinder to me than you and others who knew my dear mother." In such like sad complaints she bemoaned her lonely state, till love came to brighten the scene, for a brief space.

Mary frequently took her work to Penberth and passed the afternoons or evenings with An' Joan. As the dame sold liquor from a noggin to an "anker" (keg), her dwelling was often pretty well filled with company, of an evening. And Mary often said that such gatherings of neighbours, to hear news, sing songs, or relate old stories, reminded her of home, as she called Brittany.

Now, it so happened, a few months after Mary again settled in Chynance, she was one afternoon on a visit to An' Joan, when a young officer, home on a furlough from a man-of-war, entered the dwelling, saluted An' Joan—who had known him from a child—and called for brandy and cordials to treat the dame and himself; by the time they were seated for cosy chat, Mary entered with baskets of fruit from the orchard. The young sailor rose, saluted her, and seemed surprised to see one—apparently an inmate of Joan's—with the dress and demeanour of a lady; her broken English, with Breton accent, betokened her to be a foreigner. "Don't 'e disturb yourself, Mr. Pendar," said

An' Joan, "this young lady, poor dear, all the same to me as a daughter, is the damsel Mary I'an."

Mr. Pendar—who is said to have been one of those who then lived in Pendrea—had heard some gossip, on his first arrival at home, about the good looks, rare accomplishments, and strange history of this waif of the I'an's; and how she had refused many offers of marriage from farmers' sons that were thought good chances for her. Young Pendar took a liking at first sight to the poor orphan, and his love was not more sudden than honest and constant; and her feelings towards the young sailor must have been equally favourable, one may suppose, as they often met at Penberth and elsewhere, and purposed to be wedded on his next return from a short voyage. But the artless sailor and simple maiden made their calculations without his parents' consent. Little thought Mary, and less cared her lover, about what the old Pendars styled the stain on her paternity, or their talk about disowning or disinheriting. The brave heart of oak but little regarded his mother railing in bitter terms, of Mary's poverty and base birth, and of Beaton's youthful failing; or his father saying, "that as he made his bed he might lie on it; that if he wedded one of nought, he should be cut off with a shilling." But more devilry was set to work than the youngster knew of.

At parting, to join his ship, he told his father to keep his shilling, as he cared not for anything he had to withhold or bestow, that he saw no reason why the daughter should suffer for her parents' failings; he thought they had undergone more than enough themselves, and that he was determined to win fortune and choose a wife for himself. On taking leave of Mary he assured her that when he returned from a short voyage he would make her his bride.

Pendar left home to join his ship, which he thought would make but a short voyage.

Many months elapsed, but Mary had no tidings of her affianced lover; and, about the time she expected his return a report was circulated that he was killed in a naval engagement. As months rolled on and brought no other intelligence, Mary too readily believed the common talk; and, poor grieved soul, for many an hour she would sit, all alone, on a rock beside the shore, look wistfully out to sea, and chant some old Breton melody about meeting her true-love in the fairy orchards of Avalon. And her wild song, by the moaning waves, was sad to hear as a funeral dirge. Like a blasted flower she pined and died, and was laid beside her parents, when the young seaman, her lover, was hastening homeward in hopes to make her his bride.

Pendar arrived at Penberth with a good store of prize-money, heard, with anguish, how Mary had died of a broken heart, all through a vile scheme of his parents, who spread the sad rumour, and had no reason to think him dead; because they, unknown to him, contrived to have him drafted to a cruiser that was sent to protect merchantmen in distant seas. He was kept in ignorance of his destination, and had no means to inform Mary that years might elapse before his return. He left home without seeing his father or mother, and never more returned to Buryan; yet 'tis said that he became renowned as a brave naval commander, and died unmarried.

Within a few days of Mary's death, her uncle made a trip to Fowey, with a cargo of contraband goods, and on his return voyage, shaped his course for the Land's End, intending to land in Mount's Bay, to visit his niece, and persuade her to return with him. His ship approached land off Penberth; the sea being smooth, he ran her close in, near the cove, that he might be taken ashore in his ship's boat. It so happened that his old craft was running for the cove in this Autumn evening's twilight with a thick fog. The *Mur's* crew mistook I'an's vessel, beating the same course, for a revenue cutter, and one of the hands fired a random shot between "wind and water" that killed their former commander, as he was about to step into his boat; some say it was on the very evening of his niece's funeral. The Breton crew fired on the *Mur*, and sunk her. Almost all Penberth men were on board, and the greatest part of them were drowned within hail of the cove and their dwellings. I'an was taken home to be buried, in Brittany, and his family dropped all intercourse with their father's native place.

It was not known here till years after the fatal mishap that I'an was killed by a shot from the *Mur*, or that it was his ship's company who sent many of his old crew to a watery grave.

THE I'AN'S GHOSTS.

We have no title-deeds to house or lands,
Owners and occupants of earlier dates
From graves forgotten stretch their dusty hands,
And hold in mortmain still their old estates.

LONGFELLOW.

Now that ghostly visits are rare, many persons may be sceptical of what is said of this haunted house, and we shall only relate a few of the most remarkable stories. Shortly after Beatrice died, noises like the rumble of a spinning-wheel and clicking of cards, with unnatural shrieks, were often heard in "Beaton's chamber," which remained locked up, with its furniture just as it was when she died; persons passing by the house at night, who had courage to cast a glance at its windows, saw in that room and others a glimmer of light, and shadowy forms flitting to and fro. But almost everybody hurried by without casting an eye towards the house, or took a roundabout way rather than run the risk of having a fright or their rest disturbed by a remembrance of those strange apparitions.

Over a while it seemed as if more spirits joined those that first arrived, till at length they made such a 'rattle-cum-stave' throughout the whole house that it was left for years unoccupied,—by mortal tenants at least. The turn continued its rumble upstairs, and what had formerly been kitchen, hall, and parlour, seemed filled with a revelrout all night long, and folks were often dismayed by unnatural appearances outside the house. Towards night clouds of fog would roll in from over sea, settle around the I'an's premises, and become denser and darker till the place seemed shrouded in thunder-clouds; then lights would flash around the house, and such sounds be heard as if made by discharges of small fire-arms, with a roar of cannon now and then; one would, also, hear the surging and splashing of waves, flapping of sails, creaking of blocks and tackle, with other sounds usually heard on shipboard, till this apparition rose high above the houses, drifted away seaward, and disappeared.

Sometimes all lights in the house would go out, at the same instant, without any visible cause; this was such a common occurrence that the inmates would merely say, "that's Beaton come again; but, never mind, we shall soon hear her spinning, then we may light the candles again, and hope to be left quiet for a time." When people would persist and occupy the house, it was often troubled by day, and all its mortal inmates, both man and beast, would be seized with fear, and run to doors, at times when nothing unusual was seen or heard. Often in the height of a clear summer's day, a blast of chilly air, with a grave-like scent, would pervade the old dwelling; then children would screech, dogs howl, cats, with their hair bristled up, rush out of doors, or smash through windows, if doors were closed. The cats never returned, and died of fright when they couldn't escape the house. There's no end of stories about the ghostly pranks that were acted here for more than a century, and we shall only relate another.

A carpenter, who was working about the place, said he didn't believe that all the I'an's spirits would make him quit the house or Beaton's chamber even; and he waged a pint of brandy that he would see, that very night, what made the racket there, and hail the spirits if he saw any. That he might have a sight of them, without more ado, he bored an auger-hole in Beaton's chamber door. Having primed himself with drink, when night came, and the usual noises began, he fixed himself close to the door and peeped in. At first he only beheld a faint light glimmering over the bed, and what looked like a dead man stretched thereon, with shadowy figures moving about the room; then he saw more distinctly, and made out a woman, dressed in grave clothes, sitting on a chair beside the bed.

Then the chamber became so dark that he could see nothing of the figures on the bed and in the chair but their eyes, that shone with purple light. The woman's eyes—he could see nothing else but her eyes glistening like coals of fire—arose from the bedside and approached the door, and still the carpenter could only see a pair of flaming orbs when they were within a few inches of his face; and he—terror-struck or spell-bound—had neither power to move away, nor to withdraw his gaze. There he stood like one rivetted to the spot for minutes, that seemed hours, till a blast of cold air smote his face, and something pierced his eye like a red-hot nail. He fell on the floor, was found insensible when raised, and he ever remained blind of one eye.

There was but little rest for anyone dwelling in the I'an's house until some years after Parson Corker came to Buryan; and, at first, he made many fruitless attempts to confine those unresting spirits to their graves. He ordered that the locked-up chamber should be opened, and all its furniture burned—as no one would venture to make use of anything therein—and he would try again what could be done.

So one night the reverend gentleman came over from Tresidder—where he lived with his cousins the Tresillians;—a good number assembled; they broke open Beaton's chamber-door, and began to throw out the furniture, but they found it a more difficult job than was expected. Turns, chests, chairs, tables, were soon cleared out, and a great hanging-press was smashed to pieces, tossed through a window, and added to the blazing pile on an open space fronting the house. They found it, however, no such easy work to break up the grand carved-oak bedstead, which must have been made and put together in the room, because neither its tester nor its head would pass through the doorway. In this bed-head were two deep recesses, ornamented at their backs and all around with carved foliage, framing the names and ages of some old I'an or Ivan and his wife, who probably had this bedstead made when their house was built. High up on either side of these recesses, between them and the tester—among flowers and creeping plants—were boldly carved faces, supposed to be those of the family; they were all very much alike, with peaked beards, wonderful high foreheads, and long noses,—straight as a line. Bedding, rich hangings, and old raiment, very grand in their day, were rotten and gone to dust. When all was at length cleared out and blazing in the town-place, the parson entered to conclude his work by sprinkling salted water all about; at the same time he repeated long words, spells, or incantations in Latin, because that tongue was said to be more respected by devils and restless spirits than any vulgar dialect. He also performed other ceremonies, whose use and practice were only known to learned divines.

But it is doubtful whether the reverend exorcist did any good on that occasion. For whilst Treen folks made a bonfire of what had been the I'an's furniture, he or the spirits raised an awful tempest; houses were unroofed, walls blown down, and other damage done throughout the neighbourhood and far away. Meanwhile, ghostly forms were seen and unearthly voices heard, high up over flames and smoke, making derisive shouts like demons' laughter. They seemed to enjoy the fun, whilst many people cursed the parson for rising such a storm. One can't say how his best endeavours failed to lay these unruly ghosts. But

"Perchance some form was unobserved,
Perchance in prayer or faith he swerved;"

for on the following night troops of spirits arrived at their accustomed hour and made as much disturbance as ever. Then Mr. Corker—determined to rout them—sought advice and assistance from the most remarkable "spirit-queller" of that time, one parson Polkinghorne, who belonged to some parish east of Penzance.

It was believed, of this Parson Polkinghorne, that no spirits walking the earth could resist his spells, and that, when other exorcists failed to obtain a mastery over an obdurate one, this gentleman no sooner joined them than the poor ghosts would exclaim—like that of old Squire Harris, of Kenegie— "Now, Polkinghorne, thee art come and I must be gone!" And he at once sent the shadow off to its grave and there confined it for evermore.

One night, a week or so after the unsuccessful attempt, the two parsons— arrayed in their priestly vestments, bearing large books and a coil of new hempen cord—arrived at the haunted house's door, and requested all the inmates to quit it before they entered, and not to attempt to hear or see anything that might take place, nor to re-enter their dwellings for that night. When all the living inhabitants had left the house, the reverend exorcists entered it; but how they worked to get control over these troublesome spirits nobody knew but themselves, as they were no more seen till an hour or so after midnight, when they issued forth and took their way to Church-town, with the bound spirits in their company (it is supposed), and, having finished their work in the graveyard, they, about daybreak, aroused the inmates of the "Scaw-tree" inn, made a hearty breakfast, and returned to Tresidder.

Now, 'tis said that this Parson Polkinghorne had power, also, over the spirits of air, or whatever they be, that usually raise the wind, when ghosts are laid; for on this night all was so quietly done that the weather was not, for a wonder, uncommonly stormy. The I'an's ghosts, however, were settled, that's certain; they met with their match at last, and quitted their old habitation for good. From that night their old house was quiet and remained so for a few years, then part of it was again haunted by the ghost of a crazy spinster called 'Bitha (Tabitha) who also became insane from grief at her sweetheart's untimely end. But this spirit gave little trouble, compared with the former ones, and took its departure in a few years, of its own accord; at least we never heard of anything having being done to "lay" it.

About sixty years ago these almost forgotten traditions were revived. One Sunday afternoon, in summer time, a carriage arrived in Treen, stopped near the I'an's house, and a middle-aged gentleman stepped from the conveyance just as an old man drew near, who saluted the visitor, and asked if he would be pleased to accept of his services to show him the Castle? The stranger replied, in but indifferent English, that he would like to know if there were any remains in Treen of an ancient mansion, or castle, that once belonged to a family called I'an or Ivan, as he spelt it for Uncle George, who was a most intelligent old guide and the best chronicler of Treen.

"Why, there's the dwelling," said he, "that old people always called the I'an's house, though young ones, thinking to improve the name, have lately called it the John's house; but no family called Johns were ever proprietors of it that I ever heard of."

The gentleman looked at the old house, and said that he expected to find a much grander one.

"Yet, in its day, that was considered far above the common," Uncle George remarked; "and it must have cost much to build when no wheel-carriages were in use, and timber had to be dogged (dragged) many miles through narrow lanes, and stones and other materials were carried on drays, or on horses' backs. Besides, where you see nothing now but pigs'-crows and turf-ricks," continued he, in conducting the visitor towards the house, "there was once a large green-court; and at the back where you will find little else but dung-pits and heaps of rubbish, there were more buildings belonging to the house, with a large walled garden and a rabbit warren beyond."

The gentleman then informed his guide that he was a descendant of an old Catholic family who, between two or three centuries ago, owned a Castle in Treen and much land in that neighbourhood, if such traditions and documents as were preserved in his family might be credited—that he resided in Brittany, to which place his ancestors had hence removed at a time when Catholics were much persecuted here—that, being in England on business and curious to see his family's ancient home, he had come to Treen for that purpose—and that he would also like to know if there were any tombstone inscriptions, or other records of them, in St. Levan Church. Besides, he said, that others of his family had long been desirous to know something of a place respecting which they had many curious traditions. Moreover, he informed the old man that the name usually spelt I'an was an abbreviation of Ivan and equivalent to Juan or plain John; the confusion in, or the various modes of, spelling took place, probably, before J and U replaced I and V, but still the old pronunciation was retained. [The same applies to many old French names here, that seem to be spelt one way, and pronounced differently. Take Lanyon as a familiar example, pronounced Lanine.] This Breton gentleman, whom we may call M. Ivan, as he spelt his name in full, when shown through the old house was much disappointed to find its interior a mere wreck, with little to show that it had ever been a gentleman's residence, except a few fragments of carved wainscot and ornamental plaster-work in an apartment that had been a portion of hall or parlour in olden time. It seems the "gentil Breton" had heard much of Castle Treyn, and 'Uncle' was much diverted and surprised to find that he thought it was a grand building situated in the village, and hinted that it might have been his ancestor's residence.

"Faix! they must have been the giants then," said the old man to himself, "for I never heard of anybody else who ever lived there."

And, in answer to M. Ivan's enquiries where the Castle was and if any of it was still standing, "still standing, sir," he exclaimed. "I believe 'e, faith, and stand it will till Doomsday, unless one can get out of a rock the Castle-key; but when that is done, as Merlin prophecied, all will sink into the sea, whence it was raised by enchantment, they say, with the giants who dwelt there of yore. But the Castle isn't here in town; it's down to cliff," continued he, showing the way; "and we can travel there across the fields, if you please, while your carriage can go out the lane and await 'e in Pedny-vounder cliff, if so be that you would like to ride to Church-town."

As there were many interesting objects to be seen by the way, the gentleman decided to walk to St. Levan Church also, and his conveyance remained in Treen. In passing the fields Uncle George said, "Old folk, who are dead and gone, always held (and I believe it for truth) that people seldom lived in Castle Treen, or in any of our cliff or hill-castles, for more than a few days at a time; and that was when they had to seek refuge there for their old people, women, and children, with their flocks and other property, from the Danes and other northern robbers who used to land at Parcurno, Penberth, and elsewhere, to ravage the country, carry off women, and do worse mischief than that, if the hair that crops up every now and then in some families may be taken as evidence. But the red-haired pirates were soon put to rout, and then nobody remained in our stronghold of Treen Dynas except a man to keep watch from Castle Peak."

He might have remarked, too, that the old proprietors of Treen held to a tradition that Kaerkeis bowjey and barn were as old as the Castle, and were built in that out-of-the-way place for the purpose of storing fodder for cattle near the stronghold against an invasion. They also believed that valuables were, at such times, hastily buried in the Castles; those who secreted the property being slain, nobody knew where to find it. As a proof of the probability of such a belief, within the old guide's remembrance, about the quantity of two quarts of ancient Roman and other coins were found within or near Castle Maen. The coins were simply placed in a pile, on a flat stone, and enclosed by three others set on edge and capped. The whole was buried in a bank of earth and small stones that formed part of an old hedge or gurgo. Probably some of these coins may still be found among old folks of Sennen. The writer had many of them, when too young to know the value of such interesting objects.

Having passed the fields and ascended the rising ground beyond, M. Ivan asked where the Castle was—he could behold nothing like a building between them and the sea, towards which they had shaped their course.

"We are already within it," replied the venerable guide, "and have passed the outer wall through a breach where it is levelled and the ditch filled in to make a road. I ought to have pointed it out to 'e. The outer mound is little short of half a mile long. Hundreds of cartloads of stones have been carried away from the walls for building houses and hedges. Yet on Kaerkeis side, where it isn't easily reached, some of it is still pretty perfect; except, indeed, where our youngsters have bowled the stones over cliff for their Sunday afternoon's sport; and it would be just as well, or better, 'seeman' to me, that they were allowed to have their wrestling and hurling-matches at such times, to keep them from doing mischief, like they had in their great-grandfars' days, when folks were quite as good, and to my 'seeman,' better than they are now, for all that constables do and duffans say."

We can't follow the old guide through the long story he used to relate of what passed between him and the Armorican gentleman. Having shown the Castle and related the legends of giants, small people, &c., connected with this enchanted spot, they passed along the cliff to St. Levan Church. Service was over and the congregation dispersed, but the church-door key being kept at the inn, they inspected the church to see if any memorial of the I'ans was to be found, but nothing connected with them was observed in carved shields or bench-ends, nor elsewhere. Parish registers—if any remained two centuries old—he had no opportunity to see.

They also visited St. Levan's Well and Chapel. The old man pointed out a long flight of steps that may still be traced best part of the way from the spring to the ancient chapel's site. The gentleman took particular interest in the ancient cliff oratories, with their holy wells, and in every spot along their way hallowed by saintly legend. In returning from Chapel-Curno, as the little oratory over Parcurno used to be called, they were met at the foot of Carnole hill by a gentleman of Penzance, who used occasionally to preach at the Methodist Chapel in Sowah. This gentleman often returned thence to Treen (where he usually remained over night) by way of St. Levan Church and along the cliffs. He knew Uncle George very well; for they often disputed about what the old man styled a new-fashioned religion. Yet they were always great friends.

The gentlemen were introduced and walked together to Treen. By the way M. Ivan related how curiosity had led him to visit Treen, and that he was, on the whole, gratified with his visit, though quite taken down in his exaggerated ideas (as transmitted by family traditions) of their former importance here; and thought the foregoing tragic story, which the old man related in part, just as probable a reason for his ancestor's departure as that of religious persecution; yet he believed they were always attached to, and held, the old faith. When they arrived at Treen he handsomely rewarded the intelligent old guide, and was about to leave when the preaching gentleman proposed for M. Ivan to take tea with him at the house where he put up. The invitation was accepted, and he was regaled with bread, cream, and honey—the produce of what was once his family's acres.

Mr. Richard Edmonds remarks that "Treryn Castle, Maen Castle, Chûn Castle, Castle-an-Dinas, and several other cliff-castles, and hill-castles, in the Land's End district, have been in existence probably between two and three thousand years. And Treryn Castle, with its high massive vallum, deep ditch, and the foundations of its stone wall, twelve feet thick, presents so little temptation either to the agriculturist or to the builder, that its existing remains, vast as they are, need no Society's protection for their continued duration for generations yet to come.

All castles, of course, do, or did once contain dwellings of some kind for their occupants. But the low huts which once stood within the castles near Penzance (although considerable remains of such dwellings in Chûn Castle were extant in Borlase's time) have now almost everywhere disappeared. It was not, however, from these rude huts, but from the fortifications enclosing them, that our very ancient castles derived their name; and not one of them, at the present day, appears more worthy of being thus called than at Treryn Castle."

CASTLE TREEN AND ITS LEGENDS.

"I cannot tell how the truth may be,
I say the tale as 'twas said to me."

SCOTT.

OLD traditions say that the headlands of Castle Treen, or rather Trereen, on which the Logan Rock carn and adjacent crags stand, was raised out of the sea by enchantment. This portion of the stronghold, enclosed by the inner line of defence, running directly across the isthmus, is generally spoken of as *The Castle*, and that between it and the outer or landward embankments is usually called Treen Dynas.

THE KEY OF THE CASTLE.

It is not known what powerful magician raised this giant's hold, though it was believed that its security depended on a magic stone called "the key of the Castle," respecting which Merlin had something to say, as well as about many other remarkable stones in the neighbourhood. Castle Treen, however, must have stood where it is long before Arthur and his magician visited West Cornwall.

The key was an egg-shaped stone, between two and three feet long, which was contained in the cavity of a rock with a hole facing the sea, through which it might be turned round; and the opening appeared large enough for it to be passed through. Many attempted to get it out, but they always found it to hitch somewhere; and lucky (according to old folks' faith) that it did, because the sage Merlin prophecied that when the key of the Castle was taken out of the hole, Men Amber (the holy rock) would be overthrown, the Castle sink beneath the ocean, and other calamities occur.

The key was situated near the bottom of a deep chasm called The Gap, which is passed on approaching the Logan Rock by the usual path. It required a sure-footed climber, of strong nerve, to reach it, and this could only be done from land, at low water, or nearly so.

Surging waves occasionally changed the position of this magic stone, and from the direction of its smaller end, as it lay in a trough of water, prognostics were drawn with regard to the seasons, &c.

Few persons had sufficient hardihood to descend the precipitous cliff and risk being caught in The Gap by a flowing tide; and the key of the Castle

- 128 -

remained a mysterious and venerated object till Goldsmith's mischievous tars, or the dockyard men who were employed in erecting machinery to replace Men Amber (as the stone they overthrew was formerly called) heard of it and the traditions connected therewith. Then, one day, some of these wretches, on farther mischief bent, entered The Gap in a boat, and, being provided with crow bars, they broke away the edges of the rock that enclosed the key, ripped it out, and tumbled it down among the sea-washed pebbles! Some calamity has surely befallen these wretches ere this, or Bad Luck is a mere name, and powerless as an avenging deity.

Part of Merlin's prophecy was fulfilled, however, yet not in the order predicted.

The venerated nodule was what is called, among miners, a "bull's eye," or "pig's egg," of large size. It appeared to be a closer-grained and harder stone than what surrounded it.

GIANTS OF CASTLE TREEN.

The earliest inhabitants of this stronghold were giants who protected the neighbouring people in return for cattle and other necessaries with which the last-named provided their powerful friends, as was usual here in olden times.

An aged giant, his childless wife, and their adopted son, are the only ones of whom connected traditions are handed down by old folks of Treen. Not only this giant (how we wish the chroniclers had preserved his name) and his wife but all people who depended on his protection, particularly those of Treen and bordering places, were much grieved and disappointed when they found their giant and giantess were middle-aged and had no children who would aid them in old age and perpetuate the race.

The giantess, having no household to think about, grew, as most unemployed women do, peevish and troublesome. The giant, having little or no work to occupy himself with, grew fat and lazy. Quiet and good-tempered as he was, he was dreadfully tormented by his wife. She called him a lazy, useless old loon; and said he was too fat, and didn't take exercise enow. When he had nothing else to employ himself about, in peaceful times, she told him that he should log the rock, for a few hours every day, to stretch his sinews and make his blood circulate brisker, instead of dozing away all day and night in his chair, which may still be seen. "Go thee way'st," said she; "swim over to the Dollar Rocks, it's only two miles or so; dive round them and catch me a few good big congers; I want their fat to make a cake. And the pollock and cod that feed among the ore-weed thereabouts are excellent eating."

The dissatisfied woman's advice was sometimes taken. He would swim away, and, in an hour or two, bring her home a string of fish of a furlong's length.

Then he would log Men Amber for a bit. This he could easily do with the tip of his finger, when standing on the grass below it; for the rock is only 30 feet or so from the grass, and Treen giant stood at least 40 feet high, without his boots. He was stout in proportion, and his strength of arm was prodigious. Sometimes, with his staff, he kept the sacred stone in motion when seated in his chair, just opposite it. But often it happened, when getting through his exercise by the latter mode, that he fell asleep, long ere the sand was down in his wife's hour-glass. And then she, the faggot, would pelt her quiet husband with rocks, heaps of which may still be seen, lying loose, just as they flew from her hand and dropped at no great distance from the poor giant's chair. He would wake up, with a sore head, to hear her say, in a voice like a bellowing bull, "Stop thy snoring, thou confounded old fool, and work away, west ah? or I'll pommel thy noddle to browse."

"What the deuce shall I do to stop her tongue and cure her temper? Can 'e tell me, my good people?" He would often say to Treen folks and others, who visited him of a summer's evening; "she's the most troublesome woman I ever heard of!"

All kinds of employment were suggested. In those days everybody thought he could manage a discontented wife, were he her husband; but actually to do it was difficult.

"Why should she fret and fume for lack of children," he used to say to his Treen neighbours, "and what need have you either, in those peaceful times, to care whether we have descendants or no?"

Potent reasons were given both by giantess and people why they desired that their chief's race should be continued. Charms and other means were used in order to obtain the desired result.

Yet much time passed, and their rock-hewn cradle was still empty, when a happy thought struck a wise man of Treen. He advised that a baby should be *stolen* from the giant of Maen, who had a large family, and was, moreover, a very troublesome and aggressive neighbour—if one may credit stories of his hurling the rocks against Treen giant, which are still to be seen at Skewjack Moor, on the bounds of their two domains. One may judge of Maen giant's stature by the size of his bed, bowls, spoon, and other utensils, that remained in a lane on Treve, at a short distance from Sennen Church, a few years ago, and some of them may be there still.

Our giant and his wife were delighted with the sage man's advice. To steal a baby from the big man who was proud of his stronghold between Pen-von-las (Land's End) and Pedn-men-du (Black Stone Headland) would be capital revenge on him and his. "Then how nice it will be for me," said the giant's wife, "to sit on the Logan stone with the cheeld in my arms, of summer afternoons, when the waves sing lullaby, and my old man can rock us both till the dear baby falls asleep. Or he may dandle it in his arms atop of Castle Peak, or jump with it thence, from carn to carn, to Gamp-an-sees rocks and back again, whilst I skin an ox for our supper, and you, my good people, can bring us down plenty of milk to nurse him on, that he may grow apace."

A wise woman, or witch of Treen, who could take any shape, was selected as the most likely person to execute their project without causing any stir with Maen giant, who was very fierce, and proud of his descent from old blustering Bellerus, who was said to have lived thereabouts in days of yore.

One afternoon away went the witch, and, without being noticed on the road, reached Cairn-men-ellas, where she hid herself between rocks to watch. A little before sunset she saw a giant's child, of four years or so, coming that way with some common people's children, who wanted to show him how to play *bob*. Now the infant giant, though as big as an ordinary man, was still a baby in every feature, and he hadn't been long weaned; he still wore a bib, though he had out-grown his clothes, and his frock and saveall (pinafore) scarcely reached to his knees. The common boys and girls, from ten to a dozen years of age—like children in size to him—led about the great *slab*, as they termed him, and did with him just as they pleased.

The woman, seeing them place buttons (and they hadn't many) on the bob, took from her basket a string of large bright ones, shook them before the giant baby, and said, "Now kiss me, dear, and I will give 'e all these." He kissed her again and again, delighted to have the buttons. Over awhile she said, "The tides are low and I am on my way to get lempots (limpets) and gweans (winkles) from Cowloe; will 'e go, dears?"

The elder ones said it was then too late—they must be all home to Treve before sundown, or their mammies would strap them soundly and send them to bed without supper. But the babe-giant said, "I'll go, for I want some gweans to play *five-stones*, and lempots too, that my da may shoe the cats with croggans (limpet-shells) and codgey-wax (cobblers'-wax). He do dearly like that fun, and my ma do never beat me."

"Come along then, my turtle," said the witch, as she took his hand and led him off.

On the way she took from her basket many toys and showed him how to play with them. This pleased him, so that he thought no more of Cowloe, and she led him away over the Green to Brew Moors, where, to divert him she changed herself into the shape of a horse, and he trotted on her a mile or more, when she resumed her woman's form, and led him into Castle Treen, where he was received with open arms by the mistress.

It would take long to tell how he was caressed by the childless pair and fed by their people.

He often reposed, during his infancy, in a small chair that may still be seen near the large one in which the giant usually rested—the one just opposite the Logan Rock; and, until he grew too big, he frequently slept in the giant's arms.

At sunrise in summer the old giant delighted to carry him up to Castle Peak, where he placed the infant to stand on the topmost stone, which was much higher then than now, and named to him all the noted places within ken. After turning him round that he might behold the magnificent prospect on either hand of wild, sea-lashed headlands in the distance, and noble carns towering near, he would exclaim, "My dear boy, who wouldn't be proud of such a home as this? Believe me, dear son, in all this western land—from the Lizard Point, that you see yonder, to Pedn-Penwith, which lies under the setting sun—there is not another giant who owns a place equal to Castle Treen; and all shall be thine, my darling, when I am dead and gone."

When the sun shone warm he took baby down to the Castle Leas, near the Gap. This was his favourite fishing place, where a deep pit may still be seen in which he pounded *browse*, that was cast on the water to entice in fish. From these rocks, at the water's edge, the giant, like a monstrous dolphin, stretched on the sea with the boy standing on his broad back, and holding on by the hair of his head like bridle-reins with both hands, would swim out and round to the Sees—the rock that stands like an island in Gampar, (Close or Little Cove), just under Hal-dynas, and at the eastern end of the outer mound of his fortress. Having rested there awhile and given the cheeld a few shags' eggs, limpets, mussels, and such like dainties, back they would steer, but farther out; and, coasting all the seaboard of his Castle, land in Par Pry.

When a few years older the giant taught his big boy to fish from the rocks with rod and line, showed him how to make fish-hooks out of bones and *croggan*-rims—as boys out there do now, or did not long ago. In giants' times they hadn't a bit of iron, not even so much as a nail. The giantess with her distaff and spindle, spun them yarn that served for lines.

It wasn't much, however, that the giant knew to teach the youngster. Like all of great bulk he had more strength than knowledge, for as we say, "The best goods are bound up in the smallest bundles."

Meanwhile the giantess took care that the boy had an unlimited quantity of food, that he might eat and drink whenever he choose. Over a few years he was nearly equal in bulk to his new Dadda, as he called the old giant.

We like to linger over these pleasant times, for the old Titan when he took much delight in his charge. But alas! the sequel must be told in sorrow and tears for female frailty.

We don't like to—and indeed we wont—repeat all the stories handed down, which for the most part are highly unfavourable to the moral character of Treen Giantess, for fear of slandering her unwittingly. Yet it is no worse than she deserves to say that all traditions agree in representing her as a most abandoned female in her latter years.

All her care and attention were bestowed on the boy and she neglected her old husband, so that he had to dive for fish, and skin oxen, (or eat them skin, horns, and all). Sheep he could seldom get; they were dainties reserved for the young fellow. The poor old giant was often driven to such extremities that, to appease hunger, which makes brutes of the best of men, he was fain to stay his stomach on ore-weed.

To add insult to injury she often taunted her aged spouse with his weakness, which was the consequence of her neglect, and cut him to the heart by making unfavourable comparisons between him and the pampered youth who could now log the rock from sitting on the grass; and that was more, as the giantess told her husband, than he could do in the best of his time.

Worst of all, her maternal love then changed into a passion that, all things considered, one might even now, in these times of lax morality and free-love, regard as reprehensible.

The poor old giant was slow to become jealous, till he found himself utterly forsaken by his spouse and adopted son, who always stole away to sunny glades between the carns to play by themselves. That would have passed, however, without notice,—he rather liked to be left alone, to dose in his chair of afternoons—had not some Treen women, who were sharp in such things, spied what was going on, and, out of envy, told the old giant. He then became very surly and gave the doting pair much annoyance by coming on them unawares when they withdrew to enjoy their amorous diversion. They had seldom much comfort then, except when the old fellow left his castle to get provision.

One winter's day, when he was about to start for this purpose, he told his wife and the youngster that one of them should meet him on his way back to assist in taking home whatever he might procure.

They promised to do so, but time passed so pleasantly with the couple that they thought but little of their good old provider till they heard his footsteps and angry voice, about a quarter of a mile off, as he came stamping along Pedn-y-vounder cliff vowing vengeance on his ungrateful wife and foster-son.

They became somewhat frightened, and the "strollop" of a giantess, knowing that "the first blow was half the battle," prepared for the encounter by placing herself on the rocks west of the Gap, a dozen feet or so above the narrow path which the giant would have to pass. He came stamping along, an ox on his shoulders (its legs were tied together and passed over his head,) and on each arm he carried a sheep basket-fashion, their trotters bound with their spans.

He roared louder than the stormy breakers when he entered his castle's inner enclosure and found that no one, even then, came to meet him. In his fury he bounced along without noticing his wicked rib, with her bared arm and clenched fist, awaiting his approach, and as he came along the narrow ledge she dealt him a blow in his eyes, as he glanced towards her, that sent him, cattle and all, heels over head down the precipice.

When she beheld him falling a remembrance of their early loves, or something else, caused a sudden revulsion of feeling, which made her regret her rashness, and, unwilling to witness her husband's dying agony, she stepped back westward, about twenty paces, on to a level stone between high rocks, where she stood still and cast her apron over her head that she might hear less of the giant's awful moans. Though the giant's skull was very thick it was badly smashed on the boulders; yet he didn't die until he called on the Powers whom he served to avenge him, which they did instantly by changing his vile partner into stone, where she stood and where she may still be seen. The old giant, in his dying moments, thought of the young one more in sorrow than in anger—he couldn't in his heart feel very bitter against the simple-innocent hobble-de-hoy, and regarded his wife as the seducer.

Nothing more is known of the young giant, and but little of any others of the Titan race that in mythic ages dwelt in Castle Treen.

Of late the Giant's Lady, as she was formerly called, has been named the Logan Rock's Lady by those who are ignorant of our old traditions. When tempests rage, or anything else excites her, she rocks to and fro; but her movements are languid with age or sorrow. Pitiless storms have so beaten on her head for ages that one can't make out a feature, and her fair proportions are so mutilated that one can scarce discern a semblance of her gigantic form in the time-worn granite mass. She appears, indeed, of pigmy stature compared with her husband. If, however, she had never been larger than her stone image now appears the story is none the less credible on that score. For do we not, every day, see mere midges of women united with giants of men, according to our reduced scale?

DAN DYNAS.

Old folks held—and long tradition made it pass for true—that the outer wall of Castle Treen was built by a deaf-and-dumb giant, called Dan Dynas, or, as some say, Den-an-Dynas, assisted by his wife An' (aunt) Venna, who broke up the ditch, filled her leathern towser (large apron) with the soil, and put it for *filling* behind the rocks, as her husband rolled them into their places. When they had thus constructed a stronghold, in which people with their tin and cattle were safe from marauding pirates, the giantess and other women collected hundreds of cartloads of stones into heaps, near the mound, ready and handy for slinging at, or to hurl down on, the heads of besiegers. When an incursion happened to be made An' Venna, with the women and old men, defended the fortress, whilst Dan and his fighting men slew the enemy or drove them to sea. The ruins of this good couple's handiwork may still be traced from Par Pry, on the southern side, to the inlet of Gampar, or Haldynas Cove, towards the east.

A descendant of old proprietors of Treen informed me that a great quantity of stones remained, in piles, within and near the embankment, until after wheel carriages came into use. Although this part of the cliff was then common few persons cared to remove them, and none durst take a stone from the castle walls for fear Bad Luck would pursue any one who disturbed the giant's work. But of late years, great portions of this ancient rampart have been demolished and its facing-stones carried away for building.

It is also related—though the story seems somewhat fabulous—that this deaf-and-dumb giant would stand on Carnole and thence sink invading ships, entering Parcurno, by hurling rocks on them, or he wrecked them, when at a distance, with huge stones discharged from slings made of bulls' hides. When the people couldn't charge his instruments of war as quickly as he wanted them, he would roar like thunder, make signs to stand clear, kick the rocks up out of the ground, smash them to handy pieces, and fire away again.

Like all other West Country giants he was very fond of old-fashioned games, and was delighted when youngsters came down to Kaer Keis of an afternoon to play cook (quoits) or keals (nine-pins) with him; but he could never understand the weakness of ordinary mortals' frames; for, in caressing his playmates, he now and then broke their ribs or cracked their sculls—to his great grief and greater surprise. We may remark that, although some Cornish giants have been misrepresented as little better than savage cannibals—Cormovan of the Mount to wit—all traditional giant stories, in this district, describe them as amiable protectors of the common folks who lived near their castles. They were, however, almost invariably, stupid and often did mischief unwittingly by having more strength than sense; therefore, it is shameful to defame those ancient heroes and ascribe to them such vile traits as are not warranted by our popular stories.

THE SMALL PEOPLE (FAIRIES).

When our giants and other antique people left their human bodies they continued to dwell in their old homes down almost to our times. As they had no idea of any life but a carnal existence on earth, they were permitted to live there as spriggans (elves) and they seemed to have enjoyed themselves, in their small way, by imitating mortals' pleasures.

Old folks, only just departed, often witnessed their gambols amongst the carns of Castle Treen.

Fishermen, when becalmed near Pedn-y-vounder cliff, of summer's nights, frequently saw thousands of gaily-dressed little people, with lights, moving about in what looked like beautiful gardens that extended, in some places, down almost to high-water mark. At the same time low but lively music, and the scents of sweet flowers, would be wafted over the water. The fishers, however, hastily made off whenever such fairy melodies and odours reached their boats. These haunts are screened from view, landward, by towering crags. Steep precipices render them inaccessible on the sea-side; though they may be seen from the water, during summer months, gay with cliff-pinks and other flowers in places that not even a goat could reach.

Treasure-seekers, when digging in nooks and corners among the Castle carns, have been scared away even by day with ill-favoured looking fays of nearly human size; and the same uncouthly-formed elves have often been seen wrestling, hurling, and playing other games on a level place near Hal-dynas; but there is no special story relating to them that we ever heard.

ST. LEVAN WITCHES.

In days of yore ugly old hags that sold themselves to Satan merely to have their "spite out" on their neighbours, or to ride on a broomstick and play pranks but little known except among themselves, made the Castle crags their resort. When all the neighbouring witches were assembled they scampered up to the platform on the top of Castle Peak, mounted their ragworts or brooms, and took flight over to Wales to milk Taffy's cows and steal his leeks. Those who lived in Roskestal, and other places over that way, took their departure from Pedn-pen-with. On their return each one alighted, with all her plunder, in some convenient place near her dwelling. 'Tis said that, in old times, the people of this neighbourhood were much addicted to sorcery, and, from their skill in the black art, they acquired and still retain the name of St. Levan Witches.

Traditions of Parcurno.

A ghostly ship, with a ghostly crew,
In tempests she appears;
And before the gale, or against the gale,
She sails without a rag of sail;
Without a helmsman steers.

LONGFELLOW.

NOT long since a general belief prevailed in the western parishes that in ancient times Parcurno was the principal port of Cornwall, and that, until the Cove became "sanded up" there was sufficient depth of water to float the largest ships then made, in to the foot of an old caunce (paved road) which may still be seen.

One old story ascribes the choking of Parcurno and Parchapel to the mischievous spirit Tregeagle, who was sent to Gwenvor Cove and there required to remain until he made a truss of sand—to be bound with ropes spun of the same—and carried it to a rock above high-water mark. For many years he toiled in vain at his task, and his howling would be heard for many miles away when winds or waves scattered the sand he had piled up during low water.

One very frosty night, however, by pouring water from Velan-Dreath brook over his truss he succeeded in making it hold together and bore it to a rock above the flow of spring tides.

Then, as some say, that very night, as he took his way over or along the coast towards Helston, to revisit and torment those who raised him from the grave, by way of showing his exultation at having completed his task, or for mere deviltry perhaps, he swept all the sand out of Nanjisel and around Pedn-pen-with into Parcurno and adjacent coves, without letting any enter Pargwartha.

Another tradition says that sweeping the sand from Nanjisel to the east of Tol-pedn was assigned to Tregeagle as a separate task.

After this exploit the troublesome spirit was again sent to Gwenvor to make a truss of sand. There he remains toiling to this day—unable to perform what is required in order to regain his liberty, because he was bound not to use Velan-Dreath water or any other.

There is also a very old belief that spectre ships frequently visited Parcurno, both before and since its navigable channel became filled with sand, and that they were often seen sailing up and down the valley, over dry land the same as on the sea.

These naval apparitions were, in olden times, regarded as "tokens" that enemies were about to make a descent; the number of phantom vessels foreboded the sea-robbers' approaching force.

This presage of yore was held for truth by many old folks but lately deceased; yet latterly it has somehow changed its character and become connected with the history of a person who, little more than a hundred years ago, lived in a lone house called Chygwidden, about a mile inland from Parcurno. This comparatively modern story also accounts for the sand shifting, and has appropriated old traditions that had no connection therewith.

It relates that, long ago, Chygwidden was the chief dwelling-place of a family who flourished in St. Levan for a few generations and then all its branches became so reduced, through riotous living, as to be obliged to mortgage and sell much of their freehold lands.

The eldest and only son, by a former wife, of old Martin T——, who lived there, took to a seafaring life when about twenty, on account of cruel treatment received from his drunken father and a step-dame several years younger than himself. On leaving he vowed that he would never return whilst one lived who then darkened his father's doors.

Many years passed, and as no tidings had been received of young Martin, as he was still called, most persons believed him dead. In the meantime, his father, the step-dame, and her children, having all died within a few years of each other, a distant relative, as heir-at-law, had taken possession of what little property remained, and lived in Chygwidden.

Some ten years after the decease of all who had lived under old Martin's roof when his eldest son was driven thence, a large ship hove-to within a mile of Parcurno on a fine afternoon in harvest time.

People working in fields near the cliff noticed the unusual circumstance and saw a boat leave the ship with two men, who landed in Parcurno with several chests and other goods, and the ship proceeded on her course.

It was evident that one of those who came on shore was well acquainted with the place, as he struck at once into a pathway over the cliff which led, by a short cut, to Rospeltha, where he made himself known as young Martin T—— and procured horses and other help to take several heavy chests and bales to Chygwidden.

There was great rejoicing when it was known that the wanderer had at length returned to claim his own. His kinsfolks—a young man and his sister Eleanor, a damsel in her teens—were ready to resign possession, but Martin then cared little for house or land, and told them to keep the place and welcome, for all he desired was to have a home there for himself and his comrade whilst they remained, which he thought would only be for a short spell. His tastes had changed with change of scene. The place that he had once deemed the fairest on earth—but then he had seen no more of it than was visible from the nearest high hill—now appeared dreary; and the people whom—those of his own family excepted—he once thought the best in the world now seemed a forlorn set of consequential, grimly-religious nobodies to him, and above all to his mate, who, by-the-bye, requires more particular notice than we have yet bestowed on him.

Martin found the people, also, much altered from what they were in his youthful days, for about the time of his return a new sect had sprung up whose members, professing uncommon godliness, decried our ancient games and merry-makings, which were wont on holidays to unite all ages and classes. Their condemnation caused them to fall into disuse; and, on account of the censorious and intolerant spirit which then prevailed, there was much less heartiness and cordial intercourse amongst neighbours than formerly.

In a short time, however, Martin, now called by most persons "The Captain," became reconciled—one can't say attached—to his native place and the "humdrum West Country folks," as he styled them, who marvelled at his riches and the change which had taken place in his outward mien and manner. Yet the homely people's surprise at the alteration in Martin was nothing to their wonder, allied to fear, excited by his dusky companion or slave, for no one knew in what relation they stood to each other.

This stranger was seen to be a robust man, about thirty years of age apparently, with a swarthy complexion, many shades darker than the Captain's Spanish-mahogany tinted skin. Martin called this man José or mate, and he rarely spoke a word of English (though he could when he pleased) or addressed anyone but Martin, with whom he always conversed in some outlandish lingo which seemed more natural to the Captain than his mother tongue. A tantalizing mystery shrouded the dark "outlander;" for his master or friend would never answer any queries respecting him. He was almost equally silent with regard to buccaneering or other adventures, and rarely spoke of anything that occurred either at home or abroad during his absence. The two strange beings often came to high words and even to blows, but they would never allow anyone to meddle in their quarrels. When Martin was drunk and off his guard he would now and then ease his mind by swearing at his mate in plain English, or grumble at him in the same, to the effect that he had risked his life and spent a fortune to save him from being hanged at the yard-arm. "Discontented devil of a blackamoor," he would say, "why canst thou not be satisfied to live here? Thou art bound to me body and soul; and do I not indulge thee with everything gold can purchase?"

José would sometimes murmur "Avast there; all our gold and diamonds can't procure us here the bright sunshine and joyous people, nor the rich fruits and wine, of my native clime."

He seldom, however, made other reply than by gloomy looks or fiery glances which soon recalled Martin to his senses. It was remarked that after these outbursts of passion he was for a long while like the humble slave of his mate.

The boat in which they landed was kept at Parcurno, except for short spells during stormy times of the year, when she was put into Penberth or Pargwartha for greater safety; and, weeks together, they would remain out at sea night and day till their provisions were used; then they would come in, their craft laden with fish, and this cargo was free to all-comers. Stormy weather seldom drove them to land; they seemed to delight in a tempest.

Before winter came they procured a good number of hounds, and great part of the hunting season was passed by them in coursing over all parts of the West Country. Often of winter's nights, people far away would be frightened by hearing or seeing these two wild-looking hunters and their dogs chasing over some lone moor, and they gave rise to many a story of Old Nick and his headless hounds.

When tired of the chase, weeks were often passed at a public-house in Buryan Church-town. Martin treated one and all and scattered gold around him like chaff. The tawny mate, however, at times restrained Martin's lavish expenditure, took charge of his money-chests, and refused him the keys.

José would occasionally condescend to express his wishes to Eleanor, who was mistress of the rare establishment. She understood and humoured the pair, who took pleasure in decking her in the richest stuffs and jewels that their chests contained or that money could procure, and she frequently stayed up alone best part of the night to await their return.

After being at home a year or so the Captain had a large half-decked boat built, and several rocks removed in Parcurno to make a safer place in which to moor her. They then took longer trips, and were not seen in Chygwidden for months running. The two eccentric beings passed many years in this way, and held but little intercourse with their neighbours.

At length Martin perceived tokens of death, or what he took for such, and made his man swear that when he saw signs of near dissolution he would take him off to sea, let him die there, and send him to rest at the ocean's bottom. He also bound his kinsman by oath not to oppose his wishes, and invoked a curse on any one who would lay his dust beside the remains of those who had driven him to range the wide world like a vagabond.

They might have complied with his strange desires, but ere they could be carried out he died in a hammock, suspended in his bed-room.

Now there comes a mystery, that is not likely to be cleared up.

It was known that a coffin,—followed by the cousins, José, and the dogs, was taken to St. Levan Churchyard and buried near the ground in which Martin's family lie. But it was rumoured that the coffin merely contained earth to make weight.

The following night, however, the dark "outlander" had two chests conveyed to Parcurno, the largest of which was said to contain the remains of his friend, and the other money and valuables which belonged to himself. The chests placed on board the half-decked vessel, José and his favourite dog embarked, waited for the tide to rise, and put to sea; but no one remained at the cove to behold their departure, and no more was seen in the West of man, dog, or boat.

Eleanor disappeared on the funeral night and it was believed that she left with the stranger, who was scarcely a league to sea ere a tempest arose and continued with great fury for nearly a week; and, although it was in winter, the sky of nights was all ablaze with lightning and the days as dark as nights. During this storm Parcurno was choked with sand, and no boat could be kept there since.

The tempest had scarcely lulled when an apparition of Martin's craft would drive into Parcurno against wind and tide; oft-times she came in the dusk of evening, and, without stopping at the Cove, took her course up over the old caunce towards Chapel-Curno; thence she sailed away, her keel just skimming the ground, or many yards above it, as she passed over hill and dale till she arrived at Chygwidden.

The barque was generally shrouded in mist, and one could rarely get a glimpse of her deck on which the shadowy figures of two men, a woman, and a dog, were beheld now and then. This ship of the dead, with her ghostly crew, hovered over the town-place a moment, then bore away to a croft on the farm, and vanished near a rock where a large sum of foreign coins was disinterred many years ago, so it is said. Of late the ghostly ship has not been known to have entered Parcurno, and on account of innovations recently effected there she may nevermore be seen in that ancient port.

It may be observed that traditions of phantom-ships sailing overland were common to many places near the Land's End with which no stories are connected; these appearances were merely supposed to forebode tempests and wrecks.

The few incidents which form the groundwork of the above legend occurred but little more than a century before it was related to me by an aged farm labourer of St. Levan; yet in that short space it has assumed such a mystic garb that the simple and true story can scarcely be perceived under its embellishments.

LEGENDS OF ST. LEVAN.

They had their lodges in the wilderness,
Or built them cells beside the shadowy sea,
And there they dwelt with angels, like a dream!

REV. R. S. HAWKER.

ST. LEVAN AND HIS SISTER.

AN old habitation, in which, according to tradition, St. Levan dwelt, is still standing. This humble dwelling, situated in Bodellan, is on the eastern side of Parcurno Bottom, near its upper part within a hundred yards of the road, towards which stands the end that contains its sole fire-place. The hearth-stone may still be there, much as it was when St. Levan's sister, the good midwife, St. Breage, cooked on it the fatal chads which choked her children.

The story says that good old St. Levan was one evening down fishing from his accustomed place in Rospeltha cliff—still called Old St. Levan's Rocks. He cast in his hook-and-line, intending to take one fish only for his supper, from the multitude that always came around the rock on which he stood as soon as he cast in "browse" (garbage to attract fish). Contrary to St. Levan's wish, two chads, or young breams, fastened on his hook at the same time, and not to show favour to either he threw both of them into the sea again. And no sooner was his hook-and-line in the waves a second time than the same chads, or two others, hooked themselves together again, and were again restored to the sea. For the third time he cast in his line; and, seeing two fishes on his hook again, he regarded this occurrence as a providential intimation that he was to take them both home, and acted accordingly. When he came to Bodellan he found that his sister, St. Breage, had just arrived with two children. The chads were boiled for supper, and St. Breage's hungry children, being careless of bones, got choked, and remembrance of this event is handed down in St. Levan's parish by chads being there called "chuck-cheeld" to this day.

Some thirty-five years ago the writer often noticed, on a bench-end in St. Levan church, near the belfry door, a panel, or shield, on which two fishes, with their heads touching each other, were carved in bold relief. The fishes were much like chads, or young breams, in outline, and the foregoing legend might have suggested this design, or the device have originated the story. It is to be feared that this bench-end, and much more tastefully-designed and boldly-wrought carving, disappeared before the Rev. C. C. Anstey came to preserve and restore the interesting remains of this once beautiful church. Loads of as fine carved work, and no more decayed than what remains, were, from thirty or forty years since, carried off by the carpenters, who were, every now and then, employed to demolish the curious old oak benches, and to replace them with painted deal boxes, in many variations of ugliness.

It is said that the path which St. Levan took across Rospeltha fields to his accustomed fishing-place, may still be traced by the ground his holy footsteps trod bearing finer grain when in corn, and by the grass being greener when in pasture than in other parts of the fields.

Johanna's Garden.

St. Levan road passed by a small enclosure in Rospeltha, called Johanna's Garden, (at least it retained that name a few years ago when the writer knew it well).

One Sunday morning the holy hermit, going down to cliff to get a fish for his dinner, in passing by this garden saw a woman called Johanna gathering pot-herbs. St. Levan rested the end of his rocking-rod on the ground, stopped, and gave her a kindly greeting. But she, looking over the hedge, exclaimed, "Oh sinful man that you are, for going a fishing of a Sunday! Whatever can 'e think will become of 'e?"

"Self-righteous hypocrite that thou art," answered the saint, "in looking for other people's faults thou canst not behold thine own. Think not that thou— with thy fingers spread out and thy eyes turned up—art better than others, for a more strict or a more lazy observance of Sunday. And tell me," he continued, "sharp as thou art to mark others' faults, and blind as thou art to thine own, wherefore should it be a sin for me to take my daily fish from the sea any more than for thee to gather herbs from thy garden?"

St. Levan said much more, but all in vain were his endeavours to bring the woman to reason, for, in spite of all he could say, she would still have the last word and contend that there was more sin in catching fish than in picking greens of a Sunday.

At last the good man being provoked by her obstinacy, pretended piety, and conceited clack, raised his hand and cursed her, saying, "From this time, for ever, thou shalt be known, if known at all, as the Foolish Johanna! And thy garden shall ever continue, as now, to bear more hemlock and nettles than leeks and lentils. Moreover," he continued, "mark this—To make thy remembrance the more accursed for all time to come, if any child by thy name be baptised in the waters of Parchapel Well it shall become a fool like thyself and bad luck follow it."

Down to very recent times, so great was the fear of old St. Levan's curse that anyone in this parish desirous of having a child named Johanna took it to Sennen to be christened.

It may be remarked that, until the roof fell into St. Levan's Well, and it became choked up, the sexton always kept it clean and fetched water thence for the baptismal office.

We don't know what state "Johanna's Garden" is now in, but some thirty years ago it always bore more weeds than pot-herbs.

These simple traditions—thus handed down and kept alive by St. Levan people, who believed them to be literally true—mark a lingering veneration for the holy fisherman who, in this secluded place, led his tranquil life.

THE ST. LEVAN STONE.

In St. Levan Churchyard is a cloven rock called St. Levan's stone. For some reason, now unknown, this must have been a venerated object when the church was built, or it would have been used in the building. The common notion, however, is that long before St. Levan's time this rock was regarded as sacred, because Merlin prophecied—

"When, with panniers astride,
A pack-horse one can ride
Through St. Levan stone,
The world will be done."

It is stated that Merlin came here with King Arthur, when he slaughtered the Danes at the battle of Velan-druchar. The separation of this prophetic stone is so slow that there appears to be no danger of the world's ending just yet.

PARCHAPEL WELL.

To find the Saint's Well one should take a pathway bearing westward, from a little below the church, and which leads over Roskestal cliff to Pargwarra (we spell all names as the inhabitants pronounce them). After crossing the brook and mounting a hedge keep straight towards the sea, and on a pretty level spot the ruined walls of St. Levan's baptistry will be found, as also some traces of rude steps on a pathway that connected this holy fount with an ancient chapel and burying-ground which stood on ground so near the precipice that little, if any, of its site now remains. We have heard old folks of St. Levan (who were born there more than a century ago) say that in their younger days Parchapel Well, as they always called it, was, twice a year, regularly cleaned out and repaired, and the ground, for a good space around, as well as the steps, cleared of weeds, swept, and sanded. The first week of May being a time of general well-dressing, Parchapel Well was never neglected then, and it was also cleaned up against the feasten tide, when many christenings usually took place.

Old folks also spoke of another time-honoured observance in which the Saint's Well was shown due respect. Until within half a century or so, it was a custom on Christmas-eve for carol singers belonging to the higher side hamlets to assemble in Sowah town-place round a large flat table-like rock called the Garrack Zans (holy rock). Here they would commence singing, and proceed to Roskestal, where at another Garrack Zans in that town-place they would be joined by others, and all would thence go singing down to Parchapel Well, where they would meet with many singers from Treen and other lower-side places. At the Well many an old carol would be chanted. One was never forgotten, in which, according to our West Country version, Holy Mary says to her dear child:—

"Go thee wayst out, child Jesus;
Go thee wayst out to play
Down by God's holy well.
I see three pretty chelderen
As ever tongue can tell."

This, for its sweet simplicity, is still a favourite in the west.

The rude steps, which may yet be traced (though almost overgrown by rushes and other water-plants) will be regarded with interest, as we learn from St. Levan traditions that great sinners did penance by crawling over these rough stones on their bare knees, and that the devout who desired or aspired to acquire extraordinary grace, or indulgence, scrambled up all the way on bare knees from chapel-door to holy fount.

A LEGEND OF PARGWARRA.

My William's love was heaven on earth,
Without it earth is hell.

SCOTT.

PROCEEDING westward from St. Levan's Well we pass the next inlet, called Parleddan (Wide Cove), and arrive at Pargwarra or Pargwartha (Higher Cove), which is one of the most secluded and picturesque nooks that may anywhere be found.

Old folks also called this place the Sweethearts' Cove, from a tradition of its having been the scene of a tragical love-story, which is best known to me from fragments of a quaint old 'copy of verses,' entitled—

THE TRAGEDY OF SWEET WILLIAM AND FAIR NANCY.

This composition of a forgotten western bard related that, far back in old times, the son of a fisherman, who dwelt at Pargwarra, lived many years—off and on from a boy—in service with a rich farmer in Roskestal, and courted his master's only daughter, who, almost from her childhood, loved the young serving-man with a strength of affection beyond her control.

The youngster, being of a roving turn, often went to sea for many months in summer, and although he was then most wanted on the farm, his master always took him back again when sailors were paid off and merchant ships laid up during the stormy winter season. It was his old master's and Nancy's great delight of winter's nights, to be seated with neighbours around the fire and hear Willy tell of strange things he had beheld on the ocean and in foreign lands; they wondered at what he related of waterspouts, icebergs, and northern lights, of whales, seals, and Laplanders. And they listened with awe and surprise to what he told them of burning-mountains, where he said he had seen, from a distance, the very mouths of hell vomiting clouds of sulphurous smoke, flames, and rivers of fire. And when sailing as near these dreadful regions as anyone dared venture for the heat, and for fear of having their vessel drawn ashore, where all the nails would be pulled from her planks by the load-stone rocks that bordered these lands; of nights, he had heard high over-head, devils shouting, "the time is come but such and such a one isn't come;" soon after, one would hear doleful cries and behold black clouds of doomed spirits driven to the burning-mountains by troops of demons. He had seen the wreck of Pharaoh's chariots on the beach of the Red Sea, which, he assured them, had retained the hue from which it took its name ever since the Egyptian hosts were slain and overwhelmed, where their bones are still bleaching on the sands.

But all that was easily believed by his simple hearers, and mere nothing to the marvels he related from shipmates' stories when he told them of those bold mariners who had been farther east and seen the Dead Sea across which no bird could fly—how they had plucked from trees that bordered its black waters apples full of ashes that were tempting to the eye; they had touched Lot's wife turned to salt, and brought home some of her fingers; that was often done, he said, for with the next tide's flow they sprouted out again.

The neighbours liked above all to hear him tell about the dusky men and strange women of Levantine lands, and how the latter would shoot loving glances at British tars through peepholes cut in their thick black cloth veils.

Now William himself was a wonder of perfection, past compare in Nancy's eyes. She admired him for his stalwart form, for his strange adventures on sea and land, and for the rare presents he brought her home. The farmer, too, liked him just as if he had been his own son, yet it never entered his head that his daughter and only child would ever think of the dashing and careless young seaman as her lover.

Yet her mother, more sharp sighted, soon discovered that her fair Nancy was much in love with their serving-man. When William was gone to sea the dame upbraided her with want of proper pride and self-respect till she had fretted her almost to death's door. "What a fool thou must be," said she, "to throw thyself away, or to hanker after one so much beneath thy degree, when thy good looks and dower make thee a match for the richest farmer's son in the West Country; think if you wed a poor sailor how you will be scorned by all your kith and kin." Nancy replied, "but little care I for relations' reproach or good will, and sink or swim if ever I marry it shall be the man I love who is able to work and win." The dame prevailed on her husband, much against his will, however, not to take the sailor to live there when he returned home again; and she—watching her opportunity—slammed the door in his face and told him he should nevermore harbour beneath her roof.

But the father fearing his only child would pine to death, told her and her lover that if he would try his fortune by a voyage to the Indies or elsewhere for three years, when he returned, poor or rich, if he and Nancy were in the same mind, they might be wedded for all he cared.

That being agreed on, William got a berth in a merchant-man bound for a long voyage, took friendly leave of his old master, and the night before his ship was ready to sail he and Nancy met, and he assured the sorrowing damsel that in three years or less she might expect him to land in Pargwarra with plenty of riches, and he would marry at home or fetch her away and make her his bride. According to the old verses he said—

"Down in a valley, love, where three streams unite,
I'll build thee a castle of ivory and diamonds so bright,
That shall be a guide for poor sailors of a dark stormy night."

They vowed again and again to be constant and true; with their hands joined in a living spring or stream they broke a gold ring in two between them, each one keeping a part. And to make their vows more binding they kindled, at dead of night, a fire on the Garrack Zans (holy rock), which then stood in Roskestal town-place, and joining their hands over the flame, called on all the powers of heaven and earth to witness their solemn oaths to have each other living or dead. Having plighted their troth with these and other ancient rites—that romantic lovers of old regarded as more sacred than a marriage ceremony—they said farewell, and William went on his way and joined his ship.

Three years passed during which the old dame had done her utmost to persuade her daughter to become the wife of some rich farmer—for true it was, as she said, Nancy might have had her choice of the best—yet coaxing and reproaches were powerless to shake the maid's constancy. When three years and many months were gone without any tidings of William, she became very melancholy—perhaps crazy—from hope deferred, and took to wandering about the cleves in all weathers, by day and by night.

On the headland, called Hella Point, which stretches far out west of the cove, there is a high over-hanging rock almost on the verge of the cliff, which shelters, on its southern side, a patch of green sward, mostly composed of cliff-pinks; this spot used to be known as Fair Nancy's bed. There she would pass hours by day and often whole nights watching vessels that came within her ken, hoping to see her lover land from every one that hove in sight, and to be the first to hail him with joyful greetings in the cove. Her father and the old fisherman—anxious for William's return—treated her as tenderly as a shorn lamb, and often passed long nights with her there; at length the poor maiden had to be watched and followed for fear that in her night wanderings she might fall over the cliff or drown herself in a fit of despair.

One moonlight winter's night, when in her chamber indulging her grief, she heard William's voice just under her window, saying, "Sleepest thou, sweetheart, awaken and come hither, love; my boat awaits us at the cove, thou must come this night or never be my bride."

"My sweet William come at last, I'll be with thee in an instant," she replied.

Nancy's aunt Prudence, who lodged in the same room, heard Willy's request and his sweetheart's answer; looking out of the window she saw the sailor, just under, dripping wet and deathly pale. An instant after—glancing round into the chamber, and seeing Nancy leave it—she dressed, in all haste, and followed her. Aunt Prudence, running down the cliff lane at her utmost speed, kept the lovers in sight some time, but couldn't overtake them, for they seemed to glide down the rocky pathway leading to Pargwarra as if borne on the wind, till they disappeared in the glen.

At the fisherman's door, however, she again caught a glimpse of them passing over the rocks towards a boat which floated off in the cove. She then ran out upon the How—as the high ground projecting into the cove is called—just in time to see them on a large flat rock beside the boat, when a fog rolling in over sea, shrouded them from her view. She hailed them but heard no reply.

In a few minutes the mist cleared away, bright moonlight again shone on the water, but the boat and lovers had disappeared.

Then she heard mermaids singing a low sweet melody, and saw many of them sporting on the water under Hella; that was nothing new, however, for the rocks and sawns (caverns) bordering this headland were always noted as favourite resorts of these death-boding syrens, whose wild unearthly strains were wont, before tempests, to be heard resounding along Pedn-Penwith shores.

By daybreak the old fisherman came to Roskestal and told the farmer that he hoped to find his son there, for, about midnight, he saw him at his bedside, looking ghastly pale; he stayed but a moment, and merely said, "Farewell father and mother, I am come for my bride and must hasten away," when he vanished like a spirit. It all seemed to the old man uncertain as a dream; he didn't know if it were his own son in the body or a token of his death.

In the afternoon, ere they had ceased wondering and making search for Nancy, a young mariner came to the fisherman's dwelling, and told him that he was chief officer of his son's ship, then at the Mount with a rich cargo from the Indies, bound for another port; but put in there because his son— her captain—when off Pargwarra, where he intended to land last night, eager to see his native place, went aloft, and the ship rolling he missed his holdfast of the shrouds, fell overboard and sunk before she could be brought-to or any assistance rendered.

All knew then that William's ghost had taken Nancy to a phantom boat, and a watery grave was the lovers' bridal-bed. Thus their rash vows of constancy, even in death, were fulfilled, and their sad story, for a time, caused Pargwartha to be known as the Sweethearts' Cove, and some will have it that the old Cornish name has that meaning.

There are other versions of this story, that only vary from the above in details of little interest.

I have recently tried in vain to find anyone who knows the old 'copy of verses,' the argument of which I have for the most part followed.

The fragments I recited, however, recalled to a few old folks a newer piece called the "Strains of Lovely Nancy," that used to be printed in a broad sheet and sung and sold by wandering ballad singers of the west, forty or fifty years ago; and from what I heard of the latter one might conclude it to have been a modernised and an imperfect version of the ancient tragedy.

Traditions connected with places in the southern parishes of West Penwith having brought us within a short distance of the Land's End, we now return to St. Just and purpose to relate such as are found in that parish and Sennen.

And singular enough, almost all old stories handed down in St. Just are fairy-tales.

An' Pee Tregeer's Trip to Market on Hallan Eve.

Faery elves,
Whose midnight revels by a forest side
Or fountain some belated peasant sees.

MILTON.

ONE St. Just Feasten Monday, about thirty years since, we heard the following story told by the kitchen fireside in the "North Inn." An aged mine-captain related the principal part, others of the company helping him out when his memory or invention failed.

"I have heard the old folks tell," said Captain Peter, "how long ago—it may be hundreds of years past, for what we know—the Squire, who then lived in Pendeen, had for his housekeeper an elderly dame called Pee Tregeer, who came to a sad mishap one Hallan Eve. Some spices and other small things were wanted from Penzance for the Feasten tide, and the careful old creature wouldn't trust anyone to go for them but herself. Now, An' Pee dearly loved company on the road, and, not knowing of anybody more likely to take the jaunt with her than Jenny Trayer, who lived at Pendeen Cove, she took her basket and stick and went down to see if Jenny would go.

"This woman was the wife of one Tom Trayer. The hut in which they lived was the only dwelling then in the cove. The pair were but little seen out of the place. Tom passed great part of his time a fishing, when he wasn't smuggling; and his wife seldom left home except when she took round liquor and fish together, in her cowal, for sale. Jenny, however, was frequently visited, for she professed to be, and passed for, a White Witch, charmer, or wise-woman. On this account many resorted to her that they might be benefitted by her charms and spells. Yet, there were others that regarded her as a witch of deeper dye, and who believed that, by her strange dealings with the Old One, her husband had always a favourable wind, so as to make a quicker passage to France and back than anyone else in "the fair trade." Besides, fish, they said, always came to his hook and net when other fishermen had none. If anyone happened to offend either of the pair some strange run of bad luck was sure to follow; and nothing proved their compact with Old Nick so much as the rich wrecks which were constantly floating into Pendeen Cove when the pair lived there. Yet, as they lived on the Squire's estate, few cared to openly accuse them of practising the black art; and An' Pee didn't trouble herself about their sorcery or witchcraft, so that they furnished her with a good supply of choice liquors.

"When she arrived at Tom's door, contrary to custom she found it shut, and, hearing voices within, her curiosity made her peep through the finger-hole (latch-hole). Then she saw Tom sitting on the chimney-stool, and his wife taking on the tip of her finger from a croggan (limpet-shell) what appeared to be salve, which she rubbed over her husband's eyes.

"The anointing finished, Jenny placed the croggan in the mouth of the oven and covered it up with rags. An' Pee, seeing Tom put on his hat, and come towards the door, lifted the latch and entered. Tom didn't seem pleased at the old dame's abrupt entrance, as he went out with a very black look, but his wife made much of her, that she might speak a good word for them to the Squire whenever they wanted any favour, which she was ready enow to do for the sake of good liquor.

"'I am very glad to see 'e, An' Pee,' said Jenny, 'I have this moment been thinking about 'e and wishing you would come down to taste the choice cordials Tom and the boys brought home by their last trip.'

"Whilst Jenny was in the spence after the liquor, An' Pee took from the croggan the least bit of a greenish salve and touched one eye with it. Before she had time to anoint the other, out came Jenny with her hands full of jars and bottles. 'Now, what will 'e take, An' Pee?' said she, in placing the liquor and drinking-horns on the board, 'Will 'e first of all help yourself to some brandy from this jar, or some rum out of that, before you try the Hollands in the case-bottle, and take some of the sweet cordials afterwards? We have wine, too, in the spence if you would like that better to begin with.'

"An' Pee took a drink of all the various kinds of liquors, just to sample them. Jenny excused herself from going to town, because, being Feasten eve, she had many churs (odd jobs) to do that the place might be tidy against the morrow. Besides, she expected many customers that evening, for a supply of drink to pass the tide. She didn't choose to leave the selling of the liquor to Tom, she said; he was too easily taken in.

"It was about three o'clock when, An' Pee having filled with brandy a bottle, which she always carried in her pocket, left the cove and started for Penzance. Coming out of the dark dwelling she was surprised to find how well she could see, and the good liquor put such life into her heels that she tripped along the lanes without feeling the ground under her feet. Yet, it was almost candlelighting when she got to town. After purchasing what she wanted for the house she went down among the standings on a three-cornered plot, where the market-house is now, to buy a pair of shoes for herself. Whilst she was trying their size with a piece of stick the length of her foot, to her great surprise she saw Tom Trayer going from standing to standing as brisk as a bee, picking off everything that suited his fancy. Yet, nobody but herself appeared to see him taking rolls of leather, knives, forks, pewter-plates, wooden spoons, thread and yarn, and many other things, which he stuffed into his pockets and the knapsack he carried on his back. An' Pee, vexed to see his tricks on the tradespeople, went up to him and said, 'Tom! arn't thee ashamed to be here in the dark carrying on such a game?' 'Ah, es that you Aunt Pee,' Tom replied, 'now tell me which eye can 'e see me upon?' 'Why with both, I should think,' said she. But when she winked the eye that had been anointed, and found she only saw him on that, she said, 'I can see thee, and thy thievery, plain enow on my right eye, but the other es rather cloudy by night.' When she said this, Tom held up his finger and, pointing towards her anointed eye, said,—

"'Cursed old spy,
Thou shalt no more peep nor pry,
With thy anointed eye.'

"Then he blew on it and, laughing in her face, said, 'Take that for poking your nose where you arn't wanted, and meddling with other people's business. You shall neither see me, nor anyone else, any more with that game eye.' The old woman felt as if a needle had pierced it. She fell to the ground, and rolled about under the standings. Such was her agony she couldn't keep on her legs.

"She called on the market people to seize Tom Trayer, telling them he had put out her eye by witchcraft, and that he was going about in the dark, stealing goods from their standings and stalls. But no one, except herself, had seen him. Some said that An' Pee was drunk or dreaming, and they led her to Alverton-lane, tied her basket on her arm, wished her good night, and a pleasant journey home to Pendeen, and a merry feasten tide.

"Now An' Pee didn't return by the way of Polteggan Bottom and Boswednan, though it's the nearest, because there are so many stiles on that road and bogs near it. She took her course through Castle Horneck fields. When she came out into the high road, she drank a little from her bottle (which she had refilled in town) and went on for three or four miles, as she thought, being so distracted she couldn't tell whether she was going up hill or down dale half the time, and fancied herself much more advanced on her journey than she really was, when she beheld, a little before her, a man on horseback. By the proud way he was stuck up on his high horse, she took him for a gentleman who lived in the south of the parish.

"An' Pee was very glad to see him, and he was going so slowly that she soon overtook him, and when the old woman came up he stood stock still. 'My dear, maister,' said she, 'how glad I am to see 'e; don't 'e know me? I'm Pee Tregeer, and you can't think how I've been served out to-day.' Then she told him how she went down to the cove and anointed her eye with witch's salve—how that made her to see Tom Trayer stealing from the standings—

how he put out her eye, because she let him know, and other people too, that she was up to his tricks, and had found out which way he managed to live so easy without working like an honest man. The gentleman made no reply, and An' Pee continued to say 'In spite of being blind, foot sore, and leg weary, I'm got as far as here you see, and we can't be far from Ballaswidden I should think, and oh! my eye is still burning like fire; so, for goodness, do take pity on a poor unfortunate oman and take her up behind 'e. I can ride well enow on the flat 'cheens' of your horse without pillion or pad; it won't be much out of your way to give one a lift down to Pendeen gate, or if you will only take me over Dry Carn I won't forget your kindness all my born days. I well remember the time when you went much farther out of your way to meet me. Then, to be sure, I was young and much better looking than I am now; though you are years older than I am, yet you are still a fine-looking man, strong and lusty; all your family are good-looking boys; and how upright you sit on your horse! You have still a colt's tooth in your head, if all they say be true, but why don't 'e speak to me, are 'e gone to sleep? One would think you were takean a nap, and your horse too, it's standing so quiet.'

"Not having a word in reply to the fine speech she made to please the old gentleman, who didn't so much as turn his head, An' Pee called out as loud as she could, 'Ef you are the lord of Bosavern you needn't be stuck up there so proud that you won't speak to a poor body afoot, as ef I didn't know 'e and all belonging to 'e!' Still he never spoke. Yet she thought he winked on her, just as he used to do in his younger days. This vexed her the more, and she screamed out, 'The time was when the Tregeers were among the first in the parish, and were buried in the church as well as the old Bosvarguses, Usticks, Borlases, Milletts, and others of the quality! Ef you won't believe me, ask maister; he can tell everything from his books.' Still no speech with the horseman. 'Art ah dead drunk then? Wake up and speak to me, west ah?' screamed the old woman with increasing anger, as she took up a stone and threw it at the sleeping steed. The stone rolled back to her feet, and the horse didn't as much as whisk his tail.

"Pee now got nearer, and saw that the rider had neither hat nor wig on; nor was there a hair to be seen on his bare head, and, putting out her hand to touch the horse, she felt nothing but a bush of furze. She rubbed her eyes, and saw at once, to her great surprise, that what a moment before appeared (and she would have sworn it was) a gentleman on horseback, was nothing else but a tall cross that stands on a high bank, by the road-side, about half a mile from Santust lane's end. The old woman thought she was miles farther on, and must be so bewitched that she couldn't believe her senses.

"Fearing that Tom Trayer was still dogging her steps, she went on for dear life, and, not staying to look for the stepping stones in the stream below Cardew Mill, she splashed through with the water above her knees.

"On she went and, seeing a light on her right hand side, she thought it shone through the window of a dwelling, where she might rest awhile and dry herself, so she made for it, straight across the moors, but went on for miles, it seemed to her, without coming to it. Then the light went out and left her floundering in the bogs; yet, getting out and steering for the place from which it vanished, she at last found herself amidst the furze-ricks and pigs'-crows in Boslow. Not seeing any light in the only dwelling of this lonely place, An' Pee opened the door of an out-house and entered it, hoping she might take a few hours' rest.

"In the crow that the old dame entered she was glad to find a good quantity of straw, on which she lay down and fell asleep, but her slumbers were soon disturbed by a bosom of vears (litter of sucking pigs) which had just been severed from their dam and placed there to be weaned. The young sucklings, taking An' Pee for their dam, continued rooting round her with their snouts. All her endeavours to get a comfortable rest being in vain, she came out and, hearing the sound of a threshal (flail) going, and seeing a glimmer of light in the barn on the other side of the town-place, she thought that the old man of Boslow was up late threshing that he might have straw to serve his cattle over Sunday. 'Now,' said the old woman to herself, as she crossed the town-place, 'I shall get a spell of rest in the barn, for I feel so sleepy that no noise of threshing will hinder me from having a nap.' She made for a window, which stood open and through which the light glimmered, that she might have a peep at what was going on before she went in.

"Looking in she could only see, at first, an old iron chill (lamp) with two porvans (rush wicks) burning in it. The chill hung from a stake, driven into the wall opposite, at the head of the barn-boards. Then, in the faint light, she noticed a slash-staff (beating part of the flail) going up and down, but couldn't see anybody working it. That she might be able to reach her head farther in, to see better, she rolled close under the window a big stone, and, standing on that, on her tip-toes, she saw that the threshal was worked by a little old man, no more than three feet high, covered only with a few rags, and his long hair that hung over his shoulders like a bunch of rushes, (a bunch beaten for making sheep's spans). His face was broader than it was long; she couldn't make out the colour of his great round owl's-eyes, they were so shaded by his shaggy eyebrows, from between which his long nose, like a snout, poked out. His mouth reached from ear to ear, and they were set far back to make room for it. Pee noticed, too, that his teeth were very long and jagged, for he was so eager about his work that, with each stroke of the threshal, he kept moving his thin lips round and up and down, and his tongue in and out. He had nothing of a chin or neck to speak of, but shoulders broad enow for a man twice his height. His naked arms and legs were out of all proportion, and too long for his squat body; and his splayed feet were more like a quilkan's (frog's) than a man's.

"'Well,' thought An' Pee, 'this es luck, to see Piskey threshan; for, ever since I can remember, I have heard it said that Piskey threshed the corn in Boslow of winter's nights, and did other odd jobs all the year round for the old couple who lived here, but I wouldn't believe it. Yet here he es!' As she reached farther in and looked round she beheld scores of small people, no more than two feet high, attending on the thresher; some of them lugged down sheaves and placed them handy for him; others shook the straw and bore it off to the end of the barn. An' Pee couldn't help admiring how, when one side of a sheaf was threshed clean, Piskey, by a few quick, smart blows, would rise the sheaf on its butt-end, then knock it over quite cute like with the unthreshed side uppermost. When the corn was all out of that side, with a few sharp blows on the tongue of the bind, it was laid open and the straw sent to the lower end of the boards with the tip of his slash-staff. An' Pee declared that she never saw a smarter thresher in all her born days.

"When a heap of corn had gathered on the boards, he raked it off with the barn-rake and kicked the bruss-straw (short straw) out of it, leaving the corn just as clean as if it had been winded. In doing this job, he raised such a dust that it set him and the small folks sneezing, and the old woman, according to custom, said 'God bless 'e little men!' She had no sooner spoken the words than the light went out and all vanished; but she felt a handful of dust thrown into her eyes that nearly blinded the only peeper that she could see anything on, and she heard Piskey squeak out,

'I spy thy snout, old Peepan Pee;
And I'll serve thee out, or es much to me.'

"An' Pee felt rather uneasy when she remembered that the 'small people' have great spite against anyone who watches them or tries to pry into their doings.

"The night being clear she found her way out of the scrambly lane, leading up from Boslow to the highroad, scampered on as fast as she could, and never stopped till she reached the top of Dry Carn. There she sat down a minute, that she might recover her breath, to pass quickly over the road near Carn Kenidzek and down the Gump, as everybody then (as now) dreaded that haunted track; indeed, few go near that wisht place, about the turn of night, without hearing, if not seeing, the Old One and his hounds, hunting among the rocks for any restless spirits that might have strayed so far away from the churchyard—their only place of safety—or some other frightful apparitions, fighting and howling round the carn, or fleeing over the downs.

"She 'jailed' away—down the hill, as fast as she could lay foot to ground, thinking to be home by the kitchen fire in a quarter of an hour, and went far enough, as she thought, to have reached Pendeen gate twice over. Then she feared that she might have got into a wrong bridle-path over the downs, or that Piskey was playing her a trick, because, turn whichever way she would, the road appeared to be before her. After going on for a long while, she saw light and heard music, at no great distance. Thinking then that she must have kept too much on her left and be near some house on the road to Church-town, where they were getting in tune for the dancing on Feasten Monday night, she went over the downs, straight towards the light, feeling ready for a jig, and stopped more than once to 'try her steps,' as the lively old dancing tunes kept sounding in her ears. But, instead of arriving at a house, as she expected to, in passing round some high rocks, which hid the light a moment, she came, all at once, on a level green, surrounded by furze and rocks, and there, a few yards before her, saw troops of 'small people' holding a fair, or belike it might be their feasten market.

"Scores of little standings all in a row, were covered with trinkets, such as knee and shoe buckles of silver and gold, glistening with Cornish diamonds; pins, with jewelled heads; brooches, rings, bracelets, and strings of crystal beads, figured with green and red, or blue and gold; and scores of other pretty things quite new to An' Pee; who, not to disturb the small folks till she had seen all that was doing, crept along softly in the rear of the standings, till she stood opposite a company of dancers; hundreds of them linked hand in hand, after the old bonfire-dance fashion, were whirling round so fast that it made her head light to look at them.

"Small as they were—none more than two feet high, and rather slender in make—they were all decked out like old-fashioned gentry—the little men in three-cocked hats and feathers; full, square-skirted, blue coats, stiff with buckram and gay with lace and buttons; vest, breeches, and stockings of a lighter hue; and their dainty little shoes fastened with diamond clasps. Some few, who were rigged more like soldiers or huntsmen, wore either jet-black or russet-coloured riding boots.

"An' Pee said that she couldn't name the colours of the little ladies' dresses, which were of all the hues of summer's blossoms. The vain little things, to make themselves look the taller, had their powdered hair turned up on pads and dressed with flowers, lace, and ribbons to an extraordinary height for such dolls of things. Their gay gowns were very long-waisted, and their skirts so distended by hoops that they looked just as broad as they were long. Their shoes of velvet or satin, were high-heeled and pointed at the toes. The men were much darker complexioned than the women, yet they were all very good looking, with sparkling dark eyes, well-shaped noses, sweet little mouths, and dimpled cheeks and chins. Not one among them, that she saw, had a spotty face or purple-top nose, because they drink nothing stronger than honey-dew. Some, to be sure, appeared to be rather aged, yet, all were sprightly, merry, and gay.

"In the dancers' ring stood a May-pole about three yards high, all wreathed with flowers. Where they got them, that time of the year, to make their garlands, was a wonder. The pipers, standing in their midst, played lively old dance tunes that are now but seldom heard, and An' Pee never felt more inclined for a dance in her life than when she heard their cheery music; but how could she reel round among such little beings and have a jig without kicking them down?

"'The women,' she always said, 'were the sauciest little creatures that one ever seed; she was most ashamed to look at them—tossing up their heels, forwards and backwards, higher than their heads, and kicking off the men's hats, as they capered round and round.' Every now and then, one would unlock her hands and, breaking out of the ring, take a leap right over the men's heads, perch on the May-pole, and there spin round, on her toe, like a whirligig.

"There were lights about in all directions—lanthorns no bigger than gun-pop (fox-glove) flowers, hanging in rows along the standings, and rushlights, in paper cups like tulips, shone among the gingerbread-nuts, comfits, candied angelica, peppermint-drops, and more enticing things that are seen in any other fair. She thought, too, that all the glow-worms in creation had gathered together near the fair-ground, to help to light it up. Yet, with all these lights, there was such a shimmer over everything that the old dame got bewildered at times and could never see anything so plainly as she wished.

"At no great distance from the dancers there was a wrestling ring, where many little ladies were looking on, betting on their favourites and helping them with their good wishes and applause. Farther on, some were shooting with bows and arrows at a target. Others were playing at keals (bowls). Every here and there the lilly-bangers (raffle-keepers) with their tables and dice kept a great noise calling out, 'Come hither, sweet ladies and gentlemen, and try your luck! One in, two in, three in; who will make four in for this nice cake?' Farther off, nearly out of sight, a great number were 'hurling to the gold' (goal). She knew what was going on from hearing the old cry of 'Well done, Santusters, one and all, comrades; fair play is good play' and, every now and then she saw the little hurling-ball, as it was cast from side to side, shine like a shooting star. By that means they contrived to hurl by night.

"All games, which used to be played at fairs and merry-makings, were there carried on. Still, great part of the small folks diverted themselves in parading up and down, on the green, between the standings and dancing-ground, examining the pretty things displayed. They didn't seem to have any money amongst them to buy anything, yet they often bartered their trinkets and changed them from stall to stall.

"The old woman determined to have some of the pretty things glistening before her, but, among so much that was beautiful, she couldn't make up her mind what to take. Whilst An' Pee was considering, she saw approach the standing a little lady, tired with dancing, leaning her head on her partner, who with his arm round her waist supported her steps. The gentleman taking from the hands of a little dame who kept the stall a golden goblet of the size and shape of a poppy head (capsule) held it to the faint lady's lips. Sipping the contents she recovered in an instant, and, choosing a fan, made of a few goldfinch feathers stuck into a pearl handle, her partner took a pair of diamond buckles from his knees and placed them on the standing by way of pledge. The little couple having tripped off again to the dance, An' Pee thought how well the bright little buckles would look, fixed as brooches, on her Sunday's cap-ribbon or in her neckatee, and determined to secure them at once, fearing they might be gone with the next small body that saw them.

"As there was nothing that she could so readily turn inside-out, and drop on them, as one of her gloves, which reached to her elbows, she drew off one, inside-out, and dropped it, as it seemed to her, right on the buckles. Her hand nearly touched them; but, in trying to grasp them under her glove, a palm of pins or needles, so small that she didn't notice them, stuck into her fingers, and she cried out, 'Oh! Cuss 'e! You little buccas.' That instant all the lights went out, and all the fair, and most of the small people, vanished like shadows among the rocks or sunk into the earth, like muryans (ants) into their holes.

"Yet many of the frolicsome sprights were still about her, as she soon found to her cost.

"Whilst she was still stooping, and groping for her glove and the buckles, she felt a great number of the small tribe—a score or more—leap on her back, neck, and head. At the same time others, tripping up her heels, laid her flat on the ground and rolled her over and over. More than once, when her face was uppermost, she caught a glimpse of Piskey, all in rags as usual, mounted on a year-old colt, his toes stuck in the mane, holding a rush in his hand to guide it. There he sat, putting on the smaller sprights to torment her, making a tee-hee-hee and haw-haw-haw, with his mouth open from ear to ear.

"When she spread out her arms and squeezed herself down, that they shouldn't turn her over, they would squeak and grunt in trying to lift her; but all her endeavours to hinder their game were of no use. Somehow or other over she went, and every time they turned her face downwards some of the small fry would jump on her back and there jig away with 'heel-and-toe' from her head to her feet. In the pitch and pass of their three-handed reels, it was who and who should get on her stays; the steel and whalebone in that, she supposed, served them as a springing-board. In the finishing off of their double shuffles they would leap more than three times their height, turn a summersault over each others' heads, and so make the pass. An' Pee twisted her head on one side, saw what they were at, and tried to beat them off with her stick, but they got it from her hand, laid it across her waist, and mounting on it astride, as many as could, bobbed up and down, singing,

'See-saw-see,
Lie still, old Peepan Pee.
See-saw-see,
Upon old Peepan Pee,
Who should better ride than we?
See-saw-see.'

"The old woman, not to be beaten with such imps, tossed back her feet to kick them off; then they held her legs doubled back and pulled off her shoes; some jumped up and balanced themselves on her upturned toes, whilst others pricked at, and tickled, the soles of her feet till she fell into fits of crying and laughing by turns.

"Pee was almost mad with their torment, when, by good luck, she remembered to have heard that the adder-charm was powerful to drive away all mischievous sprights. She had no sooner pronounced the words than they all fled screeching down the hill, Piskey galloping after; they left her lying on a bed of furze, near a large rock.

"She got on her feet, and, looking round, saw, by the starlight of a clear frosty morning, that the place to which she had been piskey-led was near the bottom of the Gump; that the level spot of green on which the small people held their fair, and carried on their games, was almost surrounded by high rocks, and was no larger over than the Green-court or walled garden in front of Pendeen house; yet, when the fair was on it, through the sprights' illusions, this green spot seemed like a three-acre field.

"An' Pee only found her stick. The basket, tied to her arm, was empty and broken to pieces. She paced the ground over and round, in hope of finding her hat and shoes, and above all her glove, and the precious buckles under it. Giving over at length her fruitless search, with the help of her stick she hobbled, barefooted and bare-headed, down the hill and reached Pendeen gate.

"'Now thank the powers,' said she, as she passed through it and slammed it behind her, 'I shall be a-bed and sleepan in a few minutes.'

"Though An' Pee knew that Piskey had played her many tricks that night, and she thought he might be still dogging her footsteps, yet she was so bewildered that, until too late, it never came into her head to turn some of her clothing inside out, and now, so near home, she defied him to lead her astray.

"Inside Pendeen gate there is one road leading to the mansion and another which goes down to the mill. Between them there were two or three acres of ground, which had probably never been cleared or cultivated, as there were several large rocks remaining on it and brakes of furze, seldom cut, because the old Squire, or his family, had stocked this piece of rough ground with fancy breeds of tame rabbits, and the wild ones which came among them from not being chased or shot at, became so tame that they continued their frisky gambols, without showing any signs of fear when persons passed near them; and, for the pleasure of seeing the bunnies sport, furze was allowed to grow here and there over great part of this ground.

"In passing to the house An' Pee avoided the stony road and walked on the green, because her poor bare feet were cut and sore.

"Now hundreds of times—drunk and sober—on the darkest nights she had gone along the grass beside the bridle-paths, without once missing her way to the Green-court gate. Yet, that Hallan Eve she, somehow, went too far from the road, got in on the grassy patches between the furze, and, before she knew that she had missed her way, found herself down by the mill-road. She followed up that track, and in making a new attempt to reach the house, she again got among the furze and wandered about on the patches of green between them for hours without coming to either road. Yet, as usual, with piskey-led persons the path appeared either before or close beside her, until, tired out, she lay down to wait for day and fell asleep.

"The Squire and all his household were very much concerned because of the old woman's absence, well knowing that no ordinary matter would keep her from home on the feasten tide. During the night the servants had been sent to the villages round, to inquire if anyone had seen her in Penzance or on the road, but no tidings were obtained of her. The Squire rose by break of day and called up his servants to hunt for her. In passing along the road towards the gate, only a few yards from the house, he heard somebody snoring in a brake of furze bordering on the path, and there he found his housekeeper very ragged and torn. Some say he discovered her by finding on the road her knitting-work, with the yarn hanging to it, and, by taking up the yarn, he went by it till he found the dame with some of the ball in her pocket. However that may be, he roused her with great difficulty, and, without opening her eyes, she said,

"'I wan't turn out to please anybody till I've had my morning nap; so go away, go, and shut my chamber door!'

"At length her master, having brought her to her senses, helped her up and asked what made her take up her lodgings on the cold ground?

"In passing slowly along, and stopping awhile at the Green-court gate, she told him of her mishaps.

"The Squire didn't think one half of what she said could be true; indeed he questioned whether she had been to Penzance at all, and thought it quite as likely that she had stayed tippling at the cove till near dark, starting for town, had missed her way, and, wandering over the Gump, had there, or where he found her, fallen asleep and dreamt great part of what she told him.

"'Belike Pee,' said the Squire, as she was about to go down the Green-court steps, 'what you took at the cove had something to do with rising the spirits you saw.'

"'Oh! you misbelieving man,' cried she, turning round, and holding towards him her uplifted hands, 'if I like a drop of good liquor to cheer my heart, now and then, I never took so much as to do me harm in all my born days; and, leave me tell 'e, that with all your learning, and doubting, you know but little about the 'small people.' There es more taking place in the region of spirits, as I've heard the parson say, than you can learn from your books, and for want of faith, I fear me you will never be enlightened. Yet as sure as my name is Penelope Tregeer, I seed, heard, and what is more I felt, all that I now tell 'e.'

"'Go in and sleep the spirits out of thy noddle, that thou mayest be in time to see about the feasten dinner,' said the Squire, as he turned away, and took his favourite morning's walk to the cove.

"When he came in, after a turn round the cliff and up by the mill, he found the old woman, never the worse for her journey, busy preparing the feasten fare, and the ladies and gentlemen of his family, and numerous visitors, at an early breakfast that they might have time to proceed to church in grand state on the feasten day."

PENDEEN OF OLD.

Capt. Peter, having taken a pull from the pewter pot, continued with—
"Believe me, comrades, Pendeen didn't then look wisht at feasten tides nor at any other time, when one saw, (and smelt, too), the sweet scent of turf-smoke that curled up from chimney stacks, which now look down sorrowfully on cold hearths; and one saw fair faces peering through the

casements, numbers of ladies and gentlemen walking about the garden alleys and courts of the old mansion, or when the cry of hounds and the winding of the horn echoeing through the house, called one and all to the hunt at early morn. And, I can but think," he continued, "how strangers visiting Pendeen for the first time, after riding over miles of open downs with scarce a dwelling in sight, must have been surprised when they caught the first glimpse of the noble old seat, which is only seen when close at hand, and the track of rich cultivated land between it and the sea; it must have appeared to them like a place raised by enchantment, as we hear of in old stories. And the old masons, who took pride in their art and did their work truly, were right to bestow such labour on the beautiful chimney stacks of the old mansion, because they are there first seen, and from parts where little else of the house is visible; and the first sight, like first love, is never forgotten, mates."

Capt. Peter paused, drained the pewter pot, which had stood foaming before him, handed it to the cheerful old landlady to be replenished, and took a smoke. A tinner, who sat by the fire knocking the ashes out of his pipe, said, whilst he cut up his roll-tobacco, rubbed it in the palm of his hand, and refilled:—

"I don't understand very well Capen what is meant by enchantment, only that it's something strange and wonderful. Now, to my mind, the greatest wonder about the place is the Vow. One end of it we know is within a few yards of the mansion, but no one knows where the other is to be found. Ef there be any truth in old traditions about that cavern, adit, fougou, or whatever it may be called, it runs for a great distance (some say miles), yet most people believe that the eastern end was once open at the cove. Others will have it that old tinners, who lived before part of the roof had fallen in, travelled in it for ten times the distance from the house to the cove, and burned more than a pound of candles without finding the end. They always returned frightened, and what they saw to scare them they could never be got to tell.

"Perhaps the Spirit of the Vow, that many have seen at the entrance, in the appearance of a tall lady, dressed in white, with a red rose in her mouth, at all seasons of the year, may take a more fearful form within the cavern.

"Who can tell," he continued, "but that money and treasures may have been secreted there in troublesome times of old, and I wonder why the Squire don't have the mystery about the Vow cleared up; there can't be much of the roof fallen in, and, for my part, I'd willingly give all my time, out of core for a month to help clear away the rubbish and take the venture upon shares."

"I am very much of thy mind, my dear," Capt. Peter replied, "Ef the Squire would give us leave we'd pitch cost as soon as the feast is over, and I don't think we should find there many spirits to frighten us away. I believe that many of the fearful stories about the Vow were invented by smugglers. When the fair trade was in its glory the Vow was a convenient place for storage, and I think that the smugglers, who didn't want any faint hearts, with weak heads and long tongues, to come near them, invented many fearful stories to scare such away. One never finds any so fond of prying into other people's business as the foolish ones, or 'Grammer's weak children,' as we say."

How Piskey Left Boslow.

Tells how the drudging goblin sweat
To earn his cream bowl duly set,
When in one night, ere glimpse of morn,
His shadowy flail hath thresh'd the corn.

MILTON.

"No doubt," said the tinner after a pause, "Piskey threshed the corn and did other odd jobs for the old man of Boslow, as long as he lived, and they said that after his death he worked some time for the old widow, till he took his departure from the place about three score years ago. Some say"—

"Stop a minute, my son, I can tell 'e a story about that," said Capt. Peter, taking the pipe from his mouth, and holding up his finger:—"One night, when the hills were covered with snow and winter had come severely, the old widow of Boslow left in the barn for Piskey a larger bowl than usual of gerty milk (boiled milk, thickened with pillas, or oatmeal). Being clear moonlight she took a turn round the town-place, stopped at the barn-door, and looked in to see if Piskey were come to eat his supper while it was hot. The moonlight shone through a little window right on the barn-boards, and there, sitting on a sheaf of oats, she saw Piskey eating his gerty milk very hearty. He soon emptied his wooden bowl, and scraped it with the wooden spoon as clean as if it had been washed out. Having placed the 'temberan dish and spoon' in a corner, he stood up and patted and stroked his stomach, and smacked his lips in a way that was as much as to say, 'that's good of 'e old dear; see ef I don't thresh well for 'e to-night.' But when Piskey turned round, the old woman was sorry to see that he had nothing on but rags and a very little of them.

"'How poor Piskey must suffer with the cold,' she thought and said to herself, 'to pass great part of his time out among the rushes in the boggy moors or on the downs with this weather—his legs all naked, and a very holey breeches. I'll pitch about it at once, and make the poor fellow a good warm suit of home-spun. We all know ragged as Piskey es, he's so proud that he won't wear cast-off clothes, or else he should have some of my dear old man's—the Lord rest him.'

"No sooner thought than she begun; and, in a day or two, made a coat and breeches, knitted a pair of long sheep's-black stockings, with garters, and a nightcap, knitted too.

"When night came the old woman placed Piskey's new clothes, and a bowl of gerty milk on the barn-boards, where the moonlight would shine on them to show them best. A few minutes after leaving the barn she came back to the door, opened its upper part a little, and, looking in, saw Piskey standing up, eating his milk, and squinting at the clothes at the same time. Laying down his empty bowl he took the new breeches on the tip of his hand-staff, carried it to the window, and seeing what it was, put it on over his rags, dragged on the stockings, and gartered them, donned coat and cap, then jumped over the barn-boards, and capered round the barn, like a fellow light in the head, singing,

"'Piskey fine and Piskey gay,
Piskey now will run away.'

"And, sure enow, run away he did; for when he came round to the door opening into the mowhay he bolted out and took himself off without as much as saying, 'I wish 'e well 'till I see again' to the old woman, who stood outside the other door looking at am. Piskey never came back and the old woman of Boslow died that winter."

AN OVERSEER AND A PARISH CLERK OF ST. JUST
ABOUT SIXTY YEARS AGO.

"It was no wonder if persons coming from Penzance to Pendeen of a dark night should miss their way and think themselves piskey-led," said the tinner.

"There was neither bridge nor house in the place called New Bridge before wheel carriages were in use, and the only St. Just road from Penzance this side of Cardew Water was a mere bridle-path or rather a great number of horse tracks, often crossing each other and twisting about far and wide round rocks and intervening patches of furze, over miles of open downs and boggy moors, with no hedges near the road to keep it within bounds. When one track was worn too deep it was never repaired, as there was plenty of room to make a new one. Bridges then were few, and for the most part made by placing flat slabs to rest on the stepping-stones in some of the deepest streams, for the convenience of foot passengers. These old foot-bridges were ugly things to cross by night and the stepping-stones were worse."

"We have all heard about the old stepping-stones in Nancherrow Water," said the tinner, who finished the foregoing story, "how, after day-down, no one could pass over them in going to Church-town without some mishap, and no person would venture to return that way until daybreak. Shortly before the first bridge was built there, one of the overseers was a farmer who lived in the North of St. Just. Few persons then could either write or read, except one here and there, who passed for a great scholar if he could sign his name and read a chapter in the Psalter without much spelling. The overseer not knowing how to write or cipher, kept the accounts of his monthly disbursements on the dairy-door, in round o's for shillings and long chalks for pence. The last Saturday of each month he took the dairy-door on his back and carried it to Church-town, that the clerk might enter his accounts in the parish book.

"One Saturday, in the season when days are short and streams high, the overseer couldn't make out his accounts and reach Nancherrow Water before dark; and, in passing, with the door on his back, over the wet and slippery stones, he lost his balance, and fell into the stream. By good luck the door was under, and floated him down to a place where the water spread out shallow and there he landed, but all the accounts were washed out. 'Tis said that the overseer's mishap was the reason why the first bridge was built over Nancherrow Water."

"I can tell 'e another sad case," said the Capt. "We elderly folks have all heard of Uncle Will Ben, who was the parish clerk and the best fiddler in the parish, a little before I was born, and everybody says he was what we call a 'peathy old fellow, with plenty of gumption.'

"One Feasten Monday Uncle Will was rather late in going to Church-town with his fiddle, in a case, under his arm, to play during the night in a public house. Being Feasten Monday, like enough he had stopped to take a drop at neighbours' houses on the road; however, in crossing Nancherrow Water, his foot slipped from the stepping-stones and his fiddle fell from under his arm into the water, floated down the stream and in under a high bank where it was caught in some brambles. A gentleman riding through the water, saw Uncle Will a little below trying to get at something with his stick, and asked what was the matter. Uncle Will told him of his mishap. 'I pity your case,' the horseman replied, and rode on.

"'I don't care a cuss for the case if I'd only got my fiddle,' replied Uncle Will.

"This gave rise to the saying which is still often heard, 'I don't care a cuss for the case, if I'd only got the fiddle,' as Uncle Will Ben said.

"This old jewel of a parish clerk and fiddler said many other things which are still remembered and used as every-day sayings.

"It was the custom then for the great farmers to invite the parson and clerk to supper on goolthise (harvest-home) day, and the sexton usually came to work and see his reverend master safe home. Often all three came in time to lend a hand about the corn carrying. If two farmers had their goolthise on the same day the parson and sexton favoured one and the clerk the other. It happened, one day, when Uncle Will came alone early in the morning to help, and to enjoy the feast, that the weather was very lowering, and such was the fear of rain coming before the corn was in ricks, and thatched, that the carrying was continued all day for dear life, without stopping to take any other breakfast or dinner than such snacks as the corn carriers could catch, when there were more trusses round the ricks than the builders could put away for some time. The corn was then, except on a few large farms where ox-wains were just coming into use, all carried on the horses' backs, and the chasers, as they called the leaders who kept the trusses steady on the horses, were fond of coming in together that they might have a race back to the field, made the mowers work very irregular; it was gallop and stop half the time. That day, however, all worked with such a will that the corn was in and thatched in good time before the rain came.

"The supper being served, the clerk, in the absence of the parson, was asked to say grace. Uncle Will hesitated a moment; then, rising, he said, 'Thank God we have carried all the corn and had very fine weather; so here's grace for breakfast, dinner, and supper together.'

"Yet what is usually known as Uncle Will Ben's grace, is, 'God bless the meat and now let's eat!'

"Another saying accredited to Uncle Will—that 'Job had patience, but Job never had such a splat of black petates in his life'—is owing to An' Mary, his wife, having been a parson's daughter from upwards, and 'brought up like a lady' as he was fond of saying sometimes. When Will was a young and smart militia man, and An' Mary a girl in her teens, he fell in love with her and she fell in love with him, and came with him to St. Just. In their time potatoes were just coming into use; gentlemen and some farmers planted a few in their gardens as a curious vegetable to be used on extraordinary occasions. Will Ben, not to be behind the fashion, had a small spot planted in his garden. When his potatoes were high enough for hoeing Will told his wife Mary, who kept the garden in order, to hoe the 'splat of petates,' and be sure to hoe them clean. When William came in from his work in the fields, he said, 'Well Mary, hast a hoed the petates?' 'Yes, William dear, and hoed them nice and clean; just go out and look at them whilst I take up the supper.' 'William dear' went into the garden, but he saw no potatoe-plants, for Mary had cut them all out of the ground, not knowing them from weeds. 'Dear William' came in swearing on his wife for hoeing up all the precious petates, telling her that it had been ten times better for him if he had wedded the sexton's dafter, as she would have made a better farmer's wife. An' Mary (who, as I have heard say, was always a dear gentle soul) only replied, 'Sweet William, have patience and they will grow again. Remember Job, William dear, and think, cheeld vean, how he had patience.'

"'Oh! d———n Job,' replied sweet William, 'don't tell me about Job. Job never had such a splat of black petates in his life!'

"And now, my dears," said Capt. Peter, holding up a pot of foaming ale, "here's health and luck to 'e all, my hearties, and a merry Feasten-tide to 'one and all.' There's no sense in being miserable, and, for my part, old as I am, I'd go ten miles this night to dance to the music of as good a fiddler and as honest a man as Uncle Will Ben."

THE FAIRY MASTER, OR BOB O' THE CARN.

Out steps some Faery, with quick motion,
And tells him wonders of some flowrie vale.

MARSTON.

JUST fifty years ago, one Tom Treva lived on a small lone tenement near the foot of Carn Kenidjack hill. He had a large family and disliked for any of them to go in service. The boys, as they grew up, worked in the mines, and helped about the tillage of their few acres of crofts 'out of core.' The eldest daughter, Grace, remained at home to assist her mother, who took pride in making her handy in doing all such simple work as was required in their humble household. But as it was hard for them to make both ends meet, the poor girl had no best clothes except such as were made out of old gowns which had belonged to her grandmother. These were very gay, to be sure, yet so old-fashioned that other maidens, who worked at the mines and procured more modish dresses, wouldn't be seen anywhere from home with Grace and her grammer's old gowns. She didn't much mind their company, however. Her mother and 'the boys' (her brothers) promised her, year after year, that against the next Feasten-tide, if they could only lay by a few shillings, they would buy her as smart a rig-out as any of the proud hussies could show. But, with so many mouths to be fed, it was hard for them to save a farthing. So tides came and went, and Grace "had nothing for bettermost wear that was fit to be seen in Church-town or anywhere else from home," so the bal-maidens said, and they "wouldn't be seen going to preaching or to games with her;" yet she didn't mind it much, and seemed contented enough to stay at home, in the evenings listening to old stories related by her father and others who gathered round his hearth, because they, too, were not rich or smart enow to follow the fashions then upsetting all old customs among such Santusters as 'got a sturt to bal.' Grace would go about her work, indoors and out, singing like a lark. She was nearly sixteen, when a cousin of about her own age, who had been away only a year in farmer's service, a few miles off, came to see them the next Feast, dressed out quite like a lady, to Grace's seeming; for she wore a blue shining dress and earrings, and necklaces of red, green, and yellow beads that she changed more than once a day, or wore them altogether, while the flowers in her bonnet were the admiration of all beholders.

"I should be glad, cousin Grace," said she, "to put thee up to Church-town to the fiddler a Monday night, and wish I had only brought home one of my frocks for thee to wear; but really, cheeld, grammer's old gowns would make thee a laughing-stock to the youngsters, and not one of them would dance with us. Go thee way'st in service, cheeld, that thee may'st get a stock of clothes fit to be seen in, and a sweetheart that thee west soon want to have as well as other maidens! But the Lord help thee and the young fellow who would come a courting and take thee to Morvah Fair even in that old rorey-torey gown, with red and blue flowers so large that the birds are nesting in them."

Grace became very dissatisfied after this vision of grandeur, and never gave her mother any peace till she consented for her to go in service next summer. She was the more ready to let Grace try her fortune away, as other daughters were growing up to help her. So, during winter, she and her mother spun and knitted for dear life that they might earn a few extra shillings to provide changes of under clothing against she set out to look for service.

For weeks Grace had been going round saying good-bye to the neighbours, and she rose one fine morning and gave the last kiss, and said, "I wish 'e well, for the last time," to all the family round. Her father, on parting, charged her not to go more than a day's journey from home, and be sure to keep far away from Penzance or any town, for fear she should be kidnapped, and they should nevermore see her. He told her how strange sailors, that frequented such places, often prowled about for miles, and no maiden was safe within their reach. Grace promised to be on her guard, took her fardel, and started on her journey towards the southern parishes where gentlemen farmers lived.

On her way she thought upon what her smart cousin had told her to go over to the other side of the country, get into good farmer's service, where she might soon qualify herself to live in a gentleman's house and get higher wages. She had advised her not to pay much heed to what old folks said in their fears, about conjurors, witches, small people, and such like, that are seldom met with now-a-days. "Up here amongst the hills you know but little of the world," said the cousin, "and your old drolls arn't altogether to be believed." Grace couldn't help going out of her way a little to take a last look of Carn Kenidjack, where she had passed many happy hours, for youngsters were accustomed to meet there of Sunday afternoons to play about amongst the rocks or listen to old folks' stories. Then she went on with a pretty good heart till she reached high ground, from which she could only just see the smoke curling over the house-tops below. She turned round, took a farewell look, her eyes blinded with tears; then she went a little farther and sat down on a rock by the road-side, to have a good cry and ease her heart.

She wept aloud to think she was going to an unknown country to live amongst strangers—that she might nevermore behold her parents and old playmates. But still, determined to go on, even if she went as far as daylight would take her, she dried her eyes with her apron; and, looking up, she saw standing close beside her a very nice-looking gentleman. He wished her good morrow and asked why she wept.

"Oh, sir, I have left home," she replied, "and am on the road to a strange country to look for service."

"Well now, good luck has directed me," said he, "for, hearing there were tidy girls up this way, I started early this morning and am come so far to seek one that might take care of my house and little son, and a nicer maid than you one needn't wish to find. Indeed you look as fresh as a rose in morning dew."

He then sat on the rock beside Grace and told her that he was left a widower with one little boy, who had nobody but an old great-aunt to look after him; there was little else to do but the dairy-work after one cow, and a few poultry to take care of. "Come along home with me, Grace," said he, rising and taking up her bundle, "you can but try, and shall stay with me, if you don't like it, till you hear of some other place that may suit 'e better."

Grace wondered how he came there, for she hadn't seen him coming over the downs; and was surprised that he knew her name. Yet she said nothing, because her mother had often told her not to ask questions but to use her ears and eyes to learn.

The gentleman looked so handsome and spoke so kind, that, without hesitation, she went on with him and related how her parents had a large family, that her mother had taught her dairy-work, to cook in a plain way, and to spin and knit. "You will do, I'm sure," said he, "and if you had time to spare I suppose you wouldn't mind helping me weed the garden or pick fruit in the orchard."

"There's nothing I should like better," she replied, "for the work about one cow and a child can't be much."

He told her that his name was Robin, though most of his acquaintance called him Bob o' the Carn, or Bobby Carn.

In such like talk they went on, down hill, towards the Low Countries; and Grace, with her eyes fixed on her companion, didn't notice their road, and that for some time they had been walking through green lanes, hedged with trees; honey-suckles, and such sweet flowers as she had never seen hung over head. The gentleman remarking her surprise, said, "These trees and flowers are nothing to what you will see, ere long, where I dwell; but up in your high country no trees and but few flowers grow; that's how you think these so wonderful."

Over a while they came in sight of a large house; "Oh, sir, es that a king's palace?" demanded she, "and see, the trees around it are higher than church towers!"

"No, my child, there's many such dwellings down this way, and even larger ones, but no kings reside here," answered he.

Grace hadn't ceased wondering at the grand building when they came to where four roads met, and kept straight on, still going down hill, all amidst spreading trees which shaded the road by the side of which were rills of clear water, that every here and there sunk into the grass and re-appeared. Where streams crossed their road Grace's companion lifted her over them that she mightn't even wet her foot.

She had no notion of the distance they had gone, for he gave her cake and cordials ever so often, and talked so pleasantly that the time seemed as nothing, and she would have gone on with him to the world's end.

At length they came out of the wood near a river and she saw it was nearly sunset. "We are now all but come to my dwelling," said her master. (We may as well call him so since she had made up her mind to live with him).

He bore her over the stepping-stones that crossed the river near the foot of a towering carn of grey rocks that rose amidst a wood close by the water side. They passed up by the river a little way and entered an orchard. Grace wondered at the trees, bending down with loads of red and yellow apples and many kinds of fruit that she had never before seen. By a winding alley they came to a green, all surrounded with blossoming trees and dotted over with curious beds of sweet flowers, most of them unknown to Grace, who, without perceiving that they left the garden, entered what looked like an arbour and found herself in her master's dwelling before she noticed it, hidden as it was by roses and flowering plants which spread over its walls and roof.

Yet the kitchen was light enough for her to see rows of pewter that shone like silver. A wood fire blazed on the hearth, though it was high summer time; and beside it, on a chimney-stool, sat a prim sour-looking old woman, knitting. She looked at Grace as if her eyes would bore holes through her, when the master said, "I'm come, Aunt Prudence, with a tidy maid that I had the good luck to meet on her way to look out for a place."

"I see thee art come, Robin," she replied, still keeping her eyes on Grace; "and it seems to me thee hast brought hither a young giglet that will use her tongue more than her hands! We shall see."

"So we shall," remarked he, rather affronted with Prue's remarks, "and when you have shown her what is to be done, you needn't take the trouble to come here often. And where's the boy?" he asked.

"Here I am, dadda!" exclaimed a little fellow, bounding in to kiss his father, who took him on his knee; and An' Prue, as was her wont, mumbled to herself "we shall see."

The boy from his size appeared no more than six or seven years old, but his face looked like a cunning old man's, and his eyes were uncommon sharp.

Grace looked from one to the other rather confused, when her master said, "My little Bob, here's a nurse for 'e, who will give ye your milk, wash your face, and anoint your eyes, just like your mother used to; I hope you will like her." "That I can't tell yet," said the urchin, eyeing Grace for all the world just like An' Prue, and he looked then almost as old. The master, however, without more palaver, placed on the board, bread, cheese, apples, honey, and other things, sat down, told Grace to do the same, and eat what she liked; and, that after milking-time she could cook a good savoury supper. She had never before tasted such nice white bread and other things; after making a hearty meal, she said, "I may as well pitch to." "Rest thee till milking-time," said An' Prue, "a new broom sweeps clean, faix," mumbled she, in taking another survey through her spectacles.

Over an hour or so Robin told Grace that she had only to take the pail, pass through the orchard into a meadow by the waterside, call "Pruit, Pruit," and the cow would come to her; she did as directed, and from amidst the trees came a beautiful white cow, which stood with her udder right over the bucket and showered down her milk, so that in a minute it was full and running over. Grace rose to fetch another vessel that the milk mightn't go to waste; but when she lifted the bucket, the cow lowed, and, before the maiden left the meadow, disappeared in the wood. Grace told her master how the cow was gone off with the best milk. "That pailful will do for the night," said he; "the cow is far away by this, but if at any time you wish to have more you may take two or three pails, and 'Daisy'—that's her name—will fill them all, but she won't wait for 'e to fetch more things." "She must be a jewel of a cow, for sure, and I'll have all the pans full to-morrow," thought Grace, as she strained the milk, and washed the strainer and bucket, and did other jobs so handy, that even the old dame looked less sour on her. The master went out to feed his horse—he had a beauty in the stable close at hand—and that while Prudence said, "Now mind, Grace, you must always put the child to bed by daylight, and as you sleep in the same room go 'e to bed then too; if your master be home, he can do without you; and should he be away, you need not wait up for his return; you are not to go into the spare rooms, nor to meddle with what don't concern 'e; nor ask any questions, except about your work, and then I'll tell 'e as much as you are required to know. And let me warn 'e, that if you enter your master's private room, you will rue the day as long as you live. In the mornings rise with the sun; take the child to a spring, that he can show 'e, wash him well and then anoint his eyes with this ointment," continued she, in showing Grace a small ivory box of a greenish unguent, that she took from the cupboard; "a bit, the size of a pin's head or less, is enow to be put in the corner of each eye. Then milk 'Daisy,' and give the child this bowlfull and no more," said she, showing Grace a china-basin that would contain a pint or so; "make flowery-milk for breakfast, and when the breakfast things are washed away, scald the evening's milk, and clean up the house."

Just as the precise dame had finished her instructions, the master came in and said, "I think it's high time for 'e to go home, An' Prue, whilst there's daylight for 'e to find your way across the water." "My room is more welcome than my company," mumbled she, in hobbling out; "but we shall see how they will get on without me to keep them to stays."

Grace told her master that she wasn't used to go to bed so early; he answered, "please yourself on that score, and stay up as long as you mind to." He then brought her a basket of fruit, and told her to eat what she pleased of them; afterwards, he gave her a cup of cordial that she found delicious; and by the time she had drunk it to the last drop, she forgot her home and playmates among the hills; her brothers and sisters, her father and mother even; she no more remembered her former state, and only thought of her kind master and the delightful place in which he lived; and she dreamt that night of nothing else.

In the morning Grace was up betimes; finished her work in a hour or so, and 'looked over her shoulder for more,' when An' Prue came in, examined the house, and seeing nothing to find fault with, she merely said, "A new broom sweeps clean, but an old one es good for the corners," and told Grace she might work in the garden for an hour or so, till time to get dinner, if she had a mind to, that her master was there and he would show her what to do.

Prudence returned to her dwelling, where she kept a school; and Grace, glad to escape the old dame's piercing eyes, went into the garden to look upon the more pleasing countenance of her master, who said, "You have made a good beginning, cheeld, only hold to it, and we shall get on very well; come now and help me weed a flower-bed, that I may show 'e what to pull up and what to let grow." She weeded so handy and minded her master's instructions so well, that he, to show his satisfaction, when a bed was finished, clasped her in his arms and kissed her, saying, "I can't tell 'e any other way how well pleased I am at your handy work." She redoubled her efforts to please him that he might again show his satisfaction.

Time passed so pleasantly in the beautiful garden—which Grace thought must be like Paradise—that they forgot the dinner hour, till the boy came home from school and ran out into the garden, shouting, "Dadda! Dadda! I want my dinner; An' Prue always had it ready in time." "Run in my good girl," said his father; "give him bread and honey with milk to drink, or anything to stop his squalling, we can have apple-pie; pick a few of the ripest from yonder tree."

Having given Bob his dinner, Grace gathered such golden apples as she never beheld till then, indeed, she thought them too rich to cook, and that their perfume was enough to satisfy one, for roses and gilly-flowers were less sweet to her seeming.

Dinner over and Bob sent to school, master and maid passed a pleasant afternoon in the garden gathering fruit. Prudence, having sent her scholars home, took a nap, for she had talked herself sleepy over the horn-book. She soon waked up, however, and hurried over to find that Grace had gone a milking, and Robin was in a quillet (paddock), near by, grooming his horse. Seeing all about the house in apple-pie order, she looked rather sour, for the crabbed dame dearly liked to spy faults; that's how she was so much disliked by Grace; so without a word to anyone in the garden-dwelling, she tucked up her skirts and picked her way back to her own house, mumbling, "It seems my room es more welcome than my company, but we shall see how long they will get on without my advice."

Grace found her new life so pleasant that she took no count of time; months passed like a summer's day; she never thought of her old home or people, for all her care was to please her agreeable master. Of a morning he frequently rode away through the wood dressed like a gentleman going a hunting; and Grace took delight to keep his boots polished, and to buckle on his silver spurs that she might see him mount and ride away in gallant style. Grace always wondered where her master got out of the wood; she had gone a long way on the road he took, but saw no end of the winding, shady, alleys.

He always told her to be sure not to leave his grounds; on no account to venture outside the orchard gate during his absence; and, for her life, not to go near the high rock, for at its foot—hidden by thickets—there was a low hole, from which Bucca-dhus often issued, and carried away people who were nevermore seen here. One afternoon, however, when Robin was away and the boy at school, Grace felt weary of being so long alone or with only the poultry—that followed her everywhere about the place,—and went to the outer gate. On seeing a pleasant walk winding along by the waterside, where all was shady and quiet, she passed out and down the road till near the high rocks; she wondered whither the bowery path led; thought she heard the sea murmuring, and had a mind to go farther on, when all her thoughts were put to flight by hearing a voice say, "Stop there, my sweet pretty maid; I'll soon be down by the river-side and give thee a diamond ring." Looking up towards the place whence the voice came, she saw, on the topmost stone, a dark man dressed like a sailor, who then made signs for her to pass farther down the road. Grace hastened in, followed by the screaming hens, which roused the dogs, and their barking alarmed An' Prudence, who hurried over, gave her a good scolding, threatened to tell Robin how, by her gadding about, she had narrowly escaped being carried away. As Grace was still uneasy from fear, she waited up for her master and made a pie; he seemed well pleased to have a hot one for his supper, and the girl to pull off his boots; seeing her disturbed, he asked what was the matter; she confessed her fault with tears, and promised never to disobey him again. "I'll let it pass," said he, "as it's the first time you have disobeyed;" and, to assure her of his forgiveness, he treated her to a cordial that produced sweet sleep and pleasant dreams.

Grace finding her master well pleased that she had waited up for him, continued to do so in spite of all An' Prudence told her. "Now since thou hast again scorned my counsel, I'll leave thee to thy devices," said she, one day; "as if Robin wanted thee, forsooth, to unbuckle his spurs or pull off his riding boots, and to cook him a supper that he is better without."

Contrary to the austere dame's advice, Grace continued to take her own way, and her master seemed pleased; she wanted for nothing, yet she was always saying to herself, "Whatever can be in that locked-up parlour and the chambers that I am forbidden to enter?" At last, from always thinking about what didn't at all concern her, the fool—she couldn't rest by night or by day. One afternoon whilst An' Prue was cleaning up the parlour,—not thinking Grace was near,—she suddenly went out and left the door ajar; that instant the curious maiden peeped in, and spying lots of rare pretty things, she stepped over the drussel, and saw what she took to be conjuring implements, and trembled to behold—on shelves, in cupboards, and elsewhere about the room—men's heads, and heads and shoulders without arms; over the fire-place there were even whole bodies of small ones, all turned to stone; they were whiter than corpses and quite naked, like what she had heard of in old folks' stories as being done by enchantment; she didn't stay to notice much more and was leaving the room backwards when the old dame, coming behind, thumped her head and exclaimed, "Now thou perverse strollop since thou hast entered the forbidden room to thy cost, thou shalt work in it for a punishment; so take the waxed cloth and rub up that piece of furniture," continued she, in pointing to a long dark chest, that looked to Grace like a coffin resting on a table-frame, "Rub, rub away, rub harder and quicker till thou canst see thy poking nose in it, and stop thy whimperan or I'll crack thy numbscull." Grace burst out crying but still rubbed away so hard that she lifted the article off its legs or its frame, and, falling back with a jerk, something within it gave out a doleful sound so like a dying groan that she,— thinking it must be the voice of a spirit or of an enchanted body confined therein—was overcome with fright and fell down in a fit.

Prudence fearing for the consequences, pulled her out by the heels in great haste but not before Robin was informed, by a wailing from the chest or coffin, that something had gone wrong in his private apartment. When Grace came to her senses he said to her, "Ignorant chit thou art become so froward as not to regard Aunt Prudence in anything; this is thy second act of disobedience, for the third there's no forgiveness, and if thou any more seekest to gratify thy troublesome curiosity against my desire thou wilt have to get a new place, so beware."

After this it was many days ere Grace's master sang to her or played with her again, as was his wont, and she redoubled her efforts to please him and show her regret till he again kissed her to prove that the past was forgiven.

A sight of the forbidden appartment, however, only served to make Grace more dissatisfied because she couldn't understand all the mysteries of the place and its inmates. She noticed that the boy looked very knowing for one of his age, and thinking that by means of the ointment he saw things invisible to her, she resolved to try its effects; and, one morning, when her master had gone away, she took double the quantity used daily for Bob's eyes and rubbed them on her own; it made them smart so much that she thought them to be turning inside out or bursting from her head.

To ease their burning pain she ran down and washed them in the pool. Looking into the water—a minute after—when her eyes ceased smarting a little, she saw there, deep down, what looked like another world with trees, birds, and people in great numbers; the people were so small that many of them perched themselves on branches amongst the birds. Yet what surprised her most was to see her master below moving from place to place among them; he was here, there, and everywhere. Being somewhat frightened she left the pool and soon after, on looking around the orchard, there, too, she saw small people and amongst them her master dressed in his hunting-suit. "Now I know for sure that this is an enchanted place," said she to herself, "my handsome master must be a conjuror, and in spite of their fern-seed I shall soon discover more."

Grace passed that day very uneasy and in the evening Robin came home with several strange people bearing baskets of cakes and other dainties such as she had never before seen; these being placed away Robin told her to put the boy to bed and that she wasn't wanted below stairs any more for that night.

The dissatisfied maid went to bed but not to sleep, for in a few hours she heard the ringing of cups and glasses with other sounds which made it known to her that a banquet was being held in the stone-people's apartment.

Over a while she heard singing and music there; the entry and staircase being dark she crept down, and peeping through the partly open door, saw two smart gentlemen, besides her master, and three ladies dressed in white trimmed with green. In their ears, round their necks, and on their arms, the ladies wore diamonds that shone like stars; but most of her attention was drawn to a fair haired one who sat beside the long box or coffin, and, by thumping on it with both hands for dear life she made the body or spirit within it give out finer music than a dozen fiddlers all in a row could make with their fiddles playing altogether, so she said.

From her dark corner she listened and watched till the music ceased and the company rose to depart; then, from her chamber window, she spied Robin in the garden kiss the ladies all round, on taking leave.

Grace cried herself asleep, but for why she couldn't tell.

In the morning she found the parlour door locked, and seeing glasses, china, and other things, on the kitchen table, she washed and placed them on their shelves, and did her morning work; when her master came in and, seeing all in order, said she was a good girl, put his arm around her and was going to show his satisfaction in his usual way. But she repulsed him saying, "Go and kiss your little white and green ladies; you shall touch me no more; for you arn't of common human kind, but a changeling small-body that for nine years at a time can appear as such; yet with all your fern-seed none of 'e can deceive me any longer by your enchantment and what not."

"Hold thy foolish clack thou silly girl," said he, "thy head is turned with old folks' drolls; there's nothing uncommon here, 'tis only thy ignorance that makes thee think so. But I see," he continued with a stern air, "that thou hast rubbed thy eyes with the green ointment, and now as I find that nothing can lay thy impertinent curiosity, or check thy prying into what don't concern thee, we must part. Thy last year will be ended to-morrow, so prepare at once to leave early in the morning, and I will take thee behind me on horseback over the hills to the place in which I found thee, for thou wilt never be able to find the way back alone."

Seeing that all her promises of amendment were of no avail, and that Robin and Prudence—who was now reinstated—determined on her departure, Grace with much grief packed up her fardel, and from what her master and old sour Prudence had given her, from time to time, she had a good stock of clothing. She didn't know what wages was due to her, poor fool, nor how long she had lived there, for years had passed like a summer's day, until she longed to know too much. She was almost heart broken to leave the flowers that she loved like living things, the poultry she had reared, the pigeons that nested over the wood-corner ate from her hand and followed her over the place; the rabbits and hares that played about the garden and in the house; above all she grieved to part with a tame robin that kept in the dwelling and sang whenever she entered it.

Besides it fretted her to find that old sour Prudence was brought back to be mistress of Robin's garden-dwelling.

The discreet dame, however, not knowing what might turn up, took care to keep Chypons—as the place in which she resided was called. She was very proud of her snug habitation, because, a little below the carn, a foot-bridge crossed the stream close by her house and nobody lived so near it as to interfere with her wise management.

At daybreak she crossed the river and went on as her master had directed her; he soon overtook her, and placing her on a pillion behind him, they cantered away through dark lanes for miles, going up hill all the time, and Robin spoke not a word. Grace, blinded with tears, saw nothing of the road till they came up into broad daylight and an open country. Still the horse went like the wind, and in a few minutes she saw Carn Kenidjack.

Robin stopped his horse, sprung from his saddle, lifted Grace down and placed her on the rock from which he had fetched her. In answer to her entreaties to be taken home with him again, he only said, "Prudence and I shall try to get on without other help, yet if we can't I may come for 'e again." Grace mounted the rock and looked after him as he rode away, but in a few minutes he was out of sight. She lay on the heath and wept till near night ere she arose, slowly descended the downs, and reached her parents' dwelling.

The old folks were much surprised to behold her as they had given her up for lost or dead long ago. Her mother, however, in welcoming her home, lost no time before she opened her bundle, and found enough good clothes to last a lifetime, and amongst them a bag containing more money than they had ever seen before.

Grace's story seemed strange to all the neighbours, but most of the elderly ones concluded from all she told them that one of the changeling small people had taken her away to his underground dwelling or into his habitation in a wood—as such places used to be their common haunts—and there she had lived with him nine years that seemed less than one to her.

She could no more endure her old home—and, showing but little regard for its inmates, loathed their homely fare and old fashioned ways. Neither could she make up her mind to work steadily as of old, but like one distraught wandered away almost every day to the rock where she had first and last seen Robin of the Carn. She took but little pride in her fine clothes and money, and people thought she would go mad or fret herself to death. Yet, in a little less than two years, which seemed eternal to Grace, a neighbour's wife died leaving several small children; the widower came a courting to the distracted maiden, and, pushed his suit so vigorously, that at length she married him, and, as it happened, her husband had no cause to regret his venture, for the care of his children and plenty of work so far cured her vagaries, that in a few years she almost forgot and little regretted her life with Robin of the Carn.

Grace may be still living; it is only a few years since we were told her story, and then she was a hale old woman with a numerous brood of grandchildren.

There is a similar story told in Zennor of one Cherry who left home to seek service in the low country parishes, and was met on Lady Downs by a fairy gentleman, a widower, who took her to live with him; all went well, till, from curiosity, she disobeyed his orders and was discharged, but not until she had become so much attached to her fairy master that she died with grief on being taken back to her old home.

Though 'modern instances' make up these stories, we have many old fragmentary fairy tales that contain the same fancies; the loss of happiness through inordinate curiosity.

A TINNER'S FIRESIDE STORIES.

THE KNOCKERS OF BALLOWAL.

Blest be that spot, where cheerful guests retire,
To pause from toil, and trim their evening fire.

GOLDSMITH.

A FEW years ago, in talking with a Lelant miner about the sprites that haunt many old mines, he told us the following story, which we give in his own words, as an example of West Country dialect.

We wish to correct an error that many persons, not Cornish, entertain with regard to the language of Cornish working people. Their mistake originates, in many instances, from seeing in stories—misnamed Cornish, and for the most part written by strangers to the country—such an uncouth jargon, put into the mouths of West Country folks, which is no more the common dialect of Cornwall than it is of Jericho. Our English will bear comparison with that of any rural district, and, in most cases, be found more correct, though somewhat antiquated. Many of our peculiar words, such as agricultural or mining terms, a few names of plants, &c., are genuine old Cornish.

"I know that strangers," said Uncle Bill, "and grand learned folks like our passen, don't believe in the sperats we cale knackers workan in the bals, and say that the noise, made by these old ghosts of tinners, is caused by water oazan out of a lode and drippen into a pit; as ef the water fallan from ever so high, could sound like hammer and boryer, or pick and showl (shovel) workan away. But, bless us, comrade, what can these strangers that come here—to instruct us, forsooth!—know about such things? Yet how they will talk about what they never heard of before they came among us, and say it es all su-per-sti-tion! Now that's a fine word, my dear, and I mean to use et on all occasions; like An' Betty Brea, up your way, who es twenty times a day askan 'Do 'e knaw the sig-ni-fi-ca-tion' of some fiddle-stick's end, or other, that she may use her one grand word, lately picked up from a local preacher.

"I've been minded lately of a story that was told me by an old comrade— Uncle Tom Trevorrow, who's many years older than I am. When I was a boy, workan at Trink Stamps, he was married; and he was then as fine a man as one would meet of a long summer's day. If you'll have patience enow I'll tell 'e the story of

TOM AND THE KNACKERS.

"Do let's have the droll, Uncle Bill," said I, and he related as follows,—

"From the time Tom was old enow to handle a pick and showl he had lived in Trecroben, and worked in Wheal Reath, till twenty years or so ago, when work fell slack here, and some bals were knacked (stopped). Then he went to Santust (St. Just) to look for a job and found work in Ballowal. Most people have heard of that queer old bal, that was worked before The Flood, they say. There the old men's works, weth their deep open coffans (pits) may still be seen, jest as they left them, only wash'd and run'd in a good deal one may suppose. That old bal, everybody in Santust will tell 'e, have always been haunted with knackers. And the burrows, in crofts and cleves around, are swarman with them, and weth spriggans, wherever anything belongan to the old bal was burred. There these sprites keep everlastan watch, though all the old men's tools or treasures may be gone to rust, earth, and dust. One don't often see them, 'tis true, but only break ground near them and they'll show their ugly faces, as many have known to their cost.

Tom and his eldest boy went over and worked a few weeks, to see how they liked the place and people before removing his wife and family. They liked the Santusters fust rate. They're a capital set of red-tailed drones—only give them their own way; but you will soon find out that one must either fight or be thorough friends with them 'one and all.' Tom took a house in Letcha—handy by the bal. When his family were moved, he and the boy worked together on tribute, and worked hard makan double cores. When it came near pay-day, the boy, for want of rest, gave out, and his father worked on alone.

Tom had heard the knackers workan, away at a distance, all the time he had been there, and took no notice of their noise, but now that the boy stopped home, they came nearer and nearer every day, till he cud hardly hear the sound of his own tools with the din and clatter of theirs. As far as he could judge by the sound they were only two or three yards off, in the level close behind him, carryen on all sorts of underground work. Some appear'd to be wheelan, some showlan, others boran; he could even hear them swab out their holes, put in the tampan, and shut (blast) like a pare (company) of regular tinners. Shuttan wasn't in vogue in their time, but they've learnt et.

One night—I think et was only two or three before servey-day—Tom got quite savage to hear their confoundan clatter, with their squeakan and tee-hee-an in a mockan way, if he made false strokes, or a clumsy blow; and, being a devil-may-care sort of fellow, he, without thinkan of anything, threw back a handful of small stones, towards the spot where they seemed to be workan, and called out at the same time without stopan or lookan up, 'Go to blazes, you cussed old Jews' sperrats; or I'll scat (knock) your brains out, I will, ef you arn't gone from here.' The words were no sooner out of his mouth than a shower of stones fell upon and around him, and frightened him most out of his senses. Still, Tom resolved to work on till mornan, and, in about an hour, when his candle was burnt down and he stopped to light another, he sat down to eat the rest of his fuggan and touch pipe a few minutes. Tom had all but finished his supper, and bean hungry, could have eat more, when he heard ever so many squeakan voices sing out, from away some fathoms back in the level,—

"Tom Trevorrow! Tom Trevorrow!
Leave some of thy fuggan for Bucca,
Or bad luck to thee, to-morrow!"

Fust of all he cudn't well make out any words, but his own name. He thought of the old sayan, 'What the fool thinketh, that the bell clinketh.' He knew that sounds heard underground often seemed to be words, like Buryan bells of a weddan day ringan, 'Poor man, undone!' or 'Go thee ways't home with ragget-tail Jone!' Then he tried again if they wern't as much like some old rhymes that children sing, such as,—

"Billy Pengelley,
Got pain in his belly,
Eatan green slones for supper!"

But no, the devil a bit; for the more and closer he listened the plainer he heard the knackers, or some other sprites among them singing the same. Only when he had eaten all there was a slight change and they sung,—

"Tommy Trevorrow, Tommy Trevorrow!
We'll send thee bad luck to-morrow,
Thou old curmudgeon, to eat all thy fuggan,
And not leave a didjan for Bucca!"

And so they kept on singan, squeakan, and tee-hee-an, in going back in the end till they were out of hearan. Tom was somewhat scared; yet he felt so tired and drowsey that he could sleep in a pullan (shallow pool). The poor fellow had worked hard and been at it nearly all day and all night for the last week. When he had smoked out his pipe he leant back, thinking to take a doze for only a few minutes. But when he waked up all was quiet. He rubbed his eyes, and, lookan away in an end, where it was nearly dark, he seed scores of knackers restan on their tools. They were miserable, little, old, withered, dried-up creatures—the tallest of them no more than three foot six, or there away, with shanks like drum-sticks, and their arms as long or longer than their legs. They had big ugly heads, with grey or red locks, squintan eyes, hook noses, and mouths from ear to ear. The faces of many were very much like the grim visages on old cloman jugs, so Tom said, and more like those of brutes than Christians. One older and uglier than the rest—if possible—seemed to take the lead in makan wry faces, and all sorts of mockan tricks. When he put his thumb to his nose and squinted at Tom, all those behind him did the same. Then all turned their backs, stooped down, lolled out their tongues, and grinned at him from between their spindle shanks. Tom was now much scared. He noticed that his candle was burnt down to the clay, and knew that he must have slept nearly two hours.

"Good Lord, deliver me," said he, risan to light another candle; and all the knackers vanished by the time he was well on his legs. They seemed to melt away, one into another, changan shapes like curlan smoke. Tom, feelan hisself very stiff, tired, and cold, from havan slept so long, dressed and mounted the ladders. He was hardly able to crawl to grass. In the blacksmith's shop, where he had stopped a few minutes to change and warm hisself, he told other men who were there, putten on their underground clothes, what he had seen and heard. The old tinners told am that they warn't at all surprised, because the levels he worked in were more infested with knackers than any other part of the bal. 'Many a night,' said they, 'these troublesome sperats have ben sen whiskan round the blacksmith's shop and gwean (going) down the Buckshaft, near by, and that do enter the level thee'st work in. This shaft es so called, because a black buck-goat, or a bucca in shape of an, was seen to go down there, but never found below.'

The tinners, one and all, blamed Tom for havan anything to do or say with the knackers in an unfriendly way, and told him that as et was an old custom he might as well have left a bit of bread on the ground for good luck.

When Tom got home he went to bed at once, that he might have a good rest. His wife fed and nussed him well, with the best she cud get for am to eat or drink, in high hopes that, before many days were passed, they would take up more an twenty pound for tin.

Tom dedn't say a word about the knackers to his wife nor boy, for fear to scare them, nor dedn't think much more of the buccas.

Next mornan Tom got up like a new one, fresh as a rose. After a hearty breakfast, he and his son started for bal. Now it happened to be Corpus Chris, and the boy was loath to go—he wanted to be off to Penzance, with other youngsters, to see the fun of the fair. "Come thee way'st along, my son," said Tom, "I know thee art still tired, but cheer up a bit; Midsummer's day will soon be here; then thee shust (shalt) have a shellan and, ef we get a good sturt (start), two or three, to go to the games, and, dash my buttons; ef I too don't go down to Priest Cove, and try a hitch at the wrestlan! I could used to show as good play, and throw as fair a fall, as any man of my size." And so Tom ded—he would often show me and others how to give the hugg, play with the back crook, and so furth.

I don't see for my part why wrestlan, hurlan, and other old manlike games should be allowed to die out for a set of sports more suitable for women than men, and I hold that wrestlan es as good as boxen, and every man should know how to defend hisself. One don't know what may turn up. 'Tes all stuff and nonsense what old women say about the wickedness of such sports. I'd rather see a boy of mine with black eyes and bloody nose every day, than for am to run from one of his size.

Arrivan at the bal, first thing on entering the level, Tom noticed that some of the temberan was bulged a great deal and ready to give way. They put in new planks, and, as Tom thought, made that all secure for the time. Whilst they were at it he again heard the knackers workan away in the end, but dedn't mind them. Then to get up some tin-stuff from below, they went to work in the adit level, on the Buck lode, to secure around and repair a winze (a small shaft with windlass) that was nearly all run'd in. Whilst he put in new tembar, the boy was kept at the winze-brace (windlass and tackle). When drivan the lafts or boards, Tom plainly heard the knackers workan against him; he had to put in new tembar in the manner of spillan. The ground seemed somewhat dangerous. The longer he was workan the nearer the knackers were coman towards him, until he saw the ground move before the lafts where the sperats worked; he then called to the boy, 'Pull me up, quick, wind away for dear life, my son!' By the time he was got up to the winze-braces, the ground began to tumble in. He had the rope tied around his body. Runnan back in the adit-level, he unwound it from the winze tree, and untied it from his waist.

Yet he came very near bean killed, for he hadn't got clear of the rope five seconds before winze, rope, and all, went down with the run. Tom, poor fellow, looked around dismayed, to find that all his tin-stuff, which was put on the winze plat, with tools and all, had gone down with the rest; so he lost his tin there and below. All his labour and time was gone for nothan.

He had to live many weeks on subsist (money advanced) and went to another lode to work in an end to tut-work (piece-work), and there, too, he was most put mad with the knackers—they wed come into the level close behind, and go on with all kinds of work, and nobody could have wes (worst) luck than followed am. He went to look so wisht and felt so bad that he had to leave Ballowal; for, go wherever he might about that old bal, the knackers were for ever tormenting am, till they fairly drove 'n away, and he came back to Lelant no better off than when he left.

And here he had still bad luck doggan am for years. He had to work to the farmers for a long spell, and, as we all know, every tinner would just as soon go to the workhouse, or union; and for my part I'd rather be tied to a bull's tail, and suffer the rest, than do either one."

Having refilled his pipe, my old neighbour continued:—

"As many bals were then stopped, and a number of hands discharged from others, all the time going from bad to worse, Tom had to live, as he cud, by farm-work for three or four years. He got all out of heart, to be all the time dung-dabban, and to see his children as ragged as colts; besides he had bad speed many ways; some said he was bewitched, and advised him to see the pellar, who came round once a fortnight. Tom thought that no use, because the conjuror won't 'good 'e,' as he do call it, unless he's well paid. Tom's wife made a good bit of money by spinnan and knittan. Unknown to her husband, she took her knittan-work, and went over to the high road, one day, when the pellar, in going his rounds, visited St. Ives. She hadn't ben long in the lane before he came by.

"I'm waitan to speak wh'y," said she; "but I'm afeard et wan't be any use, because we'r very poor."

"I know," replied he, "that you have had a long run of bad luck, and it will be all the harder now to turn it, but don't be out of hopes; I'll see Tom and do what I can for 'e. I see you're a good knitster; so you can make me a few pairs of warm stockans for winter's wear."

The conjuror remained alone with Tom a good while, each time he came round. What he did to 'good 'e' esn't known, because whatever's done to hinder a run of bad luck, or to break a spell of ill wishan, must be kept secret or no cure can be effected. In two or three months, however, Tom's fortune had a turn. Several youngsters left for America and made room for other hands. Then Tom, to his great content, went to minan-work again. In a short time, instead of looking as wisht, ragged, and dirty as 'Billy-be-damned,' or 'Old Jy,' who lived in a hole in a hedge, he and his family once more got decent meat and clothan. The pellar had the credit of doing them good, whether he deserved it or no; at any rate his promises put them in better heart, and that was some help. Tom's wife was overjoyed when he went to minan again; because she always took delight when her good man came home from bal to hear him tell her and the boys what he had done that core, and about his prospect of havan lots of tin agen next pay-day. The lads were most interested when Tom worked to tut-work, drivan an end, as you'll see.

An old boryer, hammer, gads, and other tools were kept under the chimney-stool, that Tom might show them the plainer what he'd ben doan. Now you must understand that Tom believed hisself to be as good a miner as was to be found in Cornwall. He would often brag that he cud break more ground at the same cost than any other man in the bal. His mind was always so occupied about his underground work that the form of his end was always before him. And most every night, after supper and whilst smokan his pipe, he wed work his core over again with Betty, and she, to humour him, would begin with, "Well, Tom, my son; and what hast a ben doan to-day?"

"What use for me to tell 'e; I can never make thee understand anything," he'd say; "but look here boys!" At the same time he wud take the fire-hook, stick, or anything, and, quite pleased, draw out the form of his end in the back of their old-fashioned, open chimney, and all would be told to look on, say nothan, and learn. When he had marked out, to his mind, how his end stood, he would say to his wife,

"Now thee cust see the end es about square as a was this mornan, take the boryer and show me where thee west go for a hole."

"Well, I shud put down a hole there," she wed say, pointan with the boryer in the most seemly place to her.

"Now gos't away, thou great Paddy! I tell thee, Betty, thee dosen't knaw any more about such work than a Buryan man! Thee west never larn anything! Give me the tools," he'd say, and show them all, with pride sure nuf, how he'd stand and strike the boryer in the different positions ground es subject to, and so he wed keep on for hours.

One day above all, whan they lived in Santust, Tom came home highly pleased, and told his people he had done a wonderful core. After supper he lighted his pipe, as usual, took up the fire-hook, and drawed the form of his end as he found it in the mornan.

"Now, I bored a hole there," said he, pointan with his hook, "and gauv en plenty of powder, and a ripped am forth and back like a boat-cove, and tore great rocks out of am as big as housen."

"Lor, Tom, hold thy tongue cheeld; I can hardly believe thee," said Betty.

"Well, a es truth what I do tell thee. Then—now look at this, Betty—I went there, for another hole," said he pointan, "and it tord'n like mad, and left am as square as a chest, all but a piece in the bottom. Then I went down there for a side-hole, and that end now es as square as a door, I tell thee. And now, Betty, the end es squared, where west thee go for the next hole? Here, take the tools to thee; es thy turn to show one a bit now; a es hard ground, mind, none of your farmers' men can break that."

"Well, I shud put down a hole there," said she, placan the hook in the most likly place. Then Tom, with a look and voice of great contempt wed say, "I told thee there was no wale (seam) there; thee may'st shut (blast) away a ton of powder in that hole and then a wedn't heav'n, a wed make a rouse (report) hard enow to frighten away all the chalks (choughs) in Carn Glase, and then a wedn't heav'n. I tell thee again, all of the powder that went down in the Royal George wed be no good in that hole. Thee must lev'n look down more—just so, or else a wed only be a stand to waste powder in."

And so the simple contented household wed pass night after night till bed-time.

But one evenan they nearly came to grief by Tom shuttan his holes over again. He came home late in a terrible splutter, sayan he had done a very bad core—he had shut a hole three times, and a blowed away in a vug (crevice) each time.

"Et was a hole near the bottom, Jan," said he, takan the hook as usual and havan drawn the position to his own satisfaction.

"But I shud think," said the boy, "that a was a hawful bad place to come to strike et, faather."

"Thou great noddy! Doesna know that a good man can bore a hole anywhere? Hold the hook there," said he, puttan it into his hands, "and I'll show thee how to strike 'n."

Tom turned round, snatched up the hammer in a great hurry, threw it back in order to make a stroke, knocked down Betty, missed the hook, and nearly broke Jan's arm.

Betty, though on the floor, screamed to see the boy's white face, and when she saw the blood running from his arm and felt it on her own face she fainted. And Tom, seeing them both on the floor, paced up and down calling out, when he tried to rise them, "Oh my dear Betty and Jan; I'd rather shut the hole twenty times over again than kill thee and the boy; rise up do 'e, my dears."

They soon got round. The fright was worse than their hurt.

The way in which Tom and his wife amused themselves is not singular among tinners, who, as a rule, take great pride in their work, and pass hours showing their family or comrades how they worked the last cores, and what they purpose to do next."

"Well, did Tom's good luck continue?" I asked.

"Pretty steadfast; he and his sons had neighbours' fare," the old tinner replied. "When his elder boys became men they had pretty good sturts (start from a paying tribute), saved money, and went to America, and they did so well over at Mineral Point, Galena, or somewhere that way, that they sent home enough to keep the old couple in comfort, and to bring the younger boys out to them, where they, with hundreds more from here about, are making another Cornwall for "one and all.""

OLD SONGS AND NICKNAMES.

"One would like to know," said I to the old tinner, "whether Tom heard the knackers sing what he believed he did; or if there were any old rhymes, somewhat similar, that he might, long before, have learnt and forgotten till something brought them to mind." "Never heard of any such," Bill replied. But An' Mary—who knew a rare lot of queer sayings, odds and ends of old songs and the like,—said, "In a story relating to small people (fairies), that I often heard when a child, there are some lines about leaving the buryans (crumbs) for Bucca." And one would think the tribe of small folks always made their speeches in rhymes. When I was young, it was a custom in the harvest-field, at crowst (afternoon's refreshment), observed by most old folks, to pour a few drops of their liquor on the ground for good luck; and to cast a fragment of bread over their right shoulder for the same reason. Fishermen, too, were in the habit of leaving on the sand, at night, a fish for Bucca; and they were also very careful to feed and make much of their cats, to insure them good luck in their fishing. If tinners in going to bal met with a 'bulhorn' (shell-snail) in their path, they always took care to drop before it a crum from their dinner, or a bit of grease from their candle for good luck.

Our talk about old rhymes reminds me that I have known many people who become little better than fools, because of childish verses and tunes constantly running in their numskulls; one would think that their seven senses were all stuck in their ears. "Before I was tormented with Bill there," said she nodding to her husband, ""when I was sweet and twenty," as the old song goes, I lived with farmers down westward; in one place, my fellow-servant was known by the nickname of Jenny Tweedles, because she would be all day croanan over the song,—

"There was an old couple and they were poor,
Tweedle, Tweedle, go twee."

It was enough to make one crazy to hear her croanan, over and over, a line here and there, with the burden brought in after every one. I can see her old grim visage now as she maundered about the kitchen, singing in doleful tones,—

"Oh! I have been sick since you have been gone;
If you'd been in the garden, you'd heard me groan.
Tweedle, tweedle, go twee."

You may fancy I would rather hear thunder by night than be kept awake with her droaning in my ear,—

"Now I have a request to make unto thee,
Do pluck me an apple from the russet tree.
Tweedle, tweedle, go twee."

Worst of all she could never be trusted to do any work that required attention,—if scalding milk, for instance, whilst she was tweedlean, it would boil over, and the cream be in the ashes; if cooking, for the same reason, all the fat would be in the fire."

An' Mary paused, drew from her pocket a few lengths of yarn, when her husband said, "Come, Mary, keep the kibbal gwean, there's plenty of the same sort of stuff in thy bal." She continued her knitting and said, "There was a good mate for old Jenny Tweedles that used to live in the same parish, who was known by the name of Ky-me or Rigdom, because, when a boy, he was just another such fool, and would neglect, or badly do, any work he was set about whilst whistling the tune, or singing the words, of another old song,—

"There did a frog live in a well,
Close by a merry mouse in a mill,
To my rigdom, bomminare, ky-me,
Kyme-nare, gil-de-ka-re,
Kyme-nare, Ky-me." &c., &c."

"I can match these nicknames," said I, "with another instance of a grand one acquired from a song. But we must go back more than a hundred years to the time when potatoes were only grown as curious garden vegetables; peas supplied their place, and turnips, or other green crops, were unknown as winter's provision for cattle. Farmers then held, for the most part, freehold or leasehold tenements of from twenty to fifty acres of arable and pasture ground, with, in many places, twice that extent of uncultivated land or "outs" as we call it, which furnished fuel and winter's run for cattle.

Between tilling-season and harvest there was little farm work but to cut and carry furze and turf, and to save a little hay; and from the time that all was secure in the mowhay till seed-time there were long intervals of leisure. The corn was threshed as straw was wanted to be taken out to the downs or croft to keep the half-starved cattle alive. Horses, even, were seldom housed, and as there were no stall-fed beasts, little manure but ashes was made which was carefully housed to keep it dry till wanted for dressing; then it was carried in dung-pots to the ground, ploughed in, and the crop quickly sown. After rough weather everybody was on the alert watching for oarweed, which with sand constituted almost the only other substances used for manure. Everything had to be conveyed on horseback,—furze, hay, and corn in trusses, sand in sacks, oarweed in panniers or on crooks, slung over pack-saddles.

The only wheel-carriages in use were wherries, and these were drawn by horses in traces. A wherry was a square box, containing about four wheelbarrows, mounted on three solid wheels, such as we call druckshars.

To empty this machine it was overturned, druckshars and all. Though there was little out-door work to be done for long spells, our old folks were seldom idle. Hares, rabbits, and wild-fowl were plentiful on moors and the great extent of uncultivated land, and hunting was pursued—less as a pastime than a matter of necessity—to procure a little change of diet, now and then, from the almost constant peas-porridge, fish, and other salt provisions.

Women, old and young, passed much time in spinning, and in almost every farm-house one found weaving-machines, as we call hand-looms, so that when there was little else to do, farmers, or some of their men, worked the treadles, and wove the yarn into blanketing, or other household cloth. The surplus of this serviceable material met with a ready sale in markets far eastward. The home-made clothing was almost everlasting. I knew a notable old farmer's wife who used, when bragging of her husband's stock of clothes, to say, "Our Honey (Hanibal) have got twelve coats, and only two of them "biden clath" (bought cloth). Sennen people were famous for being good weavers, and those of Escols, in that parish, regarded themselves as the best in the West Country. In this village there might have been threescore inhabitants, including all ages, who were so connected by inter-marriages, that few of them knew where or how their relationship began or ended. The descendants of one family who formerly lived there still retain the nickname of "Triddles," from their forefathers having worked the treadles as their chief employment.

Weavers were much given to singing at their work, to relieve its tediousness; and an old weaving farmer, belonging to the primitive community of Escols, acquired the nickname of uncle Plato, because, whenever he was overtaken by a lazy stitch in working his treadles, he would sing a rather solemn piece,— one couldn't call it a song,—which thus began,—

"Said Plato, why should man be vain,
Since bounteous heaven has made him great?"

The rest I don't remember; it's something about sceptred king's and beggar's dust coming to the same pass. But he seldom finished his favourite ditty; for if his wife happened to be within hearing, she would exclaim, "Peter! Peter! may the devil take thee and Plato too. I can hear thee droanan that dreary thing again, and the treadles gwean (going) lazier than with Billy, the weaver, croanan over Aaron's beard and the ointment. Come Peter vean, strike up—

"Thinking to lead a sober life,
One Monday morning I took a wife,"

or some other lively catch. I'll join in, and thee west make three throws of the shuttle for one." Uncle Plato's family continued to be weavers of more than ordinary ability. Some of them left Sennen, and established the first looms worked by machinery in the old factory at Alverton, and acquired considerable property in Penzance. Many of this family were also much given to study; one of them, a lady who lived in St. Levan—I don't know her exact relationship to Plato—was remarkable for her acquaintance with Greek and Latin authors, which she read in their originals, and for her proficiency in astronomy and other sciences.

During this lady's lifetime, however, her acquirements were not regarded as anything so very extraordinary as they have been recently; for in those old times, and in that remote part, there were many who would even now be considered good scholars. The old folks of our great-grandfathers' days were neither so ignorant nor so immoral as it is now the fashion to represent them; true, there were few sleek smoothies among them, and they would be too rude and outspoken for our taste perhaps.

Books, from their dearness, were comparatively scarce; but the few they had were read over and discussed around the winter's hearth, where neighbours assembled in a social way that is now not found in country villages.

The "Story of Troy-town,"—as they called some old translation of the "Iliad,"—almost everybody knew by heart. Hector was such a favourite, that the best horse was called after him; and Penelope had, in most families, a namesake (Pee) to commemorate her constancy.

They had also the "Seven Wise Masters of Greece," "Moore's Almanack," "Robinson Crusoe,"—which everyone knew by heart, and believed a true history,—and two or three herbals, besides religious books, of which they made little account on the whole. Culpepper was an especial favourite with elderly dames; stills being common, they experimented with his recipes, and often compounded precious balsams that would operate famously as evacuants. Many West Country gentlemen were practised astrologers; and in order to understand works that treated of their favourite science, they must have acquired a knowledge of Latin and mathematics.

We revert to our old country folks to remark that, for an acquaintance with classic fables, and much other secular knowledge, they were beholden to the plain Welsh, or native, parsons—then appointed to the western parishes who lived amongst, and associated with, their flocks in an easy, comfortable way. Yet the reverend gentlemen's familiarity and sympathy with their parishioners' joys and griefs caused no diminution of respect for their sacred office. For example the Rev. James Bevan, from Glamorganshire, who was more than forty years curate of Sennen and St. Levan, was always spoken of, by the few old people who remembered him, with affection and respect. This gentleman resided in Trengothal; and so far was he from discountenancing wrestling, throwing quoits, and other manly recreations of the time, that he and his family, with many principal persons of the neighbourhood, always attended at holiday games, on Penberth Green, where they danced with rich and poor, and their presence enforced decorum, and made our rural sports respectable.

Another usage—probably handed down from Catholic times—was then common. Prizes won at wrestling, or any other manly games, were either worn to church or suspended within it to a pillar near the door, on the following Sunday. This custom was particularly observed when the victory was obtained in another parish. I have often heard one who when young was a noted wrestler, and for many years champion of his parish, speak of the satisfaction with which he used to hang up a pair of spurs, gloves, yards of ribbon, lace, or whatever it might be, as a trophy in honour of old St. Levan.

A short time ago, it was usual for the winners of gold-laced hats to display them at Church, though the wearers—often gentlemen farmers' sons— looked for all the world like livery servants. "Many customs of no more than fifty years ago," said the old tinner, "would be regarded as strange now. One thing that I have just thought of, that stories which have been related by romancers, and are still repeated by others in books, about the savagery of old Cornish wreckers and smugglers, is vile slander. Who, I wonder, would have more right to dead wreck than the salvers; and success say I to the fair trade."

The old tinner was now mounted on his favourite hobby, and as his stories about smuggling were interminable, I wished him good-night.

**AN EXCURSION TO CHAPEL UNY WELL,
WITH A LEGEND OF THE CHANGELING OF BREA VEAN.**

These, when a child haps to be got,
That after proves an idiot,
When folks perceive it thriveth not,
The fault therein to smother,
Some silly, doating, brainless calf,

That understands things by the half,
Says that the fairy left this aulfe,
And took away the other.

DRAYTON.

THOUGH the numerous visitors who resort to Penzance in autumn are rarely satiated with our fine cliff scenery, they might, with pleasure, vary their excursions by a ramble inland, where various objects of interest are found on moorlands and hills, but seldom visited.

A pleasant day, for example, might be passed by first going to Sancreed; where, in the quiet, neat, little, embowerd Church some curiously carved portions of an ancient rood-screen are worthy of notice. In the churchyard there is one of the finest crosses in the county; it is about eight feet high and ornamented with various emblematic devices, among others, the lilly of the Blessed Virgin. The old Inn, with its quaint sign "The Bird in Hand," suggestive of ready payment, was worthy of a glance, a few years ago, when some nondescript fowl of the air, trying to escape from a hand that grasped its legs, was pourtrayed on the sign-board in flaming colours by a local artist, and, underneath the captive bird, were the lines,—

"A bird in hand is better fare
Than two that in the bushes are."

From the south-eastern side of "Sancras Bickan" (Beacon) a delightful view of Mount's Bay is obtained, and on Caer Brane—commonly called Brane Rings—the next hill towards the west, may be seen the remains of an old and extensive hill-castle.

Hence, one might descend to the famous Chapel Uny Well, situated between Chapel Carn Brea and Bartine hills; the one crowned with its ruined chapel and the other with a castle. At Chapel Uny will be found a copious spring of as clear water as was ever seen. The only remains that can be identified, as having belonged to its ancient chapel, are a few dressed stones near the well. These, from their shape, would seem to have formed part of an arched door or window.

Near by there is also a large circular Fogou, or artificial cavern, walled on both sides and partly covered with long slabs of moor-stone. The Holy Well is, however, the most celebrated object in this vicinity; a few years ago, it was resorted to on the first three Wednesdays in May by scores of persons who had great faith in the virtue of its waters, which were considered very efficacious for curing most diseases incidental to childhood, and many ricketty babes are still bathed there at the stated times when the spring is believed to possess the most healing powers.

Belonging to this well and its neighbourhood there is a somewhat curious story, which we will relate just as it has often been told us by old people of the West Country.

THE CHANGELING OF BREA VEAN.

A hundred years or more ago—one afternoon in harvest time—a woman called Jenny Trayer, who lived in Brea Vean (a little out-of-the-way place at the foot of Chapel Carn Brea) gave her baby suck, rocked it to sleep, then covered up the fire, turned down the brandis, placed fire-hook and furze-prong across the hearth for good luck, and, leaving the child alone, away she hastened over to Brea to "help cut the neck." It was nearly dark when the last handful of wheat, called "the neck," was tied up and cut by the reapers throwing their reap-hooks at it. Then it took a good bit longer to cry the neck according to the old custom of the harvest-hands dividing themselves into three bands—one party calling, three times, as loud as they could cry, "We have it, we have it, we have it!" The second demanding, "What have ye? What have ye? What have ye?" And the third replying, "A neck! a neck! a neck!" Then all join, hats in hand, in a "Hip! hip! hip! Hurrah!"

The neck was then decorated with flowers and hung over the board.

Jenny, thinking about her babe all alone, didn't stop for the neck-cutting carouse, but got a good drink of beer, and her neck-cake, to take home; and hastened away. When she opened her door, she saw, by the moonlight, that the cradle was overturned. Straw and rags were on the floor, but no child was in sight.

Jenny groped round the room a long time; then, not finding any live embers among the ashes, she took the tinder-box and struck a light. "The more haste the worst speed." It was a long time before she got the porvan (rush-wick) lit in the chill (iron lamp). In searching all the holes and corners, she came to the wood-corner and there among turves, ferns, and furze, she found the "cheeld," fast asleep. Being very tired, she took up the child and went to bed. Next morning, when she looked at the babe by daylight, it seemed to her that there was something strange about it—she didn't know what—it was hearty enow, for it seemed never satisfied unless it was all the time sucking or eating; it would roar like a bull if it hadn't its will; and always wanted to be in her arms or eating pap.

The poor woman couldn't do her "chars," and had no rest of her life with the squalling, hungry brat. Yet, with all its sucking and eating, it seemed wasting to skin and bone. So it kept on all the winter—the more it ate the leaner it became. Many of the neighbours shook their heads when they saw it, and said they feared the "small people" had played her a trick that afternoon when she went to "neck-cutting." "Whether or no," said they, "you can do nothing better, Jenny, than to bathe it in the Chapel Well as soon as May comes round."

Accordingly, the first Wednesday in May she took it on her back and trudged away to Chapel Uny Well.

Three times she put it through the water from west to east, then dragged it three times round the well against the sun. Whether the bath made it any better or not she couldn't tell in one week. The following Wednesday, however, the troublesome creature seemed to expect the jaunt, and to enjoy it as it rode away on her shoulder over hill and moor to the spring, where it had the same ducking again. The third Wednesday was a wet day; yet, not to spoil the spell, Jenny took the brat, placed it astride on her shoulder, held one foot in her hand, whilst he grasped her hair to keep himself steady, as they beat over the moors against wind and rain. The thing seemed to enjoy the storm, and crowed, like a cock, when the wind roared the loudest.

They had nearly passed round Chapel Carn Brea and were coming by some large rocks, near the open moor, when she heard a shrill voice, seemingly above her head, call out,—

"Tredrill! Tredrill!
Thy wife and children greet thee well."

Jenny was surprised to hear the shrill voice and nobody in sight. When she stopped an instant to look round, the thing on her shoulder cried out in a voice as shrill and loud,—

"What care I for wife or child,
When I ride on Dowdy's back to the Chapel Well,
And have got pap my fill?"

Frightened out of her senses, to hear the miserable little object talk like a man about his wife and his child, the poor woman cast it on the ground and there it lay sprawling, until she took courage, threw it across her shoulder, and ran back as fast as she could lay feet to ground till she came to Brea town. She stopped before some houses a little below Brea mansion, threw down the thing, that clung to her neck for dear life, on to a dung-heap beside the road.

The women of Brea all ran out to see what could be the matter. As soon as she recovered her breath she told them what she had heard. "Ah," exclaimed one, "didn't I tell thee, months ago, that thee wert nussan a small body's brat, ever since the neck-cuttan night, when thy child was spirited away, and that thing left in his place."

"Shure enow," said another, "anybody of common sense might see that. Only look at the thing there, sprawling upon his back in the mud. Did one ever see a Christian cheeld like that, with his goggle eyes, squinting one way; his ugly mouth drawn another, and his pinched-up nose all a-wry too?"

"And now, Jenny," broke in the oldest crone, "'Tis lucky for 'e that I can tell 'e what you must do to get rid of this unlucky bucca, and get back thy own dear cheeld. Now there's an old way, and I don't know but it es the best; and that es to put the smale body upon the ashes' pile and beat it well with a broom; then lay it naked under a church-way stile; there leave et, and keep out of sight and hearan till the turn of night; and, nine times out of ten, the thing will be took off and the stolen cheeld put in his place. There's another plan but I never seed et tried—to make by night a smoky fire, with green ferns and dry. When the chimney and house are full of smoke as one can bear, throw the changeling on the hearth-stone; go out of the house; turn three times round; when one enters the right cheeld will be restored."

The women of Brea—resolved to try what a beating on the ashes' pile would do towards getting rid of the goblin—threw it on a heap near at hand and commenced belabouring it with their brooms. But they had scarcely touched it than it set up such a roar that it was heard in Brea mansion; and Dame Ellis came running down the town-place to see what could be the matter. She asked what they were beating in that cruel way. Being nearly dark and the wet ashes sticking to the creature she couldn't tell what gave out such a doleful noise.

"Why mistress," says Jenny, "that thing there on the ashes' pile es what was left in our house, when my dear cheeld was spirited away, by smale people, while I was reapan in your field the very day we cut the neck. All the neighbours know the trouble I've had ever since—how this thing that looked like my cheeld have ben all the time screechan, suckan, or eatan, and have never grown a bit, nor will make any use of his legs."

"But thats nothan," said she, recovering her breath, "to what happened a few hours ago, and most frightened me out of my senses. You mayn't believe at—that when, on my way to Chapel Uny Well, with that thing astride on my shoulder, somebody that couldn't be seen by mortal eyes cried out, 'Tredril, Tredril, thy wife and children greet thee well!' Then, in an instant, good lack, that thing from my back replied, 'That little cared he for wife or child when he rode on Dowdy's back (meaning me) to the Chapel Well, and had good pap his fill.' Nobody can tell the fright I was in, to hear that thing talk like a man about his wife and child."

Dame Ellis, lifting the creature from the ashes' heap, said to Jenny, "I believe that thou wert either drunk or in a waking dream when passing round the hill, and that this child, used so ill, is as truly thine as any thou hast born. Now take it home, wash it well, feed it regular, and don't thee leave it all day lying in its cradle; and, if thee canst not make it thrive, send for Dr. Madron."

Jenny and the other women at first refused to comply with Dame Ellis's advice; told her that she knew next to nothing about such matters, and related many things to prove that the creature was no mortal's child, till the lady tired with their stories, turned to go in, saying to Jenny,

"My husband shall come out and talk to thee; peradventure he may convince thee of thy error."

Squire Ellis and his wife being quakers—a sect then but little known in the West—they were thought by Brea women, and many others, to be no better than unbelieving Pagans, "who haven't the grace," said they, "to know anything about such creatures as spriggans, piskies, knackers (knockers of the mines) and other small folks, good or bad, that haunt our carns, moors, and mines; who can vanish or make themselves visible when and how they please, as all more enlightened folks know."

They well knew, however, what concerned them more—that Squire Ellis was their landlord, and that, quiet and quaker-like as he and his wife were in their talk, and demure in their looks, they were not to be trifled with; and that their will was law for all living on their estate unless they could contrive to deceive them.

Squire Ellis came down and, finding that Jenny (with her bantling and all the others) were gone into a house, where he heard them loudly talking, he had nothing to say to them; perhaps, he kept an eye on their proceedings.

Brea women, in spite of "unbelieving quakers," as they called Squire Ellis and his wife, among themselves—determined to have their own way—waited till all was dark in the great house; then Jenny, with the bantling or spriggan, and another woman, who was very knowing about changelings, passed quietly up Brea town-place, and under a stile on the Church-way path crossing a field from Brea lane, they left the creature (then asleep) that had been such a plague to them.

Jenny returned to Brea Vean, and there stayed till morning. Being fatigued and worried she overslept herself, for it was nearly daybreak when she awoke and hurried away, between hopes and fears, to the stile; and there, sure enough, she found her own "dear cheeld," sleeping on some dry straw. The infant was as clean, from head to foot, as water could make it, and wrapped up in a piece of old gay-flowered chintz; which small folks often covet and steal from furze-bushes, when it is placed there in the sun to dry.

Jenny nursed her recovered child with great care, but there was always something queer about it, as there always is about one that has been in the fairies' power—if only for a few days. It was constantly ailing and complaining, and, as soon as it was able to toddle, it would wander far away to all sorts of out-of-the-way places. The good lady of Brea often came to see it and brought it many nice things that its mother couldn't afford to buy, and when he was about nine years of age Squire Ellis took the changeling (as he was always called) into his service, but he was found to be such a poor simple innocent that he could never be trusted to work in the fields alone, much less with cattle; as a whim would take him, every now and then, to leave his work and wander away over hills and moors for days together. Yet he was found useful for attending to rearing cattle and sheep—then kept in great numbers on the unenclosed grounds of Brea. He was so careful of his master's flock in lambing time that there was seldom any lost. Forsaken or weakly lambs were often given to him by the neighbours, and he contrived to rear them so well that, in a few years, he had a good flock of his own that Squire Ellis and everyone else allowed him to pasture wherever he and his sheep choose to wander—everybody knew the poor changeling and made him welcome. When he grew to man's estate, however, he became subject to fits, and had to remain at home with his mother great part of his time.

Yet, when the fits were over, nothing could restrain his propensity for wandering, and his sheep, goats, and even calves, always followed, and seemed equally to enjoy their rambles. He often talked to himself, and many believed that he was then holding converse with some of the fairy tribe, only visible to him, who enticed him to ramble among the carns, hills, and moors—their usual haunts.

When about thirty years of age he was missed for several days; and his flock had been noticed, staying longer than usual near the same place, on a moor between the Chapel Hill and Bartinné, and there—surrounded by his sheep—he was found, lying on a quantity of rushes which he had pulled and collected for making sheep-spans.

He lay, with his arm under his head, apparently in sweet sleep, but the poor changeling of Brea was dead.

BETTY STOGS'S BABY. [4]

LITTLE more than twenty years ago, there lived in a lonely cot on a moor in Towednack a man and his wife with one child. The woman—from her slatternly habits—was known by the name of Betty Stogs; she had been married about a year and had a baby six months old or so; when, almost every day, whilst her husband was away 'to bal,' she would pass best part of the time 'courseying' from house to house in the nearest village.

The child would mostly be left in the house alone or with nothing but the cat for company. One seldom saw the colour of the bantling's skin for dirt. When anyone asked Betty why she didn't wash it oftener, "The moor es a cold place," she'd reply, "and a good layer of dirt will help keep 'n hot."

One afternoon about Midsummer she went to get milk for the child and stayed away gossiping till dusk; it was so dark when she entered her dwelling that she could scarcely see anything within it.

She went to the cradle and found it empty; the child was nowhere to be seen; nor yet the cat that always slept with it, shared its pap, and cleaned the skillet in which the 'child's-meat,' was cooked. Whilst Betty was searching about the house her husband came home from work—last core by day,—he was in a great rage with his wife and greater grief for the loss of his 'crume of a cheeld,' as he called it.

After hours spent in fruitless search Betty sat down and cried bitterly, whilst the father went away and told the neighbours what had happened.

Everybody turned out to look for the child; they examined moors and crofts for a good distance round till after daybreak without seeing sight or sign of it; but, when it was near sunrise, Betty spied the cat coming towards her, then it went back mewling into a brake of furze. She followed it and came to a plot of mossy grass, surrounded by thickets and ferns, where she saw, amongst heath and wortleberry plants, a bundle of old-fashioned chintz; she opened it and there was her child, sleeping like a nut. It was wrapped in several gay old gowns, with mint, balm, and all sorts of sweet herbs and flowers that are found on moors or in gardens; but otherwise it was as naked as when born, yet clean and sweet as a rose.

All the old folks said it was carried there by small-people, who intended to bear it away to the hills or carns; but it took them so long to clean it first that daylight surprised them ere they had done it to their mind; so they left it there meaning to fetch it the next night.

The fright, however, that Betty had undergone, did her good and the child too, for she passed less time in courseying, and took more care of her babe for fear it might be stolen again. She made lots of frocks for it out of the old chintz; and it throve so well after the small folks' cleansing that he made as stout a man as his dad, who was usually called Jan the Maunster (monster) from his bulky form.

How a Morvah Man Bought Clothes for his Wife. [4]

"Contented toil, and hospitable care,
And kind connubial tenderness are there."

GOLDSMITH.

MOST of the dwellers in the cottages scattered over the hills to the north of Penzance (like the tinners of old) work in the mines and cultivate a few acres 'out of core.' They are also remarkable for preserving many old customs which are become extinct in less remote and more populous districts, as well as for the quaint simplicity of their manners and language. A few weeks ago a tall, middle-aged man entered a draper's shop in Penzance. His blue smock-frock, corduroy trousers, ruddy with tin stuff, and the high-poled Sunday's hat, marked him for a high-country tinner. He paused in the middle of the shop and looked around as if to select some particular one of the assistants to serve him; then going over to the counter, where the forewoman was standing, he placed three little packets of money, done up in paper, before her.

"Look-e here, my dear," says he, "here's three packats of money for three things I want of 'e. Fust of all les have somethan to make a sheft for my old oman—dowlas or calico, you know the sort of stuff, and how much will do; for my old oman es of a tidy built and shaped much like you. (The blushes and titterings among the shop girls may be imagined). She told me how much, but I have forgot, only that a must cost ten-pence a yard; so cut off as much as will make a sheft for yourself, my dear, and see if you don't find the exact money for 'n in that paper, tied up with tape."

The paper opened, the money was found right to a farthing.

"Now, my dear, that's all right. Get some sort of stuff, made of sheep's clothing, I don't know what you call 'n, for to make an undercoat for the old oman. You know how much will do by your own measure; a must be two shellans a yard, and there's the money for 'n in that paper tied up with white yarn."

To make sure of the quantity wanted, the shop woman counted the cash sent, before she cut the required length of sanford. When that was adjusted,

"Now, my dear," says he, "we are getting on cappetal, sure nuf. Next let's have a pound of blue or black wostard—must be four shellans a pound and plum (soft) like yarn; there can be no mistake about that, and there es the money in the paper tied with black yarn. Now, over all these, I spose you will give me a nackan (handkerchief) for myself, waan't 'e, my darlan?"

- 204 -

The master of the establishment, who had been rather amused at the scene, though it was nothing new to him, left the desk and desired the shop woman to open some of good quality and neat patterns, for him to choose from.

"Why, Mr. ———, my dear, havn't 'e any smarter ones than these in your shop than?"

Some old-fashioned ones, of a gay pattern, were soon found, which pleased the customer exactly. Mr. ——— gave the tinner a glass of wine besides, and asked him how he liked it?

"Well, I can't say but a wed be pure keenly stuff with a glass of gin or brandy to warm un a little."

The master replied that he had no spirit in the shop, but gave his customer six-pence to buy a dram to warm the wine, on the way home.

"God bless 'e," says our Morvah man, slapping Mr. ——— on the shoulder, "but you are one of the right sort, and when my old oman do want a smock again I'll come and buy 'n for her, I don't wender now that all the women like to go to your shop, and that young woman there is pure block tin. But I spose, my dear," says he, turning towards the one he compared to pure tin, "you think me an old Molly-caudle, don't 'e, for coman here to buy the dudds for the old oman home? But 'force put es no choice,' my dear. I'll tell 'e a minute how she esn't here herself. This mornan, when I was takan breakfast to go to bal, Jenny took off a crock of petates from the brandes, that she had, to save time, boiled for the pig alongside of the tea-kettle for my breakfast. She must always be doan two or three jobs together like the milkmaid before now. She took the crock of petates out in the court to empty away the waater, and a minute before she had put a tub of calves'-meat to cool on the caunce, and the cheeld, accordan to custom, was trying to get at 'n to splash and play in the milk. The cheeld todlan round the tub, tumbled in souce, head down, Jenny left the cover slip from the crock in her fright, and out came the boilan waater and petates all over her foot.

"Then she cried, 'Come thee way'st out here Billy and take the cheeld out of the calves'-tub; see what I've done, and a es all thy fault; why disna (dids't thou not) keep the cheeld out of the way?' Ah was no good to say anything to her, my dear, because all the women, except you, will lay the blame on somebody else, for the foolish things they do. I dragged the cheeld out of the milk, left the dog to lick 'n clean, and dipped Jenny's foot in a bucket of waater. The pigs got at the crock and made some screechan when the hot petates burnt their throats. Next I put my old oman on the bed and pulled off her stockan with as much care as ef I'd ben peelan a petate. Then, by her direction, put a linan rag, spread with raw cream, all over the scald, and, without clunkan a bit more breakfast, got ready in a jiffy to run in to the doctor for a plaster, and salve, and things, and to know what was best to do.

"'Billy,' says she, 'as sure es I'm alive, I shall be laid up for weeks, and thee west have to do the work indoors and out, but I can never put away the time doan nothan. Put on thy best hat and blue coat, thy old clothes make thee look foolish in town, and go in to Mr. ——'s shop; mind what I do tell thee. I've been savan money these weeks past to buy some underclothing for winter, the next time I did go to town, and there a all es in the skibbat of the chest, in three pieces of papar, the money that each thing will come to.'

"Then she told me all about the price and number of yards, that I kept repeatan to myself all the way in till I come to the doctor's shop and there I forgot all about et. But she told me I should find a nice motherly oman in this shop just her size, and that's you my dear, who would tell me what to do ef I forgot. Jenny wanted to have something to do while her foot was healan. I told her I didn't much like to go to shop to buy her smock and undercoat; she could ask the nearest neighbour's wife to do et for her. 'No, the devil a bit,' says she, 'that I waan't! Ask Honney's boy Tom's wife, to buy the things for me! I'll go without a sheft fust, for she will go to meetan somewhere or other every night for a week that she may tell the rest of them what my things cost (and oh! the lies they will tell about et among them); besides, we shall have the house full all the time with them, makan out they are come to see how I am. Take the cheeld along weth thee down to An' Nancy Trembaa's; leave 'n there; and ask her to step up to milkey and do the rest of the mornan work for me.' When I left the cheeld down to An' Nancy's, and told her what had happened, away she went, wethout stopan so much as to put her hat on, up to keep things to rights while I'm wantan.

"Well, soas, I've done the best I could. I've got the plaster and salve in the head of my hat, with a fuggan Jenny made me take to eat on the road. A high bell-topper es as handy as a basket to stow away the lumber in; dash me ef a esn't. None of your low billycocks for me.

"Now I wish 'e all well, my dears, and ef you will come up to see us one Sunday afternoon you shall be as welcome 'One and All,' as ef you had been my own sisters. God bless 'e all; I shall be tother side of Ding Dong in less than an hour."

Neither the master nor the shop assistants saw anything to laugh at when the tinner had told his simple story. On the contrary they felt much interested, as his 'old oman' was a well-known customer.

HOW A ZENNOR MAN CHOKED HIMSELF, BUT HAD HIS WILL IN HIS POCKET.[4]

NOT long ago a high-country farmer, after having finished his marketing, in Penzance, treated himself to a supper at a cook-shop in Caunsehead. Being in great hunger, or haste, he thought it waste of time to cut his meat into smaller pieces than he could possibly swallow; besides, solid junks would stand by his ribs and do the more good.

He made but two morsels of a quarter of a pound of beef; and in bolting the last it stuck in his throat. In an instant he went blue in the face and fell on the floor. The landlord ran for a surgeon, and by good luck found one at home, the other side of the street. "Stand clear a bit, and open the man's trap," said the doctor. With much trouble the Zennor man's jaws were forced open, and the doctor feeling a portion of the meat pulled out a piece about six inches long.

The patient was soon restored and ready for another such meal.

Then a lawyer's clerk, who had just entered, remarked;—"Why, old boy, you ought to make your will and keep it by ye before sit down to eat beef again." "Why bless 'e so I have. I always keep my will in my pocket, and you shall see am ef you mind to. I made 'n myself—no lawyers for me. Here a es." Saying this he drew from his pocket a sheet of paper, and gave it to the doctor, telling him he might keep it, if he had a mind to see how to make a will. He intended to make another the next Sunday, because he had more things to bequeath now than when he made the testament, of which the following is a faithful copy:—

"I'll make my will while I am well. I will bestow my riches. I'll give to Ellek,[5] my eldest son, my best Coat, Jacket, and my Breeches. As for my watch et es in pawn; else Elexander should have that. Neckey shall have the courage Horse, and Jan the little Sprat. Mary shall have the milking Cow, and Lystria shall have the Heifer. Fillis shall have the flock of Sheep, and wat can I do better? Old Polly shall have the Puss[6] of goold, and that will most maintain her. Sally shall have the old brass Pan, the Bucket, and the Strainer.

"Signed, sealed, and delivered, in the presence of

"COUSIN MATTHEW HOLLOW,
"UNCLE PHILIP EDDY, and
"JOHN QUICK, the Schoolmaster."

The Smugglers of Penrose.

Part the First.

In winter's tedious nights, sit by the fire
With good old folkes; and let them tell thee tales
Of woful ages, long ago betid.

King Richard II.

WHAT remains of the old mansion of Penrose, in Sennen, stands on a low and lonely site at the head of a narrow valley; through which a mill-brook winds, with many abrupt turns, for about three miles, thence to Penberth Cove. So late as forty years ago, it was one of those antique, mysterious looking buildings, which most persons regard with a degree of interest that no modern structure inspires; the upper story only—with its mullioned windows, pointed gables, and massive chimney-stacks—was just seen over the ivey-covered walls of courts and gardens that surrounded it.

There was, however, a certain gloomy air about the ruinous walls and neglected gardens embowered in aged trees, which might have conduced to such unaccountable stories of apparitions and other unnatural occurrences, as were said to have taken place there.

Some three or four centuries ago, it was the property and residence of an ancient family of the same name; little more is known of these old Penroses than what can be gathered from wild traditions related by the winter's hearth. The following among many others were often recounted by old folks of the West.

About three hundred years ago, the owner of Penrose was a younger son who had been brought up to a seafaring life, which he continued to follow till his elder brothers died unmarried and left him heir to the family estate; then, preferring a life on the wave, he kept a well-armed, fast-sailing, craft for fair-trading, or what is now called smuggling; she was manned with as brave a crew as could be picked out of the West Country; most of them are said to have been the Squire's poor relations. A favourite cousin, called William Penrose—who had been his shipmate for years—was captain of the merry men all.

The Squire often took trips to France and other places, whence his goods were brought, and it is said that in his days Penrose crew were never concerned in any piratical jobs; though we know that about that time smuggler, privateer, and pirate, meant very much the same thing, whilst the two latter were then convertible terms with most of our rovers on the deep.

Penrose and his seamen passed but little time on shore except in the depth of winter; yet the board in his hall was always furnished with good substantial fare and the best of liquors, free for all comers.

Over a few years, when the good man was left a widower, with an only child—a boy about seven or eight—he seemed to dislike the very sight of land, for then, even in winter, with his little son, his cousin William, and two or three old sailors, he would stay out at sea for weeks together; leaving, as usual, the care of his farms and household to the care of a younger brother and an old reve or bailif.

In returning from one of these trips, in a dark winter's night, their boat struck on Cowloe and became a wreck. The Squire swam into Sennen Cove with his boy, and in endeavouring to save his crew got drowned himself.

The only remaining brother, known as Jan of Penrose, constituted himself sole guardian of the heir, and master of the place and property.

Now this Jan hated all whom his late brother favoured; and in consequence of his ill-will William Penrose left the West Country—for the sea it was supposed—but whither he wandered was unknown, as no tidings of him were received in the West.

The new master, however, soon got a large smuggling craft and manned her with a crew who cared but little what they did for gold or an exciting life; being well-armed they feared nothing that sailed the ocean.

Jan of Penrose never went to sea; but gave the command to a wretch—known to have been a pirate—who was cast on Gwenvor sands from his ship wrecked in Whitsand Bay, on the night that the good Squire Penrose was drowned.

This pirate-smuggler and his desperate crew boarded many a rich merchant-man going up Channel, from which they appropriated whatsoever they pleased, and sent all who opposed them to the other world by water.

There was no Preventive Service then, to be any check on our free trade. If Revenue Cutters came near our western land, their crews dreaded to fall in with Cornish fair-traders more than our smugglers feared the King's men. As for riding officers they would ride anywhere else rather than on the cliff, when beacon fires blazed from the carns of dark nights to guide fair-traders' boats into the coves.

When the rich goods and plunder were landed, and any over-curious person remarked that they were not such as seemed likely to have been purchased from our neighbours across the Channel, the jolly crew would give themselves credit for being valiant privateers, and as such be much renowned by simple country folks, and their plunder passed as lawful prize.

People came from all over the country to purchase the goods, safely stowed in vaults and other hiding places about Penrose; and in winter the crew spent much of their time there in drunken rioting with all the reckless youngsters of the neighbourhood.

After the good Squire was drowned his brother appeared to show every kindness to the orphan heir; yet it was remarked that the child seemed instinctively to avoid his uncle and the captain, who consorted much together when the smugglers were ashore.

Whenever the boy could elude the old steward's vigilance he would go away alone to the rocks in Sennen Cove where his father was drowned, or shut himself up for hours in his father's bed-room, or wander about other parts of the gloomy north wing, which was almost in ruins and seldom entered by other inmates.

One winter's day, the ground being covered with snow, Penrose's people and many others of the neighbourhood joined for a wolf-hunt. Traditions say that in those times terrible havoc was often made on flocks by these fierce beasts, and that children were sometimes carried off by them when hard pressed with hunger.

Neither John Penrose nor the captain went to the chase; when at night the game-laden hunters returned and blew their bugle-horns, they remarked with surprise that the young heir—who was a general favourite—did not, as was his wont, come into the court to meet them. The boy was sought for in every place whither it was thought he might have strayed. His uncle seemed to be much distressed, and continued the fruitless search until it was surmised that the child must have missed his way in returning from Sennen Cove, wandered out under Escols Cliff, there got drowned by the flowing tide, and carried out to sea on the ebb.

After this, Jan of Penrose, having all his own, became more riotously debauched than ever; and his gang having taken a somewhat strange aversion to their captain, he left and was no more seen in the West.

The tapestry chamber and all the northern wing was shut up, or unoccupied, as it had the reputation of being haunted. None of the servants nor even the devil-may-care smugglers would venture into it after night-fall, when unearthly shrieks would be heard there, and strange lights seen flashing through the casements till near morning. Lights were also often seen in an orchard just below the town-place when no one was there.

These unnatural occurrences, however, put no check to the excesses of Penrose's band and the lawless castaways who joined them. By way of variety to their fun, they frequently disguised themselves and made nocturnal excursions to some village within a few miles, where they would alarm the quiet folks in the dead of night, by discharging their fire-arms in a volley; and make a bonfire of a furze-rick, out-house, or thatched dwelling.

The poor villagers in their fright, would mistake these wretches for outlandish people, come again to burn and pillage as in days of yore.

They were all the more ready to think so because about this time the Spaniards had great fondness for roving round the western coasts, and often did much damage in defenceless places; it was in Jan Penrose's time, too, that a few Dons, high by day, put off from a galley in Whitsand Bay, landed on Gwenvor Sands, and destroyed Velan-dreath Mill. To return to Penrose crew, at the height of the fright and confusion they would carry off such young women as they had before agreed on; the gallants would take their fair-ones before them on horseback to Escols Cliff or the hills, where they would be left alone by daybreak, to find their way back afoot. Having carried on this sport a long time with impunity, they became so bold at last as to make an attack on Buryan Church-town; fortunately, however, Buryan men were apprised of their intentions in time to be armed and ready to give them a warm reception; in short they lay in wait for the smugglers, drove them all into a vacant place near the cross in Church-town, and there surrounded them; when thus hemmed in the band fought desperately, and till nearly every man of them was killed or disabled they continued shouting to each other, "cheer up comrades, die one, die all, and die we merrily;" and so many of them met their end in this encounter that Penrose band was soon after broken up.

One night of the following Christmas, whilst a large company was assembled at Penrose, keeping high festival after a day's hunt, loud knocking was heard at the green-court door, and soon after a servant conducted into the hall an elderly wayfaring man who requested a night's shelter from the snow-storm.

John Penrose received the wanderer with hospitable courtesy; and charged his steward, the old reve, to provide him with good cheer; the guests continued their glee and paid but little attention to him, for begging homeless pilgrims were all too plenty here at that time.

The company was also entertained by professional droll-tellers and ballad-singers; persons of that class were then—and long after continued to be—received, as substitutes for minstrels, in gentlemen's houses of the humbler sort.

The stranger, however, regarded the company with attention, and noticed that the master of Penrose looked wretched and haggard amidst all the merriment. His scrutiny was interrupted by the steward who conducted him to another room where a well furnished board, beside a blazing fire, awaited him.

The stranger having refreshed himself, told the old steward how he had just returned from a long pilgrimage in foreign lands, and had seen many places spoken of in miracle-plays, which were acted in the Plan-an-Gware at St. Just, and how he had that morning arrived at Market-jew on board an eastern ship that traded there for tin.

He also said that he once had friends in the West Country; whether they were alive or dead he knew not, but hoped to obtain some tidings of them on the morrow.

The wanderer's voice seemed familiar to the old steward, and recalled former times; but, ere they had time for more discourse, they were invited to return to the hall and see a guise-dance, which was about to commence.

The stranger seemed interested in the quaint performance of "St. George and the Turkish Knight." A droll-teller in his character of bard, took the part of chorus; explained the intent of coming scenes; instructed and prompted the actors as well.

The play being concluded and the guisards well rewarded by the wayfarer, he withdrew and told the steward that he felt weary after his long walk though the snow and would be glad to lie down; if all the beds were occupied, he could repose, he said, in a settle by the fireside, for a few hours only, as he intended to leave early in the morning.

The old man replied that he feared any other accommodation in his power to offer was not such as he might desire,—although the house was large, with ample bed-rooms for more guests than it now contained—because a great part of the northern end was shut up for a reason that the inmates did not like to talk about. Yet as he believed the pilgrim to be a prudent man, who was, no doubt, learned in ghostly matters, he was glad to unburden his own mind and have his visitor's counsel, with his prayers for the repose of the unquiet spirits that disturbed the place.

Then he told how many of the upper rooms, though well furnished, were unused and falling to ruin on account of the unnatural sounds and sights before mentioned. To which the stranger answered that as he had a mind at ease he had no reason to dread any ghostly visitants; if the steward would conduct him to a room in the haunted wing he did not fear for his rest.

The old steward, taking a lamp, led the way to the tapestry chamber—being the best room in that part of the mansion. A faggot of dry ash-wood—already laid in the large open fire-place—was soon in a blaze, and the room well aired and somewhat comfortable.

The old man brought in bread, meat, and wine, that the guest might take more refreshment during the night, and supply his wallet in the morning if he started before breakfast. After returning with more wood and bog-turf to keep in the fire, he bade the guest good-night, sweet rest, and pleasant dreams.

Part the Second.

Blood, though it sleeps a time, yet never dies;
The gods on murd'rers fix revengeful eyes.

CHAPMAN.

After the old steward had retired from the dreaded room, its occupant was in no haste to rest himself on the large stately looking bed; but seemed never weary of examining the old portraits and quaint figures in the arras (which might have been intended for portraits too), the massive oak furniture with bold, grotesque, carvings, ancient armour, coats of mail, and other interesting objects, which were suspended from the walls, or in hanging presses, with all of which he appeared familiar; so that it was near midnight when he sat down in the long window-seat.

The storm had ceased and a full moon, shining on newly fallen snow, made it almost as light as day. He opened the casement and looked into the court, where he saw a company of young men and women passing out singly and in silence.

The visitor, being well acquainted with West Country customs, knew—as this was twelfth night—that the object of this silent procession was to work some of the many spells, usually practised at this time, for the purpose of gaining a knowledge of their future destiny with respect to what they regarded as the most important of all events—marriage and death.

So great was the desire of many young people to obtain an insight of what the future had in store for them, that they often practised singular rites,—still well-known in the West,—which are probably vestiges of ancient magian ceremonials connected with divination.

This night, however, the young peoples' intention was simply to gather ivy leaves and pull rushes; by the aid of which, with fire and water, they hoped to discover who would be wedded, and with whom, or buried before the new year was ended. There are many instances of predictions, with regard to the latter event, conducing to accomplish their own fulfilment, from their effects on people of melancholy temperament.

The pilgrim had not sat long, looking out of the open casement, when he saw the company of young men and maidens come running back, apparently in great fright. The doors were all immediately slammed to, the noisy mirth and music suddenly ceased in the hall. The house, in a few moments, was shrouded in thick fog; all was still as death about the place for some minutes, then a noise was heard like the distant roaring and moaning of the sea in a storm.

These ocean sounds seemed to approach nearer and nearer every instant, until the waves were heard as if breaking and surging around the house. In the wailing wind was heard a noise of oars rattling in their row-locks for another instant; then as of the casting of oars hastily into a boat.

This was followed by the hollow voices of the smugglers, drowned with the old Squire, hailing their own names, as drowned men's ghosts are said to do when they want the assistance of the living to procure them rest.

All this time the green-court appeared as if filled with the sea, and one could hear the breakers roaring as when standing on a cliff in a storm.

All the buildings and trees surrounding the mansion disappeared as if sunk into the ground.

At length the surging of waves and other sounds gradually died away until they were only heard like the 'calling of cleeves' before a tempest.

The steward had told the stranger of these noises and appearances, which had become frequent of late, to the great terror of the household; but he gave little heed to the old man's tales, thinking that such visions were merely the creations of weak brains diseased by strong potions.

'Tis said that when the young folks reached the outer gate of the avenue, near which they would find the plants required for their spells, all keeping silence and taking care not to look behind them—as this or speaking would spoil the charm—a female, who was a short distance ahead of the others, saw what appeared to be the sea coming over the moors before a driving fog. She ran shrieking to join her companions, who also beheld the waves fast approaching—rolling, curling, and breaking on the heath. They all ran up to the house with their utmost speed; and some who had the courage to look behind them, when near the court door, saw the curling breakers within a few yards of them; and a boat, manned with a ghostly crew, came out of the driving mist as they rushed into the house; and, not daring to look out, they saw nothing more.

The weary wayfaring man, having a clear conscience, feared nothing evil in what appeared to him an unaccountable mystery, even in that time of marvels; and, having told his beads, he committed himself to good spirits' care.

The brave man was rather soothed than alarmed by a plaintive melody, until there was a change in the harmonious strains, which grew more distinct; and mingled with them were the tones of loved and once familiar voices, calling, "William Penrose, arise and avenge the murder of thy cousin's son!"

Casting a glance towards the window—whence the sound proceeded—he saw just within it the apparition of a beautiful boy in white raiment. A light which surrounded it showed the countenance of the lost heir of Penrose. At the same time the room was filled with an odour like that of sweet spring flowers.

The pilgrim, William Penrose, spoke to the spirit and conjured it, according to the form prescribed by Holy Church, to speak and say what he should do to give it rest.

The apparition, coming nearer, told how he had been murdered by the pirate-captain of the smugglers, on the grand hunting day; and how his uncle had given the pirate a great quantity of gold to do the bloody deed—that he had been buried in the orchard under an apple-tree, that would be known, even in winter, by its blasted appearance,—that the murderer was then in Plymouth, keeping a public-house, the situation of which was so plainly described by the spirit that William Penrose would have no difficulty in finding it, and bringing the murderer to justice by means of such proofs of his crime as would be found beneath the blasted tree.

Moreover he told William that the spirits knew he was gone on a pilgrimage for their repose; and that they all, through him, sought his aid to enable them to rest in peace.

William Penrose having promised to perform all according to the wishes of the departed, music was again heard and the spirit gradually disappeared in a cloud of light.

Then the weary man sunk into sound repose from which he only awoke at break of day.

His cousin, the good Squire, had also appeared to him in a dream, and told him that concealed in the wainscot, beneath a certain piece of tapestry, he would find a secret cabinet, in which was preserved good store of gold and jewels for the infant heir; and that the key of this hidden treasury was behind a leaf of carved foliage which ornamented the bed head. He was told to take what money he required for his journey and to keep the key.

He found everything as indicated in his dream.

Jan of Penrose had often sought for this private recess—where heirlooms and other valuables were concealed, and only made known to the heir when of age, or to a trusty guardian, if a minor—but he was deterred from further search by such an apparition as made him avoid the chamber, and of which he would never speak after his fearful fright was past.

The pilgrim arose and requested the old steward to accompany him a short distance on his journey.

Before they parted the stranger discovered himself, to the old man's great delight, to be the long-lamented William Penrose; told him that he was about to undertake a long journey for the repose of the dead; that he would return when he had accomplished his mission; and bade the steward adieu, without speaking of the apparition or the cause of disturbances in the mansion.

William Penrose, having arrived in the ancient town of Plymouth, and entered the mean public-house to which he had been directed by the apparition, saw the person he sought lying stretched by the fireside in a squalid apartment that served for kitchen, guest-chamber, and sleeping room.

The former pirate-captain looked like a deserter from the churchyard (as we say); the face of this child-murderer was the colour of one long in the tomb; with but little signs of life except in the lurid glare of his sunken eyes.

William Penrose with much difficulty induced the 'wisht-looking' object to converse; and, after a while, led him to talk of the West Country, then of Sennen. From that the pilgrim spoke of Penrose, and asked him if he knew, in Penrose orchard, a certain apple-tree, which he pointly described. He had no sooner mentioned it than the inn-keeper exclaimed, "I am a dead man."

The miserable wretch begged the pilgrim to have mercy on him and listen to his confession, in which he declared he was driven to commit the murder by his evil spirit that made him dislike the child, because he had long hated his parents, more than from any love of gold given him by Jan of Penrose, to remove the only obstacle to his possession of the estate.

William Penrose—who was still unknown to the inn-keeper—wondered what cause of ill-will he could ever have had against the good old Squire or his wife, until the former pirate told how he was the prodigal son—long supposed dead—of an ancient, respectable, but poor family, whose ancestral seat was within a few miles of Penrose—how, almost from his childhood, he had long and truly loved, and as he trusted, had his love returned by the lady who became the wife of Squire Penrose,—how that he had left his home in St. Just on a desperate privateering expedition, in hopes of soon gaining sufficient riches to make the lady's parents regard him with favour,—how, whilst he was returning with gold enough to buy the parish, Penrose had wooed and won the lady—his first and only love, for whom he had toiled and suffered every hardship during many years.

He also related how when he came home so altered, by the burning suns of the Spanish Main, that his nearest relatives knew him not, and found out the ill return his lady-love had made him, that his only solace was the hope of revenge.

Some of the gold that he had sweat blood to gain, for the sake of the faithless fair, was laid out in a fast sailing craft, which might pass for a merchant-man, privateer, or pirate, as she was all in turn during a few years that he roamed the British seas.

The vessel was manned with a desperate crew, most of them his old comrades, who would do anything to please him. The design he had formed, more through hate than love, was to carry the lady off to some foreign land.

A year or so after his return he landed one night in Whitsand Bay, accompanied by a great part of his well-armed crew, who took their way towards Penrose, where he learned ere their arrival, that his design of carrying off the lady was frustrated by her having been laid in the grave a few days before.

After this he wandered over sea and land by turns, caring nothing what became of him, until cast on Gwenvor Sands—poor and naked, as his ship foundered in deep water, when all but himself were drowned; and, as bad luck would have it, he reached the shore on some loose part of the wreck.

The worst portion of his story from this time is already told; but no one can tell, as he related, how the desire of gold—to enable him to recommence his roving life, far away from the hated sight of the land and everything else that recalled a remembrance of his blighted youthful hopes—maddening drink, and a wicked heart, farther irritated by Jan Penrose, made him murder the child that he would have given a hundred lives to restore before he received the uncle's bloody gold.

Since then he had never a moment been free from remorse. He wished for death, but feared to die. If he drank himself mad, that only increased the horror of his thoughts.

He had scarcely finished his sad tale when William Penrose discovered himself to be the well-remembered playmate of the wretched man's innocent youth; and he had only time to beg Penrose to bestow in alms his ill-got store, for the scarcely hoped for mitigation of future punishment, when he breathed his last.

When William Penrose returned to Penrose and made himself known, to the great joy of old servants and others, he found that what was thought to be merely the gloomy and morose temper of its master frequently made him shun all society, and wander about the hills or cliffs and other solitary places, for days and nights together.

No one either loved, feared, or cared enough about the surly man to pay him any regard. He was absent then in one of his melancholy moods, and William with the steward, aided by other old trusty servants, removed the child's remains from beneath the blasted tree to Sennen churchyard; and out of respect to the honourable old family, little was said or known about the sad occurrence.

Jan of Penrose was no more seen alive in the old mansion, for the same night that his nephew's remains were buried in consecrated ground, he hanged himself in the malt-house; and he haunted it long after.

Following the spirit's injunction William Penrose had still to find and remove the bodies of the old Squire and his crew. Now it was supposed that they were 'sanded'—that is sunk in the moist sand and covered by it during a flowing tide—near Gwenvor Cove, because corpse-lights had frequently been seen, and the drowned sailors had been heard there "hailing there own names," as they are still accustomed to do when requiring aid of the living.

Next day Penrose and others found the bodies of the old sailor-squire and his crew near the place where fishermen had heard the "calling of the dead," and their remains were laid to repose, with all holy rites, in an ancient burying-ground near Chapel Idné, where the wind and waves sing their everlasting requiem in music they loved well when alive:—

"Pie Jesu, Domine,
Dona eis requiem.
Amen."

William Penrose, now heir-at-law of the bartons of Penrose, Brew, and other farms in the West Country,—disliking to live in the place connected with such melancholy events—gave up his rights of heirship to another branch of the family; resumed his pilgrim's staff; and was supposed to have died in the Holy Land.

The Penroses still in the West are said to be descended from a younger branch of the ancient family of Sennen; with whom the Pendreas or Pendars were intermarried.

The family of Jones purchased the Penroses' West Country property, and it remained in their possession until the beginning of the last century.

We hear again of smugglers being kept in pay by the last Jones, of Penrose, and by others who succeeded him. From the facilities afforded by this secluded place for concealing contraband goods, it was always noted as a favourite resort for western fair-traders.

Many people about the Land's End believe the old mansion was always haunted; and it is said this was the principal reason for taking down and rebuilding a portion of it a few years since.

TREGAGLE.

In Cornwaile's fair land, bye the poole on the moore,
Tregeagle the wicked did dwell.
He once was a shepherde, contented and poore,
But growing ambytious, and wishing for more,
Sad fortune the shepherde befelle.

JOHN PENWARNE.

ONE may almost every day hear West Country folks make allusion to Tregagle; for instance, a squalling child is called a Tregagle; and to a blusterer they often say, "Hold thy bleatan, thee art worse than Tregagle roaran before a storm."

But little is known here of the living man's history—which belonged for the most part to the neighbourhood of Bodmin—all our common sayings, connected with him, refer to his troublesome ghost at Gwenvor.

Our vague traditions, however, represent him as having been a most unscrupulous lawyer; and say that he rose from low estate, by taking bribes to lose his poorer client's cases, by bearing or procuring false witnesses; forging documents relating to the bequest of property; and other nefarious transactions which resulted in his acquisition of much riches and consequent power.

He is also said to have been so cruel in his domestic relations,—by having despatched several wives, who were rich heiresses—that he is regarded as a sort of Cornish Bluebeard, who sold his soul to the devil that he might have his wishes for a certain number of years.

All our western legends agree, however, in stating that the particular business which was the cause of his being "called from the grave" was this:—

A man who resided in the eastern part of the county, lent a sum of money to another without receiving bond or note or anything for security, as the transaction was witnessed by Tregagle; for whom the money was borrowed; and who died before the money was repaid.

Soon after Tregagle's death, the lender demanded his money, and his debtor denied ever having received it.

The case was brought before the court at Bodmin assizes; and when the plaintiff said that Tregagle was the only witness, the defendant denied it with an oath, and exclaimed, "If Tregagle ever saw it I wish to God that Tregagle may come and declare it."

The words were no sooner uttered than Tregagle stood before the court, and, pointing to the man, said, "I can no more be a false witness, thou hast had the money, and found it easy to bring me from the grave, but thou wilt not find it so easy to put me away." Wherever the terrified man moved about the court Tregagle followed him; he begged the judge and long-robed gentlemen to relieve him from the spirit. "That's thy business," said they, one and all, "thou hast brought him, thou may'st get him laid."

The man returned home, but whithersoever he went Tregagle followed, and would seldom quit his side or let him rest by night or by day.

He repaid the borrowed money, gave much in alms, and sought to get rid of the spirit by the aid of parsons, conjurors, and other wise men, before they succeeded in binding it, for a while, to empty Dosmery Pool with a crogan (limpet shell) that had a hole in its bottom.

Having soon finished that task, he returned to the man that brought him from his grave, and followed and tormented him worse than before, until he procured the help of other powerful exorcists who were more astute. The first thing they did was to draw a circle, out in the town-place, and put the man to stand within it. The spirit then took the form of a black bull and tried to get at him with horns and hoofs, but the man was safe within the line traced. A parson continued reading all the time, while others kept an eye on the spirit that took many shapes. At first the holy words of power made him furious; by turns, he bellowed like a mad bull, hissed like an adder, or roared like a wild beast, that he might be heard for miles away. Yet, by degrees, Tregagle became as gentle as a lamb, and allowed the spirit-quellers to bind him with a new hempen cord; and to lead him far away to Gwenvor Cove.

There they doomed him to make a truss of sand, to be bound with ropes made of the same material, and carry it up to Carn Olva.

Tregagle was a long while at his tiresome task without being able to accomplish it, until it came to a very cold winter, when, one hard frosty night, by taking water from Velan Dreath brook, and pouring it over his truss, he caused it to freeze together and bore it in triumph to Carn Olva.

He then flew back to the man who raised him, and he would have torn him in pieces, but, by good luck, he happened to have in his arms an innocent young child, so the spirit couldn't harm him.

Without delay the terrified man sent for the nearest parson, who, however, was not able, alone, to cope with Tregagle; the most he could do was to prevent him from harming the man until other spirit-quellers were brought to his assistance; with whose aid the furious spirit was again bound, led away to Gwenvor, and required to undertake the same task, without going near fresh water.

So Tregagle was matched at last, for he is still there on the shore of Whitsand Bay vainly trying to make his truss of sand; and he is frequently heard roaring for days before a northerly storm comes to scatter it.

I well remember that when a boy, and living in Rafra, St. Levan, how elderly men would go out into the town-place, last thing before they went to bed, to "look at the weather,"—in harvest particularly,—and come in saying, "Tregagle is roaring, so we shall surely have northerly wind and a dry day to-morrow," or, "the northern cleeves are calling," by which they meant the same, and unconsciously used somewhat poetical figures of speech.

A legend which connects Tregagle's escape from Gwenvor with the sanding up of Parcurnow has been noticed (on page 140); other stories, however, say, that job was imposed on him as a separate task, which he quickly accomplished just before he was finally settled at Gwenvor.

DEVIL'S MONEY.

There needs no other charm nor conjurer,
To raise infernal spirits up, but fear.

BUTLER.

NOT long ago it was believed that Old Nick frequently appeared in the form of a bull, and that he often placed money to tempt the unwary. The following story—told us of the late Sir Rose Price's huntsman—will help to explain notions which are not yet wholly exploded.

When the huntsman was a boy his parents lived in Nancledra, and sent him daily to a school two or three miles off, till he was about thirteen years old. He had his dinner sent with him, and he often minched. One morning he wandered away over the moors in search of birds' nests and rabbits' burrows. He had a good pasty in his dinner-bag and the day passed pleasantly in birds-nesting, searching for young rabbits, and playing about a tin-stream, three miles or so up the Bottom, where he stayed till the streamers left work. Then he took his course for home, over hedges and ditches, wandering wherever his fancy led him, till almost dark, when he found himself in a large hilly field not far from Nancledra. In making a short cut for home he crossed this field, and, when near the middle of it, he heard a bull bellowing, and shortly saw a large black one making towards him with tail up and head down; sometimes it would stop to tear up the ground, and fling its horns as if to get in practice to toss the boy; who being far from any hedges, there seemed no way of escape from the field before the bull could overtake him. But, luckily, within a few yards, there was a large rock, to which he ran and climbed it, a moment only before the bull came to it.

The brute kept on, for a long time, going round and round the rock, bellowing and tearing up the turf as if in a rage, till at last, tired with his vain endeavours—as it seemed—to get at the boy, it hoisted its tail like a flag-staff, galloped off, and vanished in a minute.

The boy didn't venture from his fort for sometime after the bull left. At length he 'cramed' down over a shelving side of the rock on all fours, head foremost—it was too dark to see where to put his feet. When he touched ground with his hand he felt and took up what he thought, by the feel of it, to be a penny-piece or a large button. He ran home and saw, by light shining through a window, that he had found a penny. When the way was clear, he made a place to hide it, in a hole over the chimney-stool—the fire-place was a large open one for burning furze and turf.

Next night, about the same hour as on the preceding, he went on the rock, 'cramed' down again, and found two penny-pieces, which he hoarded in the hole; and, night after night, he visited the rock, found the money doubled each succeeding night, and picked up silver money in other places where one would the least expect to find it, till his hiding-place was nearly full in a few weeks.

How much longer this luck would have continued there is no knowing; for, one night, when he thought there was nobody about, his mother came in and found him standing on the chimney-stool so earnest about something that he didn't see her watching him, and he kept handling his money till she said,

"Whatever hast thee got there between the stones, that thee art always stealing into the chimney, whenever thee dost think nobody is noticing of thee."

"Only my buttons and marbles, mother," said he.

"I don't believe thee," replied his mother; "stand away, and I'll see for myself."

Saying this she took up the fire-hook, ran the point of it into the hole, and dragged out a lot of money.

"Now tell me, or I'll kill thee, thou lying thief," said she, "where didst thee get this money; if thee hast stole it I'll murder thee, I will."

The boy didn't much mind his mother's threats—terrific as they seem—he was used to it. Yet she made him tell how he came by the money.

"Oh! good gracious mercy on us," cried she, before he had finished telling her; "oh! thou wicked boy; thee hast frightened me out of my life. Now tell me true," moaned she, wringing her hands, "hast thee used any of the devil's money, put there to entice thee to sell thyself to him, body and soul?"

"No, mother, please sure I han't," said he, "I was savan all to buy a gun."

"Well, thank goodness," groaned his mother, "that I have found all out in time to prevent thee shuttan thyself or somebody else with the devil's gun. I should never more rejoice if I thought thee hast used a farthing of en. Know, thou plague of my heart, that what seemed to thee a bull was the Old One hisself. He placed the money there for thee, and, when the bull seemed to vanish, he only changed to an adder, a toad, or something else that suited his purpose, and he was watchan thee all the time."

Whilst talking to the boy she raked all the money on to a fire-shovel, and threw it under a brandes, around which there was a good turf-fire. In a few minutes all the money melted away, and was gone like hailstones in sunshine.

Next morning she carried out all the ashes, strewed them about the town-place, and swept the hearth nine times before she lighted a new fire. The poor woman never rested till she told old Parson Stephens. He didn't altogether believe the boy's story, but said that if it was the devil's money she did right, or she might have—brought it to him.

The boy was so terrified by what his mother said, that, for years after, he never ventured to wander by night, even when he hunted for Sir Rose, and was as stout a man as one might see of a market day; and the sight of a black bull or anything he took for such would always make him tremble.

There are many stories of this class about people having been enticed with devil's money, but few of them have so fortunate an ending as the old huntsman's relation.

THE SLIGHTED DAMSEL OF GWINEAR.

Trust me no tortures that the poets feign
Can match the fierce, th' unutterable pain
He feels who, day and night, devoid of rest,
Carries his own accuser in his breast.

JUVENAL.

THERE is a general belief, in the western part of Cornwall, that if a greatly injured person, the last thing before death, reads or recites the 109th Psalm, usually called the "Cursing Psalm," applying its comminations to the injurer, the dying maledictions are sure to take effect.

Nearly a hundred years ago there lived in Gwinear Church-town a young man called Thomas Thomas, who for many years courted his cousin, Elizabeth Thomas, of the same place. She was much attached to the young man, who often promised to make her his wife; but, when she had shown her utmost trust in him, on some little disagreement, he slighted her and proposed to wed another damsel of the same village.

One Sunday afternoon he took his new love for a walk, passing by his old sweetheart's door, purposely to spite her.

Soon after they had passed the cot of Elizabeth's parents, the betrayed and wronged girl, who was of a very hasty temper, took a rope and a prayer book, went into a road-way field, and hanged herself near the path by which her faithless lover and his new fiance had passed, and would, probably, return.

They came home, however, by another road. On their arriving in Church-town, somebody asked them if they had seen Elizabeth, and remarked that no one knew where she had gone, as she had been sought in vain all over Church-town.

"Good God," exclaimed Thomas, "has she made away with herself? For more than once she vowed that she would if I slighted her."

Then, as if tokened by her spirit, he went, followed by others, direct to the tree on which they found her hanging and dead.

On the ground, at her feet, was her open prayer book. He took it up and found a leaf turned down at the "Cursing Psalm;" on a leaf too he read her name followed by "When this you see remember me."

Thomas then knew how she had doomed him; and he exclaimed "I'm ruined, I'm ruined, for ever and ever."

For a long while he wandered about like one distracted, working in various parts of the country, sometimes at mining, other times at husbandry, and never returned to Gwinear Church-town.

Little was seen of him, by anyone who knew him, until after some years, when he went to live in Market-jew. He would never venture to church or chapel for fear of hearing read the 109th Psalm; he dreaded even to pass near a school for the same reason.

He was several times hurt in the mines, in which he worked; and he attributed all his misfortunes and bad luck to the curse of Elizabeth, whose avenging ghost often appeared to him—as well by day as by night—with an open prayer book in her hand.

He could never sleep without a comrade in his room; and seldom even then, for, after a short slumber, when worn-out with fatigue, he would start up in bed, crying in agony, "Oh, dear Betsy, shut the book. Do shut the book."

Notwithstanding the distraction of his mind, he was still a fine, strong, lusty, man, and many of his comrades advised him to get married, saying there was nothing like a living wife to drive away the spirit of a dead sweetheart. Taking their advice, he paid his addresses to several young women of the neighbourhood and others farther away; but they, one and all, flouted him with scorn, for the history of his unfortunate first love was blown far and near. If he persisted in his suit the indignant damsels would ask him with a sneer if he wished to bring all the ill-wishes of the "Cursing Psalm" on their heads, too.

At length, however, a widow in Market-jew took pity on Thomas and consented to venture her lot with him; and Betsy's ghost ceased persecuting him—for a bit.

But on the road to St. Hilary Church—whither Thomas and the widow proceeded to get married—the weather suddenly changed; from a calm and sunshine it became a tempest, with thunder and lightning; it was harvest time, and a cloud, black as night, hung over them, and rain poured along churchway-path, whilst they saw people binding barley in the fields on either hand.

Thomas, trembling with fear, saw his sweetheart's ghost, with her open book, standing menacingly in the path before him; and he would have turned back, had not the widow urged him on, saying that she saw no ghost, and didn't mind her nor yet her book; and got him married. He lived for a few years pretty tranquilly; and his wife bore him two children. Then he was again disturbed with visits from the avenging ghost; and some misfortune or sickness always closely followed its appearance; until Thomas—worn-out in body and mind—when less than forty years of age died, and was buried in St. Hilary.

THE WRECK OF ADMIRAL SIR CLOUDESLEY SHOVEL.

WE are reminded by the above of the wreck of Admiral Sir Cloudesley Shovel's ship, the "Association," at Scilly; and of a tradition, common to the Islands, which attributes that disaster to the reading or reciting of the 109th Psalm, shortly before death, by one of Sir Cloudesley's crew, whom he unjustly condemned to be hanged.

The Admiral was returning with his fleet from Toulon, when, on the evening of the 22nd October, 1707, his ship struck on the Gilstone, about three miles and a half from St. Agnes; and in a few minutes afterwards she went down, and everybody on board perished, except one man, who saved himself by floating on a piece of timber to a rock called Hellweathers,—about two miles and a half from the Gilstone,—where he remained some days before the weather permitted any boat to approach and take him off to St. Agnes.

He is said to have stated that the day before the Admiral's ship was wrecked, one of the crew, who was a native of Scilly, and well acquainted with the channel, represented to Sir Cloudesley that the course the ship was taking would bring her on Scilly rocks. The Admiral and his officers were incensed at the man's interference; and because he persisted in affirming that the ship's way was wrong and would bring them to destruction, Sir Cloudesley Shovel—rather summarily, one might now think—condemned the man to be hanged for insubordination and endeavouring to excite a mutiny.

When the poor fellow was tied to the mast, preparatory to his being suspended by his neck, from the yard-arm, he begged, as a last favour, that a Psalm might be read before his execution. His request being granted, he selected the 109th, and repeated certain imprecatory portions of it after the reader; and the last words he uttered were to the effect that Sir Cloudesley Shovel and those who saw him hanged should never reach the land alive.

His body, shrouded in a hammock, with a shot to sink it, was cast into the deep, and but little heed paid to the dying sailor's sentence. Shortly after, however, the sky, which had been gloomy all day, became much darker; black, lowering, clouds, hung over the fleet like a funeral pall, and the gale rose to a violent tempest. Then the hanged man's curse was dreaded; and lo, to the crew's consternation, they beheld his corpse—divested of its rude winding-sheet—floating near the doomed ship, which it closely followed, with its face turned towards her,—in all her varying course, through eddying currents,—until she struck on the Gilstone; when the hanged man went down with the ship and his messmates.

At this unfortunate time there perished, besides the Admiral, several officers, and about two thousand men, belonging to the "Association" and other vessels of the fleet.

Sir Cloudesley Shovel's body was washed ashore at Porth-Hellick Bay, in St. Mary's, about eight miles from the Gilstone. It was quite naked, and on the hatch of a ship, on which he had endeavoured to save himself,—and a little dog lay by him,—when he was found by a soldier and his wife, who only knew him to be the Admiral by a diamond ring on his finger. They buried him in the sand, where a pit on Porth-Hellick Bank still marks Sir Cloudesley Shovel's grave. The pit never fills up in the greatest storms; and no grass ever grows on this blasted grave, although the ground around it is often green.

"So the hanged seaman had as sweet a bit of revenge as one could wish for," said our narrator, with a motion of his head which showed his satisfaction at the Fates' award.

Connected with this unfortunate occurrence, there is a gratifying bit of true history—we cannot say so much for all the above—which says that Lady

Shovel, on having her husband's ring,—by which his body was identified,—sent her by the soldier, she gave him a pension for life; and the Admiral was deposited in Westminster Abbey, where his monument recalls the direful tale.

A Night's Ride to Scilly.

No repares en eso, Sancho, que como estas cosas y estas volaterías van fuera de los cursos ordinarios, de mil leguas verás y oiras lo que quisieres, y no me aprietes tanto, que me derribas; y en verdad que no sé de qué te turbas ni te espantas, que osaré jurar que en todos los dias de mi vida he subido en cabalgadura de paso mas llano: no parece sino que no nos movemos de un lugar. Destierra, amigo, el miedo, que en efecto la cosa va como ha de ir, y el viento llevamos en popa.

*   *   *   *   *   *   *   *

Bien es verdad que sentí que pasaba por la region del aire, y aun que tocaba á la del fuego; pero que pasásemos de allí no lo puedo creer.

D. QUIJOTE.

MANY persons, not at all given to lying, assert that they have been carried up and away by Old Nick, in the form of a horse. For the most part, they affirm that they were taken "towers high;" and, when their infernal steed descended it threw them off violently, and vanished in fire and smoke.

We know a man called Jackey—never mind his surname—who had long been a sober character, and was so particularly veracious that he prefaced all his stories by saying, "I won't tell 'e a word of a lie, and know it!" Indeed this common affirmation of his has become an every-day saying, when anything doubtful is related. Well, Jackey has often told us, and many others, that, when a young man, and not so good as he might have been, he dwelt in the north of St. Just, and courted a girl who lived in Tardinney with her parents, who either rented a few acres or some dairy cows. One Sunday afternoon he went early to see his sweetheart. Whilst she was out milking, and he with her, the old woman, her mother, made a nice heavy currant-cake for tea. All was ready on the board when they returned from milking. Jackey made a hearty tea, or supper, as we should say; but, when that was over, the old woman said, "I've made a junket for thee, Jackey, as it's the first Sunday in May; it's in the dairy, 'runn'd' by this time; I'll bring it to thee in a minute."

"Don't think I can find room for it," said he; "I'm as full as a tick."

"Hold thy tongue," said she; "go thee wayst out and take a few jumps down from the heaping-stock, and pack the tea and trade away! Junket is no fillan, any more than drink; it will only quaff (puff) one for a bit."

Jackey went out and exercised himself a few minutes, by leaping over a stile; came in and found on the table a basin of junket well spread with thick cream and honey. It was no shabby allowance either, for the bowl held a quart or more. Whilst Jackey dispatched his junket his sweetheart rigged herself in her best, and then away they went down to Sennen Church-town to Methodist meeting. There they met several of his comrades with their sweethearts. Preaching over, they all went into the "First and Last" for a drop of something to drink. Santusters are always free enough in treating the women—and everybody else for that matter—so each of the fair ones had a glass of gin-and-peppermint or of brandy and cloves, or both if they liked, and most of them did like to taste both cordials and a glass of shrub besides. The men had a few mugs of shenackrum (gin and beer) with a dram of rum all around to finish off. They were a score or more going to St. Just; and all kept together till they came to the Burying-place Downs, where they parted company, and all the Santusters went Brea way, singing snatches of some well-known revival hymns to lively song tunes, except Jackey, who had to put his sweetheart home by the other road.

It was between ten and eleven o'clock when they got to Tardinney, and found the old folks gone to bed. A glowing turf-fire burned on the hearth, and they stayed courting till about one in the morning. But before Jackey left, his kind-hearted dear had tempted him to a slight supper of half a dozen eggs that she had saved up during the week unknown to the "old 'oman," and which were boiled over the turfy-fire. Jackey ate them with some bread and butter, then he had a good piece of cold cake, left from tea, with a bowl of milk; kissed; said good-night; and started for home.

Jackey had been tramping about nearly all day. He had a tiresome walk before him of nearly four miles; and to foot it, all alone, seemed doubly wearisome. He walked on pretty fast till he came half-way over Kelynack Downs. There he sat down to rest a minute and felt tired enough to sleep in a pool of water. He couldn't help wishing, when he rose to proceed, that an old horse might come in his way,—there were generally plenty of them on the common. He hadn't gone more than a hundred yards, when he saw what appeared to be an old black horse standing stock-still, as if asleep, close by the road. Jackey untied and took the halter it was spanned (hobbled) with from its legs, placed it over its head, mounted, and did his utmost to keep it on the road. But, in spite of all he could do, it took off westward over the Downs, going slowly at first, but soon quickened its pace till it went like the wind, and he was nearly blown off sometimes, with the rush of air occasioned by their speed, for there was no wind to speak of.

The night was so clear that he saw the Longships light nearly all the time, till they came to the cliff near the Land's End, to the best of his judgment. He felt no fear to speak of. The thing he bestrode took him over cliff—not right down, but sloping away gently. It went off through the air—just skimming the sea—straight to Scilly, and arrived there very quickly:—he thought it might be in a quarter of an hour or thereaway, from the time he left the Longships behind his back till they came to St. Agnes flashing light.

There was no stay when it came to the islands; for away it went all around and across them so high up that he saw all Scilly isles spread out like a map, and so plainly that he always remembered their position. Then without any control from the rider, Jackey's steed turned tail on Scilly and brought him back—about daybreak—to Kelynack Downs again, within a stone's throw of the rock where he mounted, shook him off pretty gently, and vanished in flame and smoke—as usual.

The Devil carried Jackey easy enough; but, for nearly a week after his ride, he felt very stiff and sore all over.

If any doubting body questioned the truth of this story or hinted that perhaps he fell asleep on Kelynack Downs and had "the stag," or got "hilla-rodden," (night-mare) he would reply,

"Don't 'e believe it, my dear; not sure nuf; and, as a proof that what I tell 'e is true, if you will give me a piece of chalk I'll mark out all the islands as I seed them, and as correct as anyone who had lived there all his time. Yet I had never been to Scilly before, nor have I since that night. Bless the Lord, I had a narrow escape; but didn't stay so late a-courting any more, and a few months after that night's ride, Mally and me—we got married."

One can't see what motive Old Nick had in this case, to take such trouble, unless it were for a mere freak, because he never seemed to claim any recompense from his rider.

To be "hilla-ridden," and to have the "stag," are the only names known to old country folks for the "night-mare," which is a word one never hears among them. There is, however, some difference in the signification of our two local terms. The former means to pass the time in an agony of tormenting dreams; the latter is used for obstructed respiration, or a feeling of weight on the chest, that prevents a person from moving.

ANCIENT BRIDAL CUSTOMS.

With the past and with the present,
Quaint old manners still are link'd;
Olden customs, grave and pleasant,
Ling'ring still, though nigh extinct.

C. T. C.

SOME West Country folks still observe a few old-fashioned marriage usages; one of which the following sketch will explain. It was given us, as inserted, by a young man who was one of the wedding guests.

"In the winter of 1860 we were invited to a wedding at a place called the Grambler in Sancreed; with strict orders to be in time to accompany the "weddenars" to church at ten o'clock the following Saturday morning.

Not caring to take part in the ceremony, we only left Penzance at one o'clock in the afternoon. On our arriving at New Bridge we found a messenger awaiting our arrival to guide us to the bride's parents' house where the wedding was being held. He also brought a bottle of brandy which An' Nancy, the bride's mother, sent for the "strangers from Penzance to drink on the way, to keep out the cold."

On nearing the house, we heard music and dancing, when our guide hastened on before to let the party know we were come. "My dear boys," said An' Nancy, meeting us at the door, "come 'e in quick out of the cold, we've ben afeerd you woddan coman."

All the company received us with hearty kindness; being placed at the board, our host said, "We've had dennar, my dears, but there's plenty left for 'e," at the same time pitching on each of our plates a piece of roast beef of not less than four pounds, "Aet that fust," he continued, "then you shall have some more." My companion looking rather surprised at the liberal supply, An' Nancy exclaimed, "What's the matter weth thee my boy, dossena like et? Well than thee shust have somethan else;" and without waiting a reply, took away the plate of beef and replaced it with one of roast goose and a dish of boiled pudding, saying, "Now there, my dear boy, aet that, I s'ppose the beef was too tough for 'e."

Meanwhile the wedding-party—most of whom were young people—awaited us in another room; we soon joined them and found good drink and cakes in abundance. Uncle Will, the bride's father, being called upon for a toast, he gave:—

"Here's to the bridegroom and the bride,
May they stick to each other's side;
I hope their life will be of joy,
And that the fust will be a boy."

which was received with roars of laughter and stamping of feet. Aunt Nancy took from a buffet several bottles of cordials for the women and others who liked them; amongst others were poppy and blackberry syrups, sweet-drink (mead),—that had been kept some years for this happy occasion—and peppermint water, of her own distilling. Presently the fiddle struck up with a jig. "Les have the double shuffle, Uncle Will," said the young people. Up he jumped as lively as a kid, though he was near eighty, and footed it out to the delight of all.

Young Jan of Santust (St. Just) followed, making the fire fly from the heels of his boots, like flashes of lightning; and all the company were quickly whirling, in reels, without much order.

Now, whilst the gaiety was at its height, the newly-wedded couple had contrived to slip out quietly, and hasten to their new home. "They're off, they're off," cried several voices; "come on soas, or else we shall be too late; they will be in bed and lock the door." Away they all flew, like mad devils, scampering over hedges and ditches for nearly a mile. We followed—fortunately for us it was a clear moonlight night.

When we got to the house the foremost of the party were up stairs. "Come 'e up, boys," shouted they; up we went and found the bride and bridegroom in bed, with their clothes on, having had no time to lock the door even, as the wedding guests were close on their heels.

We shall long remember the scene we then witnessed; the guests were beating them in bed, with stockings, straps, braces, or anything they could lay hands on. "Give them pepper," shouted young Jan, the groom's best man; "give et them, boys," and pepper them they did right merrily. Not wishing to be behind the rest, we took off our braces and followed suit. They continued this strange sport for a good while, until the leader said, "Les go back, soas, or else we shall be all ill-wisht, for et's nearly twelve a'clock."

Away they again rushed back to the old folks' house; and each one on arriving, before speaking, touched the cravel, (lintel or head-stone of the hearth) with his or her head, for good luck.

The old couple seemed well satisfied when we returned, as it was not quite midnight.

Many elderly folks had arrived late in the evening to drink health and long life to the newly-married; they assured us that it was an old custom to tan young married people to bed, or else they would meet with bad luck all their days. The good old souls had arranged for us to stay over night; but as we deemed it best to return home, they made us take more to eat and drink, to keep out the cold and help us on the road, they said. Then amidst hearty leave-takings and promises to visit them again soon, they allowed us to depart.

Well, somehow, we arrived home about daybreak, but often wished that we had stopped at the Grambler till sunrise.

At more modish weddings the guests merely enter the bridal-chamber and throw stockings—in which stones or something to make weight are placed— at the bride and bridegroom in bed. The first one hit, of the happy couple, betokens the sex of their first-born.

It was an old custom, religiously observed, until lately, in Zennor and adjacent parishes on the north coast, to waylay a married couple on their wedding-night and flog them to bed with cords, sheep-spans, or anything handy for the purpose; believing that this rough treatment would ensure them happiness and the "heritage and gift that cometh from the Lord," of a numerous family.

MADRON WELL.

ON passing over a stile and entering the moor in which the well is situated, cross the moor at a right-angle to the hedge, and a minute's walk will bring one to the noted spring, which is not seen until very near, as it has no wall above the surface, nor any mark by which it can be distinguished at a distance.

Much has been written of the remarkable cures effected by its holy waters, and the intercession of St. Madron, or Motran; when it was so famous that the maimed, halt, and lame, made pilgrimages from distant parts to the heathy moor.

It is still resorted to on the first three Wednesdays in May, by some few women of the neighbourhood, who bring children to be cured of skin diseases by being bathed in it. Its old repute as a divining fount has not yet quite died out, though young folks visit it now to drop pebbles or pins into the well, more for fun and the pleasure of each other's company, than through any belief that the falling together, or the separation of pins or pebbles, will tell how the course of love will run between the parties indicated by the objects dropped into the spring; or that the number of bubbles which rise in the water, on stamping near the well, mark the years, in answer to any question of time; but there was not such want of faith, however, half a century ago.

A short time since I visited an elderly dame of Madron, who was a highly reputed charmer for the cure of various skin ailments; I had known her from my childhood; and my object was to glean what I could about the rites practised, within her remembrance, at Madron Well, the Crick-stone, and elsewhere.

She gave the following account of the usages at Madron Well about fifty years ago. At that time, when she lived in Lanyon, scores of women from Morvah, Zennor, Towednack, and other places, brought their children to be cured of the shingles, wildfires, tetters, and other diseases, as well as to fortify them against witchcraft or being blighted with an evil eye.

An old dame called An' Katty, who mostly lived in the Bossullows, or some place near, and who did little but knitting-work, picked up a good living in May by attending at the well, to direct the high country folks how they were to proceed in using the waters.

First she had the child stripped as naked as it was born; then it was plunged three times against the sun; next the creature was passed quickly nine times around the spring, going from east to west, or with the sun; the child was then dressed, rolled up in something warm, and laid to sleep near the water; if it slept, and plenty of bubbles rose in the well, it was a good sign. I asked if a prayer, charm, or anything was spoken during the operations? "Why, no, to be sure," my old friend replied, "don't 'e know any better, there musn't be a word spoken all the time they are near the water, it would spoil the spell; and a piece rented, not cut, from the child's clothes, or from that of anybody using the well must be left near it for good luck; ever so small a bit will do. This was mostly placed out of sight between the stones bordering the brooklet, or hung on a thorn that grew on the chapel wall.

Whilst one party went through their rites at the spring, all the others remained over the stile in the higher enclosure, or by the hedge, because, if a word were spoken by anybody near the well during the dipping, they had to come again." The old woman, An' Katty, was never paid in money, but balls of yarn, and other things she might want, were dropped on the road, outside the well-moors, for her; she also got good pickings by instructing young girls how to "try for sweethearts" at the well. "Scores of maidens"—the dame's words— "used, in the summer evenings, to come down to the well from ever so far, to drop into it pins, gravels, or any small thing that would sink." The names of persons were not always spoken when the objects which represented them were dropped into the water; it sufficed to think of them; and as pins or pebbles remained together or separated, such would be the couple's fate. It was only when the spring was working (rising strongly) that it was of any use to try the spells; and it was unlucky to speak when near the well at such times.

The old woman that I visited said she had never heard that any saint had anything to do with the water, except from a person who told her there was something about it in a book; nor had she or anybody else heard the water called St. Madron's Well, except by the new gentry, who go about new naming places, and think they know more about them than the people who have lived there ever since the world was created. She never heard of any ceremony being performed at the old Chapel, except that some persons hung a bit of their clothing on a thorn tree that grew near it. High Country folks, who mostly resort to the spring, pay no regard to any saint or to anyone else, except some old women who may come down with them to show how everything used to be done.

There is a spring, not far from Bosporthenes, in Zennor, which was said to be as good as Madron Well; and children were often taken thither and treated in the same way.

Such is the substance of what the dame related; and she regarded the due observance of ancient customs as a very solemn matter.

In answer to the questions of "What was the reason for going round the well nine times? Leaving bits of clothing? Following the sun, &c.?" It was always the same reply, "Such were the old customs," and everybody knew it was unlucky to do any such work, and many things besides, against the sun's course; no woman, who knew anything, would place pans of milk in a dairy, so as to have to unream (skim) them, in turn, against the sun, nor stir cream in that direction to make butter.

By following down the well-stream or hedge, mentioned above, we come to the Chapel. In its southern wall may be noticed an opening for letting water from the brook, which runs near it, flow into a baptistry in the south-western corner of the Chapel. Entering the doorway, on the northern side, one may remark that this primitive fount appears to have been arched over, after the manner of our old bee-hive huts, by the upper rows of stones slightly over-hanging. The altar table-slab, or mensa—still remaining at the east end—has a square pit worked in its centre, probably to mark the spot—over reliques—on which the monstrance was placed. A step makes the division between the little nave and sacrarium; there are also the remains of stone seats which were carried all around against the walls.

Let no rude hand remove,
Or spoil thee; for the spot is consecrate
To thee, and thou to it.

THE CRICK-STONE, OR MEN-AN-TOL.

IN a croft belonging to Lanyon farm, and about half a mile north of the town-place, there is a remarkable group of three stones, the centre one of which is called by antiquaries the Men-an-tol (holed stone), and by country folk the Crick-stone, from an old custom—not yet extinct—of "crameing" (crawling on all fours) nine times through the hole in the centre stone, going against the sun's course, for the cure of lumbago, sciatica, and other "cricks" and pains in the back. Young children were also put through it to ensure them healthy growth.

Antiquaries are undecided with respect to the purpose for which these mysterious stones were erected. Some hold that it is a sepulchral monument, as well as the Men Scryfa (inscribed stone) half a mile further on, because there is a tradition that a little below, in Gendhal moor, there was once so great a battle that the streams ran with blood. Others think the object of its erection was for the computation of time; among the latter is Professor Max Müller, who, in the *Quarterly Review*, for August, 1867, after stating that the three stones are in a line bearing nearly east and west, says:—

"This Men-an-tol may be an old dial, erected originally to fix the proper time for the celebration of the autumnal equinox; and, though it may have been applied to other purposes likewise, such as the curing of children by dragging them several times through the hole, still its original intention may have been astronomical."

He also thinks that the Menheeres (long stones) served the same purpose, as they are mostly found in pairs bearing nearly east and west.

The Tolmen, in Constantine parish, and holed stones in other parts of the county, were used the same way as Lanyon Crick-stone for curing various ailments.

To cure boils and rheumatism, persons "crame" nine times against the sun, under a bramble growing at both ends.

The notion is that going against the sun will backen a disease but in all other cases the sun's course must be followed.

CHARMS.

THERE are persons in every parish west of Hayle, and in many east of it, who charm for the cure of various ailments. The members of a family, formerly of Sennen, are believed to possess peculiar virtues as charmers, which is said to have been obtained, hundreds of years ago, from a forefather of theirs, dwelling in Escols, who found, washed in on Gwenvor sand, a very old man, almost dead, whom he took to his house, had him well cared for, so that he soon recovered and prepared to depart. Before leaving, however, he told his host that he had neither gold nor silver to pay him for his hospitality; yet he would bestow on him and his what would be of more value; and imparted to the old man of Escols most of the following charms, which a descendant of the family gave me by word of mouth; if written they are useless, and the giver of a written one thenceforth loses the power to cure by charming.

Charm for a scald, wild-fire, burn, or any other inflammatory diseases.

The person to be charmed gathers nine bramble leaves, which are put into a vessel of spring water; then each leaf is passed over and from the diseased part, whilst repeating three times to each leaf as follows:—

"Three ladies come from the east,
One with fire and two with frost;
Out with thee fire, and in with thee frost,
In the name of the Father, Son, and Holy Ghost."

A stick of fire is then taken from the hearth and passed over and around the diseased part whilst the above is repeated nine times.

Charm for a prick of a thorn, boils, kennels, &c.

"Christ was crowned with thorns,
The thorns did bleed but did not rot,
No more shall thy finger (*or whatever part it may be*),
In the name of the Father, Son, and Holy Ghost."

Charm for staunching blood.

"Christ was born in Bethlehem,
Baptised in the river Jordan;
There he digg'd a well.
And turn'd the water against the hill,
So shall thy blood stand still.
In the name, &c."

Charm for a tetter.

"Tetter, tetter, thou hast nine sisters.
God bless the flesh and preserve the bone,
Perish thou tetter and be thou gone,
In the name, &c."

"Tetter, tetter, thou hast eight sisters.
God bless the flesh and preserve the bone,
Perish thou tetter and be thou gone,
In the name, &c."

The charm is thus continued until it comes to the last, which is:—

"Tetter, tetter, thou hast no sister,
God bless the flesh and preserve the bone,
Perish thou tetter and be thou gone.
In the name, &c."

"Christ pass'd by his brother's door,
Saw his brother lying on the floor.
'What aileth thee, brother?
Pain in thy teeth?
Thy teeth shall pain thee no more.'
In the name, &c."

The charmer places his or her thumb on the diseased part in all but the first charm.

Divination with a Bible and key; seeking a response to doubts from the first words the eye may glance on in letting a Bible fall open; and various other superstitious practices, common to all England, are well known here and need not be described.

THE FAIRY TRIBES.

BELIEF in fairies is far from being extinct in Cornwall, though our country folks never call them by that name.

A few days since, a woman of Mousehal told me that not long ago troops of small people, no more than a foot and a half high, used—on moonlight nights—to come out of a hole in the cliff, opening onto the beach, Newlyn side of the village, and but a short distance from it. The little people were always dressed very smart; and if anyone came near them they would scamper away into the hole. Mothers often told their children that if they went under cliff by night the small people would carry them away into "Dicky Danjy's holt."

Another kind called spriggans, which simply means sprites, are believed to guard treasures buried in cliff and hill castles.

Not long since a tinner of Lelant dreamt, three nights following, that a crock of gold was buried in a particular spot, between large rocks within the castle, on Trecroben hill. The next clear moonlight night he dug up the ground of which he had dreamt. After working two or three hours he came to a flat stone which sounded hollow; whilst digging round its edges, the weather became suddenly dark, the wind roared around the carns, and looking up, when he had made a place for his hands to lift it, he saw hundreds of ugly spriggans coming out from amidst the rocks gathering around and approaching him. The man dropped his pick, ran down the hill and home as fast as he could lay foot to ground; he took to his bed and was unable to leave it for weeks.

When he next visited the castle he found the pit all filled in, with the turf replaced; and he nevermore dug for the treasure.

Piskey still leads benighted people astray; this sprite wanders alone and is always spoken of in the singular. It is somewhat remarkable that a green bug, frequently found on bramble bushes in autumn, is called by this name. After Michaelmas, it is said, that blackberries are unwholesome because Piskey spoils them then.

Places frequented by goats are believed to be the favourite haunts of fairies.

It is uncertain whether Bucka can be regarded as one of the fairy tribe; old people, within my remembrance, spoke of a Bucka Gwidden and a Bucka Dhu—by the former they meant a good spirit, and by the latter an evil one, now known as Bucka boo. I have been told, by persons of credit, that within the last forty years it was a usual practice with Newlyn and Mousehal fishermen to leave on the sand at night a portion of their catch for Bucka. Probably from this observance the common nickname of Newlyn Buckas was derived. An old rhyme says:—

"Penzance boys up in a tree,
Looking as wisht as wisht can be;
Newlyn buckas as strong as oak,
Knocking them down at every poke."

From this it appears that Newlyn boys once considered it a matter of pride to be called by the name of their ancient divinity.

The knockers of the mines—that some class among fairy tribes—are simply believed, by our tinners, to be the spirits of those who worked the 'old bals' in ancient times.

MERMAIDS AND THE HOOPER.

WITHIN easy memory many parts of the western coast were said to be frequented by mermaids, particularly Sennen Cove. This place was also resorted to by a remarkable spirit called the Hooper—from the hooting or hooping sounds which it was accustomed to make.

In old time, according to tradition, a compact cloud of mist often came in from over sea—when the weather was by no means foggy—and rested on the rocks called Cowloe, thence it spread itself, like a curtain of cloud, quite across Sennen Cove. By night a dull light was mostly seen amidst the vapour, with sparks ascending as if a fire burned within it; at the same time hooping sounds were heard proceeding therefrom. People believed the misty cloud shrouded a spirit, which came to forewarn them of approaching storms, and that those who attempted to put to sea found an invisible force—seemingly in the mist—to resist them.

A reckless fisherman and his son, however,—disregarding the token—launched their boat and beat through the fog with a threshal (flail); they passed the cloud of mist which followed them, and neither the men, nor the Hooper, were evermore seen in Sennen Cove.

This is the only place in the west where any tradition of such a guardian spirit is preserved.

THE WRECKER AND THE DEATH SHIP.

Full well 'tis known adown the dale;
Tho' passing strange indeed the tale,
And doubtful may appear.

SHENSTONE.

PERSONS of a notoriously wicked character were said to have been frequently taken off bodily by Old Nick when they died. The following is one of many stories to that effect.

More than a hundred years ago a dark strange man appeared in St. Just; no one knew whence he came, but it was supposed, however, that he was put ashore from a pirate ship, by way of marooning him; as the crews of such are wont to do by any wretch that is too bad even to consort with high sea robbers.

He didn't appear to want for money as he soon rented a small, lone, tenement, near the shore, and married a widow of the neighbourhood.

People wondered, for a long while, how so many vessels got wrecked under the cliff that bordered the stranger's farm.

At length it was discovered that on dark winter nights—when honest folks were a-bed—he made it his practice to fasten a lantern to the neck of a horse, which he had hobbled, by tying down its head to a fore-leg; then he drove the horse along near the cliff, and the lantern, from its motion, would be taken for a vessel's stern-light.

Consequently those on board ships sailing by, expecting to find plenty of sea room, would come right in and be wrecked on the rocks. Any of their crews that escaped a watery grave the wretch would knock on the head with his axe, or cut off their hand when they tried to grasp the rocks.

He lived long and became rich by his sin. At length, however, the time came for the fiend to claim his own. When he was dying his awful shrieks were heard far away, as he cried, "Do save me from the devil, and the sailors, there, looking to tear me to pieces." Several parsons and other pious folks were sent for,—all those of the neighbourhood readily came, for the dying sinner was rich.

Though it was in harvest time and high day, the old wrecker's chamber became, at times, as dark as night. The parsons saw the devil in the room, when others could not; by their reading they drove him to take many shapes, but for all that he would not be put out; at last, when he took the form of a fly, and buzzed about the dying wretch, they saw it was in vain for them to try any longer.

During the time the exorcists were engaged, the chamber seemed—by the sound—to be filled with the sea splashing around the bed; waves were heard as if surging and breaking against the house, though it was a good bit inland.

Whilst this was taking place at the dying wrecker's bedside, two men, who were about harvest work in one of his fields near the cliff, heard a hollow voice, as if coming from the sea, which said, "The hour is come but the man is not come."

Looking in the direction whence the words came, they saw no person; but far out to sea, they beheld a black, heavy, square-rigged ship, with all sail set, coming fast in, against wind and tide, and not a hand to be seen aboard her.

She came so close under cliff that only her topmast could be seen; when black clouds—that seemed to rise out of the deep—gathered around her and extended thence straight to the dying man's dwelling.

The harvest-men, terrified at the sight of this ship-of-doom so near them, ran up to the town-place, just as the old sinner died, when his dwelling shook as if about to fall. Everybody, in great fright, rushed out and saw the black clouds roll off towards the death-ship, which, at once, sailed away—amidst a blaze of lightning—far over sea, and disappeared.

The weather immediately cleared, and nothing unusual occurred until a few men assembled to put the wrecker's ghastly remains quickly off the face of the earth; then, as the coffin was borne towards the churchyard, a large black pig came—no one knew from whence—and followed the bearers, who all declared the coffin was too light to contain any body. The sky, too, became suddenly overcast, and a tempest raged to that degree, they could scarcely keep on their legs to reach the churchyard stile, where such sheets of blinding lightning flashed around them, that they dropped the coffin and rushed into the church.

The storm having abated, they ventured out, and found nothing of the coffin but its handles and a few nails, for it had been set on fire, and all else consumed, by the lightning.

It does not appear what business the black pig had in the funeral procession; such is the way, however, in which the story is always told.

THE SUN NEVER SHINES ON THOSE WHO HAVE "SWORN AWAY A LIFE."

ONE frequently hears, in remote country places, the reproachful sayings of, "The sun wont shine on thee," or, "the sun don't shine on thee." This is regarded as a very bitter taunt, even by those who do not understand its allusion or the old belief from which it proceeds.

The following story, told me by an aged mine captain, of Lelant, will serve to explain it.

A few years ago a smuggler of Breage gave false evidence, which caused one of another crew to be hanged, on the charge of having fired a fatal shot at an officer belonging to a revenue cutter.

This perjurer, who swore away an innocent man's life, received—for informing—such a sum of blood money as made him comparatively rich, yet he remained at sea for several years, until he came to live at Hayle. Few persons there knew him; but everybody remarked that he looked deathly pale and shivered with cold, however warm the weather might be. He lived alone and rarely left his house to go beyond his garden, and his neighbours said that when he stood out in "sunshiney" weather he cast no shadow. They surmised that he had been forsworn; for he could never see the sun, and the sky always appeared dark to him; yet he saw everything else the same as other people.

After his decease it became known how he had caused an innocent man's death.

A LEGEND OF PENGERSEC.

So I your presence may enjoye,
No toil I will refuse;
But wanting you, my life is death;
Nay, death Ild rather chuse.

FAIR ROSAMOND.

MANY years ago an elderly gentleman of Gwinear told me the following story, which he had often heard related by old folks of that parish and Breage, about certain ancient occupants of Pengersec; who dwelt there long before the present castle was built by Milliton, who, according to their legend, constructed his stronghold in the time of Henry VIII, out of the ruins of a former castle which stood near the same site; and of which, they say, some out-works may still be traced towards the sea.

My friend made a point of telling the story just as it was related by old folks, and I wrote the greater part of it from his recital.

It contains, however, too many details of dreadful crimes to please general readers; and as I think it right to give our old stories unmutilated—so far as a due regard to decorum permits—I hesitated about publishing it until advised to do so by friends who thought it would interest antiquarian students.

The lords of old Pengersec Castle were all soldiers who rarely lived at home. When the last lord's father was about twenty, as there was no fighting going on hereabouts, he betook himself to outlandish countries, far away in the east, to a place inhabited by people who were little better than savages; for, instead of tilling the ground or digging for tin, they passed their time roving from place to place as they wanted fresh pastures for their cattle. They lived in tents covered with the skins of their flocks, and their raiment was made of the same material; yet these heathen worshippers of Termagaunt got plenty of gold and precious things, by sending their young men to fight, for or against, or to rob their more industrious neighbours who dwelt in houses, tilled the ground, and followed trades.

Well, Pengersec went to war with these pagans, for or against, we don't know nor care which, no more did he, so that he was fighting.

Whilst there, however, he fell in love with a beautiful Princess of the people who dwelt in towns.

He wished to carry her off, but he couldn't, because she was betrothed to a Prince of that country and jealously watched; yet Pengersec often found means to visit the lady in the dead of night; and about the time he left to return home she bore him a child, which was "put going" (made away with). In spite of all, the Princess would then have followed him, had he not vowed to return for her soon, or if, in the meanwhile, the old king, her father, died— and not having male offspring—he would marry her there and reign in his stead.

Then she took off her finger-ring, broke it, and gave him half, saying, "when this you see, remember your love in a far country;" and he swore by all she held sacred to remain unwed for seven years unless he married her.

Shortly after his return home, however, he espoused a fair lady of Helaston. There being no signs of his wife's likelihood to present him with an heir— after having been married a year or two—he became very dissatisfied; and hearing of new wars in the east he returned—before seven years had elapsed—to the country where the former Princess—now a Queen—reigned in her own right.

He renewed their former connection—taking good care not to tell her he had a wife at home—and led her troops to war against the Prince who would have had his Queen and her dominions but for him.

She lent Pengersec her father's enchanted sword—a magic weapon that brought success to the rightful possessor—and fought by his side; yet they were conquered; and the Cornish rover missed his lady-love in their confused retreat; when, to save himself, as best he could, he took ship for home and left her to her fate.

Now the Queen escaped to a port where she had many vessels, and knowing that Pengersec's castle was near a place to which they often went for tin, she embarked with an aged captain and set sail for the Mount, hoping that if the man she trusted and loved above all in heaven or earth had escaped with life, she would find him in his native land.

Meanwhile the treacherous lover had returned and found his wife with an infant at the breast; he blamed her because she had not informed him of her state before he left home. In reply, she told him how she feared to raise his hopes, not being sure they would be realized.

He had scarcely settled himself comfortably in his castle with his wife and his son—of whom he was very fond—when, one night, the Queen knocked at his gate. In her arms she held a babe that had been born at sea; weeping, she showed it to its father who refused to admit her within his doors. "What can have possessed thee to follow me here thou crazy saracen," said he, "know that I've many years been wed." "Cruel man, dos thou spurn thy little son and me from thy doors," she replied, "now that I am in this strange land poor and needy." Not wishing the inmates of his dwelling to hear or see any more of the strange lady, he led her away down by the sea-side. There, standing on a cliff, she reproached him with being a faithless, perjured lover; with having stolen the magic sword, on which the safety of her land depended; and with being the cause of all her misfortunes. He threatened to drown her unless she promised to return at once to her own country. "Alas! I have no longer a country," said she, "for thee I am become a disgrace to my people, who scorn me," and raising her hand—as if to curse him—she continued, "but thou shalt no longer flourish; may evil meet thee and bad luck follow thee to the sorrowful end of thy days."

Provoked at her upbraiding, he, in his fury, cast her over cliff, into the deep, with the infant that she clasped to her breast.

Shortly after she was found floating lifeless on the waves, with the babe asleep in her arms, by the captain and crew of her ship, who, fearing she might be unkindly received, wished to accompany her, but preferring to meet her roving lover alone, she bade them remain in the boat, near where she landed, at a short distance from his castle.

The Queen's remains were taken to her native land, and the good captain reared her child, which passed for his own son.

This old tiger of a Pengersec spent much of his time in hunting wolves, which were numerous then; the following day he was in full chase on Tregonning hill until night, when a violent storm arose. By the lightning's glare he saw, cowering around him, a drove of wild animals, that dreaded the awful thunder-storm more than they did the hunter and his dogs. Presently appeared among them a white hare, with eyes like coals of fire, then the dogs and savage beasts ran away howling louder than the tempest; the horse threw its rider and left him alone on the hill with the white hare that Pengersec knew to be the vengeful spirit of the murdered lady.

Search being made next day he was found on the hill more dead than alive from the effects of his fall and fright.

Worst of all he had lost the enchanted sword, with which he could save his life in any encounter. This mishap troubled him much, for, when in possession of this charmed weapon, he thought it mere fun to lop off the heads of those who offended him; but now he became a coward and dreaded to go beyond his castle gate without a priest beside him.

Indeed, he could never leave his dwelling but the white hare would cross his path. When the priests vainly tried to dispose of her—like other spirits—in the Red Sea, she assumed her natural shape and told them not to think they had power to bind or loose her like the spirits of those who had been in their hands from their cradle to the grave; moreover, that she wouldn't be controlled by them or their gods, but, to please herself, would quit the place until her son came to man's estate.

Pengersec's cruel treatment of his wife shortened her days; she soon died, leaving her unweaned child, called Marec, to be nursed by the miller's wife, who shared her breast between the young heir and her son Uter.

Many years passed during which Pengersec seldom went beyond his castle that he had almost entirely to himself; a few old servants only remained in the gloomy habitation, out of regard to the young master, that he might be properly instructed and cared for. Marec, when about twenty years of age, excelled in all manly exercises; being a good seaman, as well as his constant attendant and foster-brother Uter, they would steer their boat through the roughest breakers, to aid a ship in distress, when other men feared to leave the shore. His favourite pastime was taming wild horses of the hills, in which he was said to have remarkable skill.

About this time Pengersec recovered his wonted courage, so far as to venture out to see the young men's sports, and to visit Godolphin castle—a few miles off—where lived a rich lady whom he wished his son to wed.

She had often seen Marec bear away the hurling-ball, win prizes at wrestling and other games, and had a great desire for him and more for the domain to which he was heir.

Although she was passable as to looks, and only a year or two older than the young lord, he had no liking for her, because she had the repute of being a sorceress. In all the country side it was whispered that the damsel was too intimate with an old witch of Fraddam, whose niece, called Venna, was the lady's favourite waiting-woman.

They spent much time together distilling or otherwise concocting what they named medicaments, though some called them poisons; and many persons, believing the lady had evil eyes, pointed at her with forked fingers to avert their baneful influence.

Yet, from her affected horror of little failings, pretended pity for those whom she slandered by insinuations, and her constant attendance at church, simple people, that she favoured, thought her a good woman; and crafty ones, from sympathy, were ever ready to further her designs.

As the young man cared more about his sports than for the lady, Pengersec did the courting—for his son at first—but at length he married the damsel of Godolphin himself.

They had not been long wedded, however, ere she became disgusted with her old lord's gloomy fits, and, from seeing much of Marec, her passion for him became too much for concealment. Fearing lest she might betray her desires to her husband, she shut herself up in her own apartments and, pretending to be ill, sent for the witch of Fraddam, who soon discovered her ailment.

The lady complained of her dreary life shut up in the lonesome castle with her morose old husband, though he doted on her, after his fashion. Having made him promise, before marriage, that she and her children should inherit his lands and all he could keep from his eldest son, it fretted her to find that, as yet, she was not likely to become a mother. "Behave kinder to Marec," said the wise-woman, "that he and his comrades may cheer your solitude."

"Never name the uncouth savage to me!" exclaimed the lady, "he would far rather chase wolves and ride wild horses around the hills than pass any time, by day or by night, in a lady's bower." The witch being skilled in making love-potions and powders, after more converse, promised to send her a philter, by the aid of which Marec would soon become her humble slave, and pine for her love. The love-drink was fetched without delay by Venna, who waited on her young master at supper and spiced his ale; but this was a mistake, for it should have been prepared and served by the person in whose favour it was intended to work.

The waiting-maid being a comely lass, and he a handsome man, she forgot her duty to her mistress, when Marec—as the custom was with gallant youths—pressed her to drink from his tankard to sweeten it. The cordial and charms, that were intended to move his affections in the lady's favour, ended in his strolling on the sea-shore with her handmaid. The step-dame, unable to rest, wandered down on the beach, where she espied the loving pair in amorous dalliance. Her love turned to hate; without being seen by them, she returned and passed the night in planning revenge.

In the morning early the enraged lady sought an interview with her doting old husband, and told him that she wished to return to her father's house, because she was pining for fresh air, but dared not leave her room when his son was in the castle for fear of being insulted by his unbecoming behaviour; in fact, she gave the old lord to understand—by hints, which might mean little or much—that Marec then discovered such a passion for her as she failed to inspire before her marriage.

Pengersec raved, and swore he would be the death of him before many hours were passed; at length, however, his fit of anger having moderated, he assured his wife that he would get him taken so far away that it would be long ere he returned to trouble her, if ever he did.

This being agreed on, the lady somewhat pacified returned to her own apartment, and summoned her woman to attend her. Venna had no sooner entered the chamber than her mistress pinned her in a corner, held a knife to her breast, and vowed to have her heart's blood that instant—for her treachery in enticing her young master to the sea-shore—unless she drank the contents of a phial which she held to her lips.

"Have patience, my dear mistress," said she, "and I will either explain to your satisfaction what seemeth false dealing and disloyalty, or I'll drain this bottle of poison to the last drop." Venna then told her mistress that she was only following her aunt's instructions to get Marec into her toils, and—if other means failed—induce him, in the dead of night, to visit her chamber by the outer stair from the garden.

The woman also proposed to make other arrangements, of which her mistress approved.

Then the pair devised how to get rid of the old lord speedily, for—having excited his jealousy—they feared he might kill his son, or send him from the country without delay.

They little thought, however, when they had decided to poison him in the evening at his supper, that all their infernal plans were overheard by the priest and steward, who had long suspected the step-dame and her woman of hatching some plot against the young master.

In Pengersec castle, as in many dwellings of that time, there were private passages, contrived in the thickness of its walls. Such places, being known only to the master and his confidential servants, were frequently forgotten; yet the priests, who were skilled builders and great devisers of mysterious hiding-holes, mostly knew where to find them.

From behind a perforated carving, in stone or wainscot, the lady's wicked designs were found out. At supper, the old steward, as was his custom, stood behind his master to hand him the tankard of ale, that he drank with his venison pasty, and a goblet of strong waters, that stood in a buffet—prepared and spiced by the lady for her husband—beside one for herself, to take with the sweet waffels with which they finished their repast. The hall being but dimly lighted by the fading twilight and a fire on the hearth, the steward managed to distract the lady's attention, when removing the tankard, by letting it fall and spilling what remained in it on her robe, so that, without being noticed, he exchanged the two drinking-vessels' contents, and the lady took the poisoned draught which she had prepared for her spouse.

But it had little or no effect on her for the time, because, to guard against a mischance of this kind, she had long accustomed herself to imbibe poisons, in increasing doses, until she could stand a quantity that would be fatal to one not thus fortified.

After supper the priest informed Marec of the snares laid to entrap him, and of the step-dame's murderous attempt on his father.

The lady despaired of accomplishing her designs, as Marec showed by his behaviour, that he regarded her with loathing. One day, when she was more gracious to him than usual, and made advances not to be misunderstood, looking on her with contempt, he said, "Know, sorceress, that I detest thee and abhor thy shameful intentions, but thou canst neither hurt me by thy witchcraft, nor with the blight of thy evil eyes." She made no reply, but left the hall and soon after told her spouse that his son had most grossly insulted her. "Indeed," said she, "I had to defend myself with all my might to preserve my honour, and threatened to plunge a dagger into his heart unless he desisted and left my apartment." Her fabricated story so provoked the old lord that he determined to dispose of his son without delay.

That evening, the weather being stormy, Marec and Uter noticed, from Pengersec How, a vessel taking a course which would bring her into dangerous ground; the young men launched their boat, rowed towards the ship, and signalled that there were sunken rocks ahead.

Night was now fast closing in, and the land could scarcely be discerned through the mist, when the young men beheld something floating at a little distance. On approaching it, they saw it to be a drowning seaman quite exhausted, and unable to keep any longer on the surface; they pulled with might and main and were just in time to save him. Having reached Pengersec Cove, they bore him to Marec's chamber, stripped off his wet clothing, rubbed him dry, placed him in bed on sheep-skins, and lay on either side that the warmth of their bodies might help to restore him. At length his breathing became regular, and, without speaking, he went off in sound sleep.

The rescued sailor awoke much restored and just as well as need be, though surprised to find himself in a new berth with strange shipmates—as he thought his two bed-fellows. He tried to get out of bed and have a look round, when Marec well pleased to see him so far recovered—related how they had taken him into their boat the previous evening, when he was seemingly at the last gasp.

The seaman—who was called Arluth—then said, that he recollected having fallen from the "tops" into the water, and endeavouring to keep himself afloat, in hopes of being seen from his ship and rescued; but of what followed he had no remembrance. He also informed them that he was the son of a captain of an eastern ship, which frequently traded at Cornish ports; fearing his father might be in great distress, from thinking him drowned, he wished to get on board his ship as soon as possible.

Uter fetched, from the butlery, beef, bread, and beer; when the sailor and his master sat beside each other he remarked that they looked like twin brothers, from their close resemblance.

Having breakfasted, they took horses and—followed by the dogs—started for Market-jew.

When they came out on uncultivated ground, Marec proposed to hunt as they went along, that the seaman might have some game to take aboard.

They had gone but a little way when a white doe started from a thicket and ran towards the hills—followed by the hounds in full cry. The sailor's horse being an old hunter, took after them, and the rider, being an indifferent horseman, lost all control over his steed, which bore him after the hounds near to the top of Tregonning hill, where the doe disappeared and the dogs were at fault.

The sailor alighted near the same carn where Pengersec had been thrown from his horse many years agone. He had no sooner put foot to ground than lightning struck the rocks close by and they toppled over. Then he heard a voice—as if from the ground—that said, "Fear not, Arluth, beloved son of mine, to seize thy forefather's sword and with it win thy kingdom."

There was no one nigh him; but, on glancing towards the carn, he saw near it a beautiful white hare, which gazed lovingly on him for a moment and then disappeared amongst the rocks. On going to the spot, where the rocks had been severed, he found a naked sword with sparkling jewels in its hilt, and the blade shone like flame.

Arluth, having recovered from his surprise, took up the sword, and, looking round, he saw Marec and Uter near him. Surprised that it should be discovered in such a place, and at what the seaman told him, Marec said, that as he had found the magic weapon, he was destined to achieve great things.

Arluth again thought of his father and shipmates, who, not knowing if he were dead or alive would be in great trouble; he begged his companions to let him hasten to Market-jew, and their horses soon took them thither. On parting the sailor said he hoped to see his friends again; they proposed to visit him in the evening; saw him embark in a boat and pull off to his ship. The good captain was overjoyed to see him after having mourned for him as dead.

Arluth related how he had been rescued; drew the sword from his belt and told the captain where he had found it, with what he had seen and heard on the hill. The captain having examined it, said, "The time is come for me to declare that the only relationship I bear thee is through my regard and loyalty to the murdered Queen, thy mother." He then related to Arluth how the Queen had lost her kingdom and magic sword, through her ill-requited love for Pengersec; and how he had saved him when an infant. In conclusion the captain said, "Thou wilt now understand, my son—let me still call thee so— how that the young lord of Pengersec, who rescued thee last night, is thy brother. Thy name, too—which was given thee by thy mother, as soon as thou wast born—belongs to this country's tongue. The Queen, having heard Lord Pengersec thus called by his Cornish followers who attended him to her land, took that title to be one of his names, and liked it best for thee."

The captain also told the wondering sailor that he would be the acknowledged heir to their country, which had for many years been rent with civil war between divers pretendants thereto, among whom there was no one sufficiently powerful to secure the throne, since the magic sword—on which their country's safety in some way depended—had been lost, and reserved by a protecting power for him.

"Now nothing more is wanting," said he, "to enable thee to reclaim thy mother's dominions, and its people will gladly receive thee to give peace to the distracted country."

The young sailor was much surprised by what the captain related, and still more so when he said that about the time Arluth was following the white doe Pengersec came on board his ship and proposed to hire him and his crew to kidnap and carry away his son and his servant, merely to gratify a step-dame's spite. The captain said his only reply to the befooled and unnatural father's proposal was to tell him he should never leave his vessel alive if he spoke to one of his crew, and to order him over the ship's side immediately.

Being stupified with grief, he didn't think, however, of another vessel—then anchored at no great distance—that came from a city where the people mostly lived by piracy; the crew of this ship—which sailed under any colour that suited their ends—made it their business, among other things, to land in lonely places, maraud the country, carry off young people, and sell them in Barbary for slaves.

"Had I but thought of it in time," said the captain, "we would have taken off Pengersec and given him a taste of the sea, for I knew much more of him than he suspected." Having seen Pengersec go on board and leave the pirate ship, the captain and Arluth, knowing the gang would even murder their own brothers for a trifle of gold, determined to watch their proceedings, and rescue the young men if need be.

It was bargained between Pengersec and the pirates that, for a small sum, they would kidnap his son and Uter, either when they went out a-fishing— as was their practice almost nightly—or land and steal them from the castle.

Meanwhile, Arluth had arms placed in a boat; and when twilight darkened into night he saw a boat leave the pirate ship. "Now, may the gods help me!" he exclaimed, springing up and brandishing his sword, "my first use of this shall be to save my brother." Arluth with several of his crew gave chase.

Marec and Uter, being on their way to the good captain's ship, were encountered by the pirates, overpowered, and put in irons, when their companion of the morning sprang into the pirate's boat and cut in pieces every one of the gang.

Having released and embraced the captives, Arluth bore away to the pirate ship, boarded her, hanged the rest of her crew, and took the craft as a lawful prize; and a rich prize they found her.

Arluth, having returned to the good captain's ship and informed Marec and Uter how the old lord intended to serve them, said, "Come with me and never more put foot in the place whilst thy crafty stepmother's head is above ground." Marec replied to the effect that he didn't like to go away until he had furnished himself and Uter with money and needful changes of clothing. "Don't touch a thing in the accursed place," returned Arluth, "for you have a brother belonging to the land whither we are bound, who will share his last stiver with thee, and shed his heart's blood in thy defence. Nay, brother, be not surprised," continued he, in drawing Marec to him, "this brother of thine will ere long be king of the country."

"Would to heaven thou wert my brother, thou heart-of-oak, and I would joyfully go with thee to any land," replied Marec.

The captain gave the young men of Pengersec a cordial welcome, set before them the richest wines in his ship, and—smiling with satisfaction to see the brothers' attachment, and Marec's puzzled look—he related to him the history of his father's exploits, which had been told to Arluth, for the first time, only a few hours before.

Marec had been altogether ignorant of much that the old commander related of his father's youthful adventures; he rejoiced, however, to find a brother in Arluth, and to go with him, he cared not whither. Uter had such a strong regard for his master that he would gladly accompany him to the world's-end.

Arluth, having taken command of the captured pirate ship, with his brother for mate—Uter, and a few hands spared from the other vessel, as his crew— they at once made sail.

Whilst the two ships go sailing on, with clear skies and favouring gales, we will return, for a brief space, to Pengersec. About the time they got under way, the priest was told that the old lord had during the day been on board two eastern vessels; the good man, fearing this visit portended mischief, watched all night for Marec. When morning dawned, there being no appearance of the young men nor their boat—and the ships having left the bay—he sought Pengersec; found him and his wife, early as it was, in the hall. The priest and steward accused the lady of having conspired with her woman and others to destroy her step-son and husband. Venna, being summoned, turned against her mistress; the old lord, seeing how he had been fooled, ordered both women to be cast into the dungeon, mounted his horse and rode in all haste to Market-jew to see if any craft might be procured to sail after the departed ships and recover his son. Finding nothing there to the purpose, he returned at night-fall—distracted with remorse and rage—fully determined to hang his wife and her woman from the highest tower of his castle.

On nearing the thicket, from which the doe started on the preceding day, out sprang the white hare with flaming eyes, right in face of his horse; the terrified steed turned, galloped down to the shore, and, to escape the pursuing hare, took to sea. Neither the horse nor its rider were evermore seen.

The lady was released by her father's people; she became covered with scales, like a serpent—from the effects of the poison she had taken it was supposed—and she was shut up, as a loathsome object, in a dark room of Godolphin.

Venna escaped to her aunt the witch of Fraddam. The old lord having confessed, in his anguish, how he had disposed of his son and Uter, the people of Pengersec supposed they were taken to Barbary and sold as slaves; hoping, however, to discover them, the old servants took good care of everything, in order to save money and effect his ransom.

The two ships kept as near as might be on their voyage; and it was noticed that a beautiful white bird followed them from Mount's Bay; it often came within bow-shot but no one dared to aim a shaft at it, for the eastern mariners believed it to be the spirit of a departed friend who guarded them from harm.

Marec frequently passed to the old captain's vessel, when they were becalmed, for he liked much to hear him tell of eastern magicians and the wonderful things they did.

Having arrived at their destined port, they found their country in great disorder from the war waged by many pretenders to the throne, as before stated by the old commander. He had no sooner, however, presented to the people the young man, whom they had long known as his son, and related to them the history of his birth, and of the recovered magic sword, than they all flocked to Arluth's standard and proclaimed him their king.

Arluth but little valued his new dominions at first, and would have preferred the command of a good ship. Yet, to please his people, he consented to rule them, and soon became fully occupied with the cares of his government, which he regulated like the prudent captain of a well-ordered ship; he would have no idle hands nor waste of stores in his dominions.

King Arluth wished his brother to live with him as chief mate and adviser, and offered to dwell in any place he might choose, so it was near their principal port, that he might superintend the traffic.

Marec was loath to part with his brother, but his fancy was so fired with what the captain told him about a people, living near them, who were skilled in magic, that he ardently desired to visit their country, and, if possible, acquire some of their extraordinary wisdom.

Arluth, on becoming acquainted with his wishes, furnished a vessel with such merchandise as would meet with a ready sale in the wise-men's country; equipped his brother in every way becoming his rank, and dispatched him and Uter under the care of trustworthy persons.

Marec remained a long while studying among the magicians, and learned many curious arts, unknown in western lands. He also married a beautiful and rich lady, who was gifted with many rare accomplishments, and Uter wedded her favourite damsel.

In about three years, the old captain—who, in the meantime, had made a voyage to Market-jew for tin—came to the sage's country on purpose to inform Marec that his father had long been dead, and how the people on his estate had sent him money and wished for his speedy return.

Pengersec's heart then yearned for his home and his people; he told his wife how in the pleasant land, towards the setting sun, gentle showers descended, all summer long, like dews distilled from Heaven, and kept the fields ever verdant; how crops succeeded crops throughout the year, which was like a perpetual spring compared with the arid land in which they then dwelt. He said how hills and dales were covered with fat herds in that happy land, whose inhabitants had not to hunt half-starved wild animals for their subsistence, but only followed the chase for pastime; how by a process, unknown in other lands, a liquor was there brewed from grain, which made those who drank it as strong as giants and brave as lions; how the Cornish people merely washed the soil of their valleys and found metals—more precious than silver or gold.

"That is the tin, to obtain which your eastern mariners make their longest and most dangerous voyages," said Pengersec—as we shall now call Marec— "besides," continued he, "I have a strong and fair castle in a green valley by the sea; I will build thee a bower by the murmuring shore, where we will have delightful gardens and everything for pleasure." "Say no more, my beloved, about the delights of thy land," she replied, "for I shall little regard that when thou art by; thy home shall be mine wherever thou choosest to dwell; and whenever it pleaseth thee let us depart."

After procuring many magical books and other things, necessary for the practice of occult sciences, Pengersec and his lady, with Uter and his spouse, took leave of the sages and made sail for home.

On the way, Pengersec stayed some time with King Arluth, who presented him with a foal of the choicest stock of his country; he also sent on board, unknown to his brother, bales of brocade, and various rich stuffs of gold and silver tissue, besides pearls, precious stones, and other valuable things; and, promising to revisit each other, they took loving leave.

The lady passed much time on deck playing on her harp, its sweet music kept the weather fair, drew dolphins and other fishes from the depths of the sea to sport around and follow the ship to Mount's Bay; thence it came to pass that on our coast were found many rare fishes—never before seen here.

When the young lord and his beautiful bride landed at Market-jew, the people—one and all—came from near and far away to welcome them. Bonfires blazed on every hill; weeks were passed in feasting at Pengersec, where archery, hurling, slinging, wrestling, and other games were carried on that the fair stranger might see our Cornish sports; at night, minstrels and droll-tellers did their utmost to divert the company.

The lady of the castle took much delight in her new home; she often passed the mornings with her husband in hunting; she rode over moors and hills with a hawk on her wrist or a bow in her hand. At eve her harp would be heard in Pengersec towers sending joyous strains over sea and land; then fishermen would rest on their oars, and sea-birds—forgetting their nightly places of rest in the western cleeves—remained entranced around the castle.

The people were much pleased with the outlandish lady, who admired their unbounded hospitality to strangers, their primitive manners, simplicity of heart, and sincerity of intention; for they appeared to her as absolutely ignorant of fraud or flattery, as if they had never heard of such a thing; she found them to be of a free, facetious temper, though of a somewhat curious and inquisitive disposition—the women especially.

The lady thought our ancient language sounded much like her eastern tongue, and that made her feel all the more at home.

Pengersec was no sooner fairly settled than he built two broad and lofty towers—united by a gallery—on the seaward side of his castle. The easternmost tower was constructed with everything requisite for his magic art; in the other were placed his lady's private apartments, overlooking pleasant gardens, the green glen, and boundless ocean.

When Pengersec returned, his stepmother was still immured in her dark chamber. In a little while, however, she fretted herself to death, and the breath no sooner left her body than she returned to haunt the rooms formerly occupied by her in the castle. Pengersec had that portion of the building at once rased to the ground, but her hideous ghost still continued to wander about the place.

Now it was that the young lord essayed the power of his art to some purpose, for, by his enchantment, he confined her to a hole in a headland, west of Pengersec Cove, called the How, and compelled her to assume the form of an uncommonly large adder, in which shape she is still occasionally seen there, if what people of that neighbourhood say, be true.

Over a few years, Pengersec became so much attached to occult sciences that he devoted nearly all his time to their practice; he was seldom seen beyond his castle, and, even there, he almost continually shut himself up in his tower, where he was never approached except by his lady and Uter, both of whom assisted him in such operations as required help. Fires would be seen—through loop-holes in his tower—blazing all night long; and the flames ascended high above the battlements when he changed base metals into silver and gold.

If his fire happened to go out he rekindled it by sparks drawn from the sun, by means of a magic crystal. With the same glass, or another, he also saw what was being done in distant lands.

A person, who came from far to see the magician's wonders, on looking into or through this glass, beheld in the castle-court what appeared to be an uncommonly large bird carrying in its mouth a baulk of timber; on taking away the glass he could only see a duck with a straw in her bill.

Pengersec paid no attention to his farms, which left to Uter's management; the lord, indeed, had no reason to care about them whilst he could make gold in abundance.

But this untold riches was about the least important fruit of his science, for—ere he became middle-aged—he concocted a magical elixir, or water-of-life, which preserved him, his lady, and others in their youthful vigour.

The lord of Pengersec was soon renowned in all the west as a most powerful enchanter, whom everybody feared to molest—and well they might. Some one from the Mount, having a mind to his fat sheep, carried one of them down to the cliff, tied its legs together, and passed them over his head. At this instant, however, the enchanter, happening to glance at his magic glass, saw what was taking place, and put a spell on the thief that made him remain in the same spot all the night with the tide rising around him and the sheep hanging from his neck. The enchanter released the thief in the morning and gave him the sheep with a caution not to meddle with his flocks again or he would be served out worse.

'Tis said, too, that Venna, who was now a noted wise-woman or witch—living at St. Hillar Downs—often had contests with the enchanter to test the relative powers of their familiars; they contended with spells and counter-spells from mere pride of art. We omit the details because they would merely be a repetition of much that has been related in the foregoing stories of witchcraft and pellar-craft.

At times the lord would be seen careering over moors and hills, mounted on his handsome mare, brought from the east; she excelled every other steed for swiftness; a whisper from him would make her as docile as a lamb, though she was quite unmanageable with everybody else.

The castle servants were frequently alarmed by hearing the enchanter conjuring, in an unknown tongue, the unruly spirits that he required to serve him; or by loud explosions. Pungent and fiery vapours, that threatened to consume the building, often sent their strong odours for miles around. At such times the frightened inmates sought their lady's aid; who, on taking her harp to the enchanter's tower, soon drove away or subdued the evil spirits by the power of its melody. One time the magician left his furnaces and their fires to the care of his attendant whilst he went to pass a while in his lady's bower; he had not been long there when something told him that mischief was taking place in his tower. On hastening thither he found the attendant, Uter, had neglected his duty; and, by reading in one of the magical books, had called up evil spirits in such numbers that in another instant they would have destroyed him; and it required all the enchanter's power to subdue them.

Many years elapsed. The lord had a numerous family—of whom he took little heed. Some of them were settled on farms, others had been adopted by their uncle, King Arluth, who frequently sent his brother rare drugs, spices, and other things, required by him for making his precious liquor of life. The lady, having outlived all her children and grandchildren, became weary of existence in a world, or amidst a people, that seemed strange to her—all those of her own age being long dead—and wishing to rest with her children, though loath to leave her husband, she often begged him to discontinue prolonging his life; and he—as on former occasions, for the last hundred years or so—always promised her to leave the world when he had perfected some new essay of his art, which was all in all to him. His wife, however, neglected to take the life-cordial, and, at length, rested beneath the sod.

Their numerous descendants were known—as the custom was then—by the names of places on which they dwelt; only one of them is particularly mentioned by name in the legend; this was a lady, who lived in Pengersec Castle at the time that a Welsh Prince, from having heard of the Cornish magician's renown, came over to him for instruction, and before his departure married the beautiful Lamorna, who was the sage's great-granddaughter.

The Welsh Prince, having sent a quantity of black stones to Pengersec, he extracted from them a sort of liquid-fire, which, by some mismanagement, burst its containing vessels, and an instant afterwards all was in flames. The magician was consumed with all his books and treasures; the castle and all it held destroyed, leaving nothing but the bare walls.

It is said that Venna, the witch, prolonged her life also—without the aid of Pengersec's elixir—by merely enticing to her habitation, and keeping there, goats and young people. From them, by some means of her craft, she drew their youthful vigour to herself and caused them to pine and die. This wicked practice of hers having being discovered, young folks were carefully kept out of her reach; and to prevent her from doing any more mischief, one night when she was brewing her hell-broth, and the flames were seen rising high, the people—to prevent her escape—nailed up her door; put a turf over her chimney-top, and smothered her in the infernal vapours that arose from her hearth.

All the chief people of the story are ended; but had it not been for Pengersec's untoward accident he might have lived to this day.

We have preserved in the foregoing what may seem to many persons mere childish fancies; if, however, the same incidents should be found in the folk-lore of other lands, they will have an interest for those whose leisure and learning enabled them to trace our popular tales to their fountain-head.

An old tinner of Lelant, who told me the story of "Tom and the giant Denbras," brought into it the incident of Pengersec enchanting a "giant of the Mount" that came to steal his cattle. Much the same story is still told in Sennen of an astrologer, and a reputed conjuror, called Dyonysious Williams, who lived in Mayon about a century ago. This gentleman found that his furse-rick was diminishing much faster than could be accounted for, from the ordinary consumption of fuel in his own house. He consulted his books, and discovered by his art that some women, of Sennen Cove, made it a practice of carrying away his furse every night. The very next night, after all honest folks should be in their beds, an old woman of the Cove came, as usual, to his rick for a "burn" of furse. She made one of no more than the usual size, which she tried to lift on to her back, but found that she could not move it. She then took out half the furse, but was still unable to lift the small quantity that remained in her rope. Becoming frightened, she tried to get out the rope and run, but found that she had neither the power to draw it out nor to move from the spot herself. Of course the conjuror had put a spell on her, and there she had to remain throughout the cold winter's night until Mr. Williams came out in the morning and released her from the spell. As she was a very poor old soul, he let her have a burn of furse; but she took good care never to come any more, nor did the other women who soon found out how she had been served.

GLOSSARY OF LOCAL WORDS.

A or AH, he or it; *e.g.* a es, it is.
AFTER-WINDING, waste corn.
AN', aunt, an expression of regard applied to aged women.
ARREAH! (Maria?) an exclamation of angry surprise.
ARISH, stubble.

BAL, a mine.
BANNAL, broom plant.
BOWJEY, sheepfold, &c., on cliff or downs.
BRAVE, much, very well, &c.
BRUYANS, crumbs.
BUCCA, a spirit.
BUCCA-BOO (-DHU), a black spirit.
BULHORN, a large shell-snail.
BUSSA, an earthen crock.
BUSY (to be), to require; *e.g.* it is BUSY all, it requires all.

CAUNSE, pavement.
CAYER, a coarse sieve for winnowing.
CHEE-AH! word used for calling swine.
CHEELD-VEAN (little child), a term of endearment.
CHILL, an iron lamp.
CLIFF, all the ground between the shore and cultivated land. The cliff proper, or precipice, is called the edge of the cliff; the cleeves, or the carns.
CLUNK, to swallow.
COSTAN, a basket made of straw and brambles.
COURANT, romping play.
COURSEY, to linger gossiping.
COWAL, a large fish-basket.
CRAVEL, mantel-stone.
CRELLAS, the ruins of ancient bee-hive huts; an excavation in a bank, roofed over to serve for an out-house, &c.
CROGGAN, a limpet shell.
CRONACK, a toad.
CROUD, the rind of a sieve covered with sheepskin, used for taking up corn, &c.; also an old fiddle.
CRUM, crooked.
CROUST, afternoons' refreshment of bread and beer in harvest time.
CROW, a small out-house.

DIDJAN, a little bit.
DIJEY, a very small homestead.
DOWER, water.
DRUCKSHAR, a small solid wheel.
DUFFAN, a nickname for one much given to self laudation; usually bestowed on a bouncing religionist who is powerful in speech, and strong in faith, but no better than ordinary mortals in works.
DUFFY, a forthright, blunt happy-go-lucky person.
DUMBLEDORE, large black-beetle.

'E, ye or you.

FAIX! faith.
FLUSHET, a flood-gate.
FUGGAN, a small unleavened cake.
FUGGO, an artificial cave.

GADGE-VRAWS, the ox-eye daisy.
GARD, soil used for scouring.
GARRACK, a rock.
GLOWS, dried cow-dung used for fuel.
GRAMBLER, a stony place.
GRIGLANS, heath.
GRUIT, fine soil.
GUARE, play, called out by boys when they throw quoits cast a ball, &c.
GUISE-DANCE, Christmas mummery.
GULTHISE (in Scilly niclethies), harvest-home feast.
GURGOES, the ruins of ancient fences found on waste land.
GWEEAN, a periwinkle.

HILLA, the night-mare.
HOGGAN, a "fuggan" with meat baked on it; the fruit of hawthorns.

KEGGAS, rank wild plants, such as water-hemlock, elecampane, &c.
KIBBAL, a bucket used at a draw-well or mine shaft.
KISKEYS, the dried-up stalks of "keggas."
KNACKERS (knockers), spirits in the mines.
KEUNEY, moss, lichen, &c.

LAISTER, the yellow water-iris.
LEW, sheltered from wind.
LEWTH, shelter.

MABYER, a young hen.
MIRYON, an ant.
MOAR, the root; to produce roots.
MOOR-WORK, tin-streaming.
MORABS, land near the sea.

NACKAN, a kerchief.

OAR-WEED, sea-weed.
ORGAN, pennyroyal.

PADZEPAW, a newt.
PAR, cove; the word porth is never used by the natives of West Cornwall, nor does it ever occur in family names.
PEETH, a draw-well.
PIGGAL, a kind of large hoe used for cutting turf, &c.
PILF, woolly dust.
PILJACK, a poor scurvy fellow.
PISKEY, a mischievous fairy that delights to lead people astray; also a greenish bug, found on blackberries.
PITCH-TO, to set to work with good heart.
PLUM, soft, light.
PORVAN, a rush lamp wick.
PRUIT! a word used for calling cows.
PUL, mire, mud.
PULAN, a small pool, such as is left by ebb tide.
PUL-CRONACK, a small toad-like fish, found in "pulans."

QUALK, a heavy fall.
QUILKAN, a frog.
QUILLET, a small field.

REEN, a steep hill side.
ROSE, low lying level ground, moorland, &c.
RULLS, rolls of carded wool.

SEW (gone to), dried up.
SKAW, the elder tree.
SKAW-DOWER, fig wort.
SKEDGEWITH, privet.
SMALL-PEOPLE, fairies.
SOAS, sose, forsooth.
SPANISH DUMBLEDORE, the cock-chaffer.

SPRIGGAN, sprite, fairy.
SPROWL, life, energy.
STROATH, more haste than good speed.
STROLL, an untidy mess.

TALFAT, a boarded floor, for a bed-place, over one end of a cottage.
THRESHAL, a flail.
TOWSAR, a large apron or wrapper.
TUBBAN, a clod of earth.
TUBBLE, a mattock.
TUMMALS, quantity.
TUNGTAVUS, a tattling fool.
TUNTRY, the pole by which oxen draw a wain, cart, &c.
TURN, a spinning wheel.

UNCLE, a term of regard given to an old man.

VEAN, little.
VINED, mouldy.
VISGEY, a pick-axe.
VISNAN, the sand launce.
VOW, a cavern or "fuggo."
VUG, a cavity in a lode or rock.

WIDDEN, small.
WIDDENS, small fields.
WISHT, sad, like a person or thing ill-wisht.

ZAWN (pro SOWN), a cavern in a cliff.

A short time ago, two gentlemen of Penzance walked over to Chysauster, the higher side of Gulval, on a Sunday morning, to inspect the hut-circles, caves, and other remains of what are supposed to have been ancient British habitations. After a fruitless search, the gentlemen returned towards Chysauster to see if they could meet with anyone to inform them where the objects they were in quest of might be found. In the lane they overtook a woman and asked her if she knew of any caves thereabout? "Caaves! no, I don't—not fit for butchers," she replied, "but if you want any for rearan I think I can tell 'e where there es some to be found; now I look at 'e agen you don't seem much like butchers nether, nor you arn't none of our farmers about here ether! Where are 'e coman from at all? Looking for caaves of a Sunday mornan! You are very much in want of them I s'pose." The gentlemen explained that they neither wanted calves for rearing nor killing, but to find the ancient ruins. "Oh Lord," said she, "you're lookan for the old crellas, and things up in the hill! Why dedn't 'e say so than, that one might know what you meant, instead of givan such outlandish names to things. But come 'e along with me, and I'll show 'e," continued she in turning back and leading the way.

Footnotes

[1] One-eyed Joan's Tale, *p.* 213.

[2] It is somewhat curious to notice that no one who has written on the parish of Buryan, in speaking of the Boleit tombstone in the church, has pointed out that the inscription is, in accordance with a very common custom, in verse, namely in a triplet followed by a distich. It reads thus:—

Clarice, la femme Cheffrei
de Bolleit, git ici,
Dieu de lalme eit mercie.
Ke pur lalme punt
Di ior de pardun aveunt.

The word punt in the fourth line is short for prierunt. Probably there is now, or at all events, has been at some time, in the original, a small letter r above the word between the p and the u. An r has been similarly omitted in aveunt. This somewhat primitive epitaph may be thus literally translated into equally primitive English:—

Clarice, the wife of Jefferei
Of Bolleit, here doth lie.
God of her soul have mercie.
For her soul whoever prays
Shall have pardon for ten days.
        From ONE AND ALL.

[3] This story should have preceded the "QUEEN'S VISIT," but it was not obtained in time.

[4] According to our intended arrangement the three foregoing stories should have preceded those of St. Just.

[5] Alexander.

[6] Purse.
